Nuclear Agendas in Japan and Taiwan: A Comparative Approach to Science, Technology, and Society

Silvia Amato

Nuclear Agendas in Japan and Taiwan: A Comparative Approach to Science, Technology, and Society

Silvia Amato

Academica Press
Washington~London

Library of Congress Cataloging-in-Publication Data

Names: Amato, Silvia (author)
Title: Nuclear agendas in japan and taiwan : a comparative approach to science, technology, and society | Amato, Silvia
Description: Washington : Academica Press, 2024. | Includes references.
Identifiers: LCCN 2023949676 | ISBN 9781680535501 (hardcover) | 9781680535518 (e-book) |

Contents

Taiwan and Japan Book Introduction 1

Public Nuclear Agendas:
Comparative Innovation Development about Taiwan 3

Bibliography 103

Suggested Literature 125

Public Nuclear Agendas Applied to Japan in Post-Disaster Crises 131

Final Annex 259

Bibliography 269

Suggested Literature 295

Index 301

Taiwan and Japan Book Introduction

This detailed review centers on comparative innovation compliance strategies for knowledge transfer agreements and nuclear management policies maintained in Taiwan and Japan in recent years. A following discussion then introduces some major themes previously researched for this subject about the regional nuclear technology debate. While collecting information referring to Taiwanese and Japanese scientific literature, we then describe across both sections the STI (Science Technology Innovation) advanced topics that tend to converge on comparative public agency debates as well as on regional energy innovation approaches. By analysing Taiwan and Japan as regional nuclear case studies, there is to consider that technical changing policies do pertain to both cases however in a distinctive manner.

These two regional study-cases are essentially independent from one another because of emerging substantial differences that require a critical understanding about case-based STS (Science Technology and Society) knowledge transfer developments and concurrent internal factors, included in comparative research investigations. This work covers in a retrospective way descriptive arguments that point at Taiwan and Japan international nuclear science fields related to changing technological environments and NPP (Nuclear Power Plant) waste management programs surveyed after the post-Fukushima crises.

The first section focuses directly on Taiwan's specialized industrial clusters and their strategic interdependence that involves a regional competition of industrial technology activities. Through regional cluster models and local innovation plans, international authors highlight the need to redefine techno-innovation activities that mirror public and private partnerships PPP, evolving in terms of collective trading environments and regional governance regulations. The shape of regional decision-making targets in Taiwan's case points at science policy development reaffirmed through multilevel innovation initiatives that have also brought into light material implications for comparative knowledge transfer processes - which require a complete maintenance of regulative systems associated with local managerial consistent proceedings able to integrate common deliberative development schemes re-valued in East Asia.

The second and final part of this work centers instead on Japan's post-Fukushima monitoring compliance strategies for nuclear waste management policy (NWMP) model. As cross-learning processes, comparative governmental interventions, sustainability of renewable energy systems and environmental science models, lead to adaptive exploration areas referring also to the nuclear industrial policy of Japan. Through country-based studies, this section offers then a comparative overview of nuclear waste technology and scientific development transfers, where STI material expansion is fundamentally translated within comparative deliberative contexts.

What we might observe is a basic comparative formation of science and technology systematic procedures that entail an alternating interplay of policy cooperation factors. This distinctive interconnection happening in Japan's post-Fukushima tested ground has meant the establishment of common dimensions including the STS approaches fostering public knowledge clustering through regional/national/local, information distribution channels involving the managerial processing organizations.

Within both parts about Taiwan and Japan research investigation, we refer to an increasing central relationship that has evolved between the local municipalities, the energy security centres and the public networking systems determining future environmental planning activities. For the case of nuclear energy policy and technical cooperation we review environmental practice models adapted through comparative regional perspectives set at country level.

Note: This current research activity was firstly introduced for the PhD dissertation project developed at National Chengchi University, Taipei, Taiwan (R.O.C.). It has not been funded by any type of organization, association, or individual. However this project has been completed independently with unfunded follow-up revisions leading to this final book.

Public Nuclear Agendas: Comparative Innovation Development about Taiwan

General Overview

This first documentation activity introduces the reader to descriptive environmental policy investigations about Taiwan's comparative nuclear development policies. This short review has combined an argumentative understanding about transnational industry-based innovation transfers, nuclear waste policy, and public regulatory practices. In the case of East Asia with Taiwan's regional affirmative development, the progressive establishment of environmental coordination policies, local disaster risk management approaches, and knowledge transfer (KT) development agreements, has been institutionally adapted in view of comparative science and technology dynamics, and centralized regulatory facilitation mechanisms. What we argue is about the fact that regional innovation economies have required environmental safety protection plans set locally as well as comparable public-private dual partnerships (PPPs). The science, technology and societies (STS) orientations associated with technology innovating systems have entailed societal transformative implications. From this comparative literature review, we have found that in the case of nuclear power plant (NPP) managerial innovation processes and ecological industrial approaches, it comes into evidence the need to establish permanent governance measures for the (ICT) local participatory granted conditions while fostering regional technology innovation reforming schemes.

1. Introductory Notes on Nuclear Safety Innovation about Taiwan

Political democratic reforming models have been an international prominent domain.[1] In the case of the nuclear power industries established in Taiwan's democratic voting system, the actual reliability of Nuclear Power Plants (NPPs) has often been addressed through comparable perspectives.[2] Nuclear energy reviews[3] have recalled the case study about Taiwan's nuclear energy development, because of increasing disapproval fronts adhering to civic environmental parties based in Taiwan[4] such as the Green Consumers' Foundation, who in 2016 intervened in the nuclear debate concerning the reopening of a nuclear reactor at Wanli nuclear power plant, by stating its disapproval motivated by local safety issues.[5] DPP Deputy representatives and national green parties[6] have supported the local population demanding, among other conditions, a permanent anti-nuclear opposition policy, as well as, the diffusion of transparent information about the case of NPPs promotion as

[1] See: Insights on democratic local development in Taiwan can be consulted in the study of Qingshan Tan, Peter Kien-hong Yu, and Wen-chun Chen, 1996. "Local Politics in Taiwan. Democratic Consolidation." Asian Survey, Volume 36, No. 5, pp. 483-494.

[2] Note: As of 03/2021, it is stressed out that "The ruling and opposition parties [in Taiwan] had for many years debated the merits of starting operation of the power plant, but all have come to accept that no local government is willing to host a storage facility for spent fuel rods...Concerns over safety and cost of nuclear energy make operating the plant not viable [4th NPP in New Taipei City's Gongliao District]." Taipei Times, section: Taiwan News. Yang Chun-hui and Jonathan Chin, "Fourth Nuclear Plant activation 'no option': Tsai." Published in March 19, 2021, page 3. Available at: https://www.taipeitimes.com/News/taiwan/archives/2021/03/19/2003754116 Accessed 10/2023.

[3] Sung Chull Kim, and Yousun Chung, 2018. "Dynamics of nuclear power policy in the post-Fukushima era: Interest structure and politicisation in Japan, Taiwan and Korea." Asian Studies Review, Volume 42, No. 1, pp. 107-124.

[4] See: Taiwan Environmental Protection Union mandate, available at webpage: https://tepu.org.tw/?page_id=4962 Accessed 10/2023.

[5] Wu Hsin-yun, Chen Chun-hua, Wang Cheng-chung, Justin Su and Evelyn Kao, 2018. "Environmental groups protest restarting nuclear reactor." The China Post, February 6, 2018. Web-page available at: https://chinapost.nownews.com/20180206-224581 As of 10/2023 this link has been disabled. The article can be read here: https://focustaiwan.tw/politics/201802050015 CNA Archive. Accessed 10/2023.

[6] Seaver Wang, Daniel Chen, 2021. "Could Taiwan's political left reconsider nuclear power." The Diplomat, Opinion section, December 03, 2021. Webpage available at: https://thediplomat.com/2021/12/could-taiwans-political-left-reconsider-nuclear-power/ Accessed 10/2023.

renewable energy sources put also in relation to NPPs local sites management and concurrent exposition to potential seismic hazards.[7] Moreover, in prospect of a renewed referendum held in 2021, it became available to the public more detailed reports about the Longmen's nuclear power plant and its exposure to seismic risk hazards promptly analysed for local safety proceedings.[8] NPPs developed in Taiwan have required a responsive safety processing status importing local technical upgrades specifically on low-level radioactive waste (LLRW) management issues.[9] As such, renewable energy participatory models in governance have been favoured in order to facilitate independent controlling mechanisms for contextual reviews, with nuclear risk evaluation and impact analyses, connected at the local level, while strategically evolving after the 2011 Fukushima nuclear crisis in Japan.[10] Due to different configurations of administrative responsive approaches adopted at times of testing local risk disaster reduction events, public policy representatives have promoted programmatic civic interactions, in order to assess local disaster risk programs.[11] Programmatic resolutions for nuclear safety and technical

[7] Yuan-Chieh Wu, 2013. "Seismic hazard and performance for operating NPPs in Taiwan." European Nuclear Safety Regulation Group (ENSREG) Review Meeting. Institute of Nuclear Energy Research report. Available at web-page: https://www.ensreg.eu/sites/default/files/2013%2009%2024%2002_SHA%20and%20Performance%20for%20NPP%20in%20Taiwan_1020924.PDF Accessed 10/2023.

[8] Lin Cheng-kuo, 2021. "Debate over nuclear power is not over yet." Taipei Times, Tuesday, December 8. Available at website: https://taipeitimes.com/News/editorials/archives/2021/12/28/2003770303 Accessed 10/2023.

[9] Note: Sandia National Laboratories (SNL) SAND2007-0131 Report: "Taiwan has accumulated LLW from a variety of sources, primarily from commercial nuclear power generation. These wastes are currently in storage at the Lanyu Island Storage Site and on-site at nuclear power plants. In addition to LLW that is currently in storage, substantial quantities of LLW will be generated from continued reactor operations and from the ultimate decommissioning of the existing nuclear power plants. Taiwan has not yet selected a site for the final disposal of LLW, but four potential sites have been identified by the Taiwan Power Company..." In Knowlton Robert G, Cochran John C., Arnold Bill Walter, Jow Hong-Nian, Mattie Patrick D, Schelling Frank Joseph)2007. "Taiwan industrial cooperation program technology transfer for low-level radioactive waste final disposal - phase I." United States Department of Energy Office of Scientific and Technical Information. Available at webpages: https://doi.org/10.2172/900849. (or) https://www.osti.gov/servlets/purl/900849. Page 137. Accessed 10/2023.

[10] Chang-Chuan Chan, Ya-mei Chen, 2011. "A Fukushima-Like Nuclear Crisis in Taiwan or a Nonnuclear Taiwan?" East Asian Science, Technology and Society: An International Journal, Volume 5, No. 3, pp. 403-407.

[11] Note: At Institutional level is reported "in April 2013, the Taiwanese nuclear safety

protection operations coordinated at governmental level have become essential components for the aggregation of multilevel operational integrated systems, which require long term energy planning objectives, as in Taiwan' case (Chen, et al., 2006).[12]

In view of organizational changes occurring for the revision of nuclear energy transitioning processes in Taiwan, regional political advisers, local and international government experts[13] and health-care practitioners have amplified the need to increase the intensity of societal dialogues pointing at, for instance, instrumental environmental risk assessment plans (Ho, et

regulator, the Atomic Energy Council (AEC), invited the European Commission to set up an independent peer review of the stress tests of the Taiwanese NPPs, which were conducted in 2012 by the licensee, the Taiwan Power Company, and by AEC...The EU peer review noted that AEC has not identified any safety-related weaknesses in Taiwanese NPPs, which would require their immediate shutdown. Nevertheless the team recommended 'tangible further improvements' in some specific safety related areas. The peer review recommendations call for action to make the power plants more robust against the effects of large earthquakes and flooding..." Nuclear Engineering International magazine, 2013. "EU completes peer review of Taiwanese nuclear plant safety." Published on 12/11/2013. Available at webpage: https://www.neimagazine.com/news/newseu-completes-peer-review-of-tianwanese-nuclear-plant-safety Accessed 10/2023.

[12] Liang-Chung Chen, Jie-Ying Wu, and Mei-Ju Lai, 2006. "The Evolution of the Natural Disaster Management System in Taiwan." Journal of the Chinese Institute of Engineers, Volume 29, No. 4, pp. 633-638.

[13] Note: International discussion forums promoted by TW. MOST for local knowledge guidelines have involved in 2019 "[...] Representatives from national research grant agencies, and field experts on environmental change and sustainable development…By enhancing global knowledge of environmental change and sustainable development through multilateral collaborative research actions (CRAs), the Belmont Forum integrates our knowledge from stakeholders, nature, humanities, and social sciences into transdisciplinary solutions for specific actions." Department of Natural Sciences and Sustainable Development, Ministry of Science and Technology, 08/2021. "International experts and scholars gathered in Taipei for the Belmont Forum 10th Anniversary & Annual Plenary Meeting." MOST news & events section. Webpage available at: https://www.nstc.gov.tw/folksonomy/detail?subSite=&l=en&article_uid=11b7814d-8bcc-4030-a75a-38e59604517b&menu_id=eb9eb136-4319-40d6-abd3-0788bea0d3a8&content_type=P&view_mode=listView#:~:text=This%20year%20coincides%20with%20the%2010th%20Anniversary%20of,center%20and%20Apex%20Building%20in%20the%20NTU%20campus. Accessed 10/2023.

al, 2013;[14] Ming-sho Ho, 2014).[15] The triggering effects of multiple dangerous pollution hazards causing disaster crisis impacts - involving the case of post-Fukushima international environment and local NPP communication maintenance systems[16] - have been discussed number of times in regional public forums tackling the emergence of territorial environmental provisions during the unforeseen technical emergency situations (Ho, et al, 2013). To better understand socioeconomic shifts that can be explained in terms of government trusting behaviours regarding local disaster emergency management exposures, [17] the Taiwanese medical study conducted in August 2011 based on nuclear risk perception in Taiwan confirmed that respondents (2819 persons) perceived higher safety risks in local NPP operational planning site when compared with Japan (Ho, et al., 2013).[18]

Considering regulatory environmental orientations in the case of Taipei city,[19] the common alignment of disaster management systems incorporating the activities of central government units, municipalities,

[14] Jung-Chun Ho, Shu-Fen Kao, Jung-Der Wang, Chien-Tien Su, Chiao-Tzu Patricia Lee, Ruey-Yu Chen, Hung-Lun Chang, Marco C F Ieong and Peter Wushou Chang, 2013. "Risk perception, trust, and factors related to a planned new nuclear power plant in Taiwan after the 2011 Fukushima disaster." Journal of Radiological Protection, Volume 33, No. 4, pp.773-789.

[15] Ming-sho Ho, 2014. "The Fukushima effect: Explaining the resurgence of the anti-nuclear movement in Taiwan." Environmental Politics, Volume 23, No. 6, pp. 965-983.

[16] Note: Newspapers recall Taiwan on anti-nuclear protests, especially after 2011 "...The infamous Japanese nuclear accident in 2011 galvanized major protests across Taiwan, halting the construction of the country's fourth nuclear power plant and casting it into a political and legal limbo." Nicolas Freschi, 2018. "Taiwan's Nuclear Dilemma." The Diplomat, March 14, 2018. Available at webpage: https://thediplomat.com/2018/03/taiwans-nuclear-dilemma/ Accessed 10/2023.

[17] Note: In the case of a nuclear emergency, through periodic reviews the Atomic Energy Council in Taiwan promoted in 2021 Taiwan Nuclear Emergency Exercise targeting the decommissioning stages at Chin Shan Nuclear Power Plant (NPP). Atomic Energy Council, 2021. "Well prepared for the 2021 Taiwan Nuclear Emergency Exercise during the COVID-19 pandemic." AEC What's new section, September 29, 2021. Webpage available at: https://www.aec.gov.tw/english/newsdetail/pressrelease/193.html As of 10/2023 Web-link modified: https://www.nusc.gov.tw/english/newsdetail/pressrelease/194.html Accessed 10/2023.

[18] Jung-Chun Ho, et al. 2013. "Risk perception, trust, and factors related to a planned new nuclear power plant in Taiwan after the 2011 Fukushima disaster." Journal of Radiological Protection, Volume 33, pp. 773-789.

[19] Taipei City Disaster Prevention Info Website available at: https://www.eoc.gov.taipei/taipeicityems1_public_en/Introduction accessed on April 2020.

and township offices, relies on the Disaster Prevention and Rescue Act[20] involving the local government. By using comparable safety organizational approaches, in view of coordinating local protection management plans [in Finland's nuclear case "the National Programme of 2022 deals extensively with various aspects of used fuel and radioactive waste management. It includes amounts and locations of used fuel and radioactive waste as well as general objectives, principles, an estimate of the costs and schedule of waste management."][21] and corresponding administration mechanisms, it has come into attention the formation of national safety protection standards combined with specific communication knowledge tools such as the disaster prevention and rescue technology[22] which need to be adapted[23] according to the diffusion of local emergency operations coming into evidence (Ho, et al, 2013). On a similar pattern, there have been industrial environmental risks that have been linked to emergency management and contingency plans which have been monitored according to effective implementation dynamics,[24] also integrated with local regulatory measures put into place;

[20] Taipei City Disaster Prevention Info Website available at: https://www.eoc.gov.taipei/taipeicityems1_public_en/Introduction accessed on April 2020.

[21] World Nuclear News, 2022. "Finland sets out nuclear waste plans." WNN, Waste & Recycling section, 02 March 2022. Webpage available at: https://www.world-nuclear-news.org/Articles/Finland-sets-out-nuclear-waste-plans Accessed 10/2023.

[22] Taipei City Disaster Prevention Info Website available at: https://www.eoc.gov.taipei/taipeicityems1_public_en/Introduction accessed on April 2020.

[23] To note that: "The disaster prevention cycle comprises 4 elements: 1. damage mitigation, constructing disaster prevention facilities, including earthquake-resistant buildings and dams; 2. preparedness, which entails disaster prevention training; 3. emergency response, which includes rescue and the prevention of secondary damage; and 4. reconstruction and recovery." Tobishima Engineering and Construction Corporation, 2021. "Expert in Disaster Prevention Technology." Available at webpage: https://www.tobishima.co.jp/english/business/ Accessed 10/2023.

[24] Note: Planning civic training and local emergency schemes in Taiwan has also shown its vulnerabilities, as it is emphasized: "The lack of knowledge about the core concepts of emergency management such as Comprehensive Emergency Management, All-Hazards Planning, Incident Command System, Emergency Support Functions, and so forth. With no widely-accepted knowledge base of emergency management in Taiwan, and no nationally-accepted emergency management curriculum to draw from, Taiwanese authorities would have a difficult time training anyone on emergency management." Leo Bosner, and I-wei Jennifer Chang, 2020. "Taiwan's disaster preparedness and response: Strengths, shortfalls, and paths to improvement." Global Taiwan Institute, October 2020. Quote at page 16. Webpage available at: https://globaltaiwan.org/wp-content/uploads/2020/10/GTI-Taiwans-Disaster-Preparedness-and-Response-Oct-2020-final.pdf?mc_cid=

systematic assessments can be identified in terms of common evaluation analyses and local supervisory conditions interrelated with the process of strategic environmental assessments (SEAs) (Ho, et al, 2013; Liou, et al., 2004).[25] In Taiwan's case, the so-defined strategic environmental assessments (SEAs) have included precise environmental management plans supported by regional counterparts such as APEC members (Zarsky, and Hunter, 1997),[26] while incorporating local technical issues considered by ministerial state bureaus and national monitoring agencies. However, due to local operational factors at nuclear power plants involving disaster and emergency preparedness, the central governmental authorities have been in charge of the application process,[27] granting NPP licensing capacities with corresponding regulatory reforms,[28] addressing both

518eb59a56&mc_eid=ad991f7720 Accessed 10/2023.

25 Ming-Lone Liou, Yue-Hwa Yu, 2004. "Development and implementation of Strategic Environmental Assessment in Taiwan." Environmental Impact Assessment Review, Volume 24, No. 3, pp. 337-350.

26 Lyuba Zarsky and Jason Hunter, 1997. "Environmental Cooperation at APEC: The first five years." APSNet Special Reports, March 31, 1997. Website available at: https://nautilus.org/apsnet/environmental-cooperation-at-apec-the-first-five-years-2/ Accessed April 2020.

27 Note: Comparatively, the nuclear management crisis occurring in Japan in 11 March put into evidence that: "In this case, the proximate cause was the power failure at the reactor caused by a natural disaster – the earthquake and tsunami - and thus it was fundamentally different in nature than the accidents at Three Mile Island in the United States or at Chernobyl in Russia, which were caused by errors committed by the operating personnel. However, the Fukushima Nuclear Accident Independent Investigation Commission (The National Diet of Japan) determined that 'despite numerous opportunities to come up with countermeasures, successive generations of regulatory authorities and TEPCO's management resorted to delay tactics.' The commission therefore concluded that the accident 'cannot be regarded as a natural disaster. It was profoundly manmade disaster. In other words, the indirect causes of the Fukushima accident can be assumed to be an accumulation of offsite mismanagement in terms of disaster prevention and mitigation.[...]" The Fukushima Nuclear Accident and Crisis Management – Lessons for Japan-U.S. Alliance Cooperation - Final report of the SPF Research Project on "Assessment: Japan-US Response to the Fukushima Crisis." Page 6-7. Sasakawa Peace Foundation. September, 2012. Webpage available at: https://www.spf.org/en/_jpus_media/img/investigation/ book_fukushima.pdf Accessed 10/2023.

28 Note: Further limitations related to [SEA] processes have specifically been underlined about Taiwan. This study highlights that "[...] the future of nuclear power cannot be decided based on electricity provision, the nuclear waste problem, or cross generational justice in the policy planning process, because of the political context influencing energy policy planning and the SEA process." Yen-Yu Wu and Hwong-Wen Ma, 2019. "Challenges for integrating strategic environmental assessment to enhance environmental thinking: A case study of Taiwan energy policy." Sustainability, Volume 11, No. 3, pp.609.

centralized and decentralized multilevel energy production environments (Liou, et al., 2004). In association with the affirmation of national industrial innovation parks as well as technological developed areas, there has been in view the evaluation of environmental risk exposures and regional prioritization goals for Taiwan's Science Parks established in seismically open areas (Reynolds, 2016).[29] In 2012,[30] TSMC Taiwan Corporation reported on climate change mitigation adaptive plans while pointing its attention on Taiwan's natural disaster risk environment requiring collaboration between public and private sectors, moreover as TSMC statement, it specified that: "[...]TSMC is also leading the industry to collaborate with central government agencies and conduct a project to assess and mitigate climate natural disaster risk in three Taiwan Science Parks. [...]"[31] For recognizable reasons, the actual promotion of multi-risk hazards prevention campaigns has then been subscribed in order to solve comparative disaster management DM cases - which have invited digital expertise through ex. the Taiwan Internet Governance Forum or correlated international geospatial information centres[32] capacities - tackling local environmental risk pollution and field emergency responses. This type of dual science policy combination focused on contextual disaster emergency priority areas has also pointed at the direction of improving a more critical understanding about how public risk perceptions are identified, and what they have indicated in terms of regional environmental practice areas and participative innovation approaches. In essence, Disaster Risk Reduction

Available at website: https://www.mdpi.com/2071-1050/11/3/609 Accessed 10/2023.

[29] Ben Reynolds, 2016. "Understanding Risk Accumulations in Taiwan's Science Parks." Moody's RMS Report Available at the website: https://www.rms.com/blog/2016/12/19/understanding-risk-accumulations-in-taiwans-science-parks. Accessed April 2020.

[30] TSMC 2012 Corporate Social Responsibility Report, 2013. "TSMC's Climate Change Management Structure." Taiwan Semiconductor Manufacturing Company (TMSC) Report available at website: https://esg.tsmc.com/download/file/2013_tsmc_csr/english/pdf/e_8_3.pdf Accessed 10/2023.

[31] TMSC (CSR) report available at: https://esg.tsmc.com/download/file/2013_tsmc_csr/english/pdf/e_8_3.pdf Page 2.

[32] The NBR podcast series *Asia Insight* features interviews, 2021. "Lessons Learned. Disaster management perspectives from Japan and Taiwan." Podcast from Nontraditional Security Challenges in South Asia. November 5th, 2021. Webpage available at: https://www.nbr.org/publication/lessons-learned-disaster-management-perspectives-from-japan-and-taiwan/ Accessed 10/2023.

(DRR)[33] activities managed within emergency responsive monitoring systems relying on highly reliable technology tools are also crucially intertwined with local organizations and community collaborative networks, integrating technical upgraded territorial information among respective societal cohorts (Ho, et al, 2013; Liou, et al., 2004). In this line of arguments, it follows a research overview centred on science and technology environment (STS) and local industrial cooperation, while advancing further issues about public risk resilience transfers framed in reference to NPP management systems. As recognized in a 2021 Taiwan's policy plan by the Ministry of Science and Technology (MOST), climate change and surveillance technology programs considered in view of strengthening local infrastructures and improve urban resilience, can bring to timely governmental decisions, concerning also renewable energy plans "Taiwan has put in place an array of policies and actions to become a nuclear-free country and actively invested in energy transition [...] However, the types and structures of energy facilities resulting from such energy transition will be more sensitive to climate change, which implies that climate change scientific research and technology development, coping strategies, and green infrastructures still require further improvement. [...] Therefore, new technologies must be introduced to strengthen the early warning systems, disaster prevention, and disaster resilience of major cities in Taiwan."[34] Further community-action plans and ICT tools have been envisioned in relation to Taiwan major environmental risk exposures.

33 ISDR International Strategy for Disaster Reduction, 2006. "NGOs & Disaster Risk Reduction: A Preliminary Review of Initiatives and Progress Made." Background paper for a consultative meeting on a - Global Network of NGOs for Community Resilience to Disasters - Geneva. Available at the website: https://www.unisdr.org/2008/partner-netw/ngos/meeting1-october-2006/NGOs_and_DRR_Background_Paper.pdf Accessed April 2020.

34 Taiwan MOST governmental report, 2021. "National science and technology development plan. (2021-2024)." May 21, 2021. Yuan Tai-Ke-Letter No. 1100009078. Quote from page 8. Webpage available at: https://www.most.gov.tw/most/attachments/36977724-a4cd-42f3-bcd1-6e50e98b648e As of 2023 the website changed to: https://www.nstc.gov.tw/nstc/attachments/fd10ecfa-f319-44fe-8058-f379d3de22c2 Accessed 10/2023.

2. Reflections on Regional Knowledge Transfers and Regional Energy Innovation Approach

Overall science technology and society STS research areas, including academic reflections on post-3.11 Japan, [35] combining managerial knowledge transfers and socioeconomic sustainability fields retracing also migrant societies, will be further introduced in the following chapters in order to provide a comparative exploration on local development issues affecting as well Taiwan's industrial cooperation framework. At institutional level, there have been structural correlations about knowledge management transfers and technical programmatic approvals about e.g.: solar energy manufacturing sectors, that have been reviewed for local industrial development. The practical modifying issues have been fundamentally recognized through local governmental integrated programs, environment impact analyses, and disaster risk mitigation plans DDR,[36] focussed on comparative local managerial differentiation that has been consequentially put into practice.

Therefore, regional industrial innovation and technology models produced in Taiwan have required supporting and adaptive management systems able to perform in cooperation with state's risk disaster planning agencies for long term public-private mutual consolidation. Furthermore international economic analyses tend to correlate climate risks and Asia stating in particular that: "*If policy makers and business leaders can harness the region's innovative spirit, talent, and flexibility, Asia could lead a global response to climate risk by adapting and by mitigating the*

[35] Lisa Onaga, Chelsea Szendi Schieder, Kristina Buhrman, Julia Mariko Jacoby, Kohta Juraku, David H. Slater, et al., 2021. "Sources of Disaster: A roundtable discussion on new epistemic perspectives in Post-3.11 Japan." East Asian Science, Technology and Society: An International Journal, Volume 15, 2021 - Issue 4, pp. 482 - 496. https://doi.org/10.1080/18752160.2021.1997015

[36] Note: To highlight: "To this end it has become common practice for governments to use their administrative units to define the affected 'community.' Thus if an event exceeds the coping ability of a village, or local municipality, or district, or state/province or even the nation, then a specific type of disaster can be declared (i.e. local, state/provincial or national)." USAID, 2011. "Introduction to Disaster Risk Reduction." Page 8. Full Report available at website: https://www.preventionweb.net/files/26081_kp1concepdisasterrisk1.pdf Accessed 10/2023.

most severe potential consequences."[37] (Saunders, et al., 2015).[38] In this case, the multilevel implementation approaches referring to the nuclear energy industry have been aggregated in correspondence to territorial characterizations of multilateral industrial sites (Liou, et al., 2004).

At retrospective level, in the case of nuclear energy policy, the minimization of nuclear energy industrial risks and radioactive waste environmental impacts of NPPs, reviewed through public environmental risk analyses, has been arranged through national and local stakeholders involved in the region, as a precedent of disaster risks at NPPs, it is reaffirmed: "The nuclear accident at Fukushima was precipitated by natural disaster, but poor risk management, including a failure to comprehend tectonic risk in the most earthquake prone country in the world, and an institutionalized complacency about risk, were major factors increasing the likelihood of a major accident and fumbling crisis response."[39] To consider that nuclear international bodies, regional scientific expertise groups, including NEA panels,[40] and changing advisory members have been identified across national steering committees, directly associated with the Atomic Energy Council (AEC),[41] for the technical preparation of preventive and security protection

[37] McKinsey Global Institute, 2020. "Climate risk and response in Asia." Report on *The Future of Asia: Climate risk and response in Asia*, quote: page 2 (ii). Webpage available at: https://www.mckinsey.com/~/media/McKinsey/Featured%20Insights/Asia%20Pacific/Climate%20risk%20and%20response%20in%20Asia%20Research%20preview/Climate-risk-and-response-in-Asia-Future-of-Asia-research-preview-v3.pdf?msclkid=09f3f56baa3811ec8b2079a4972c4613 Accessed 10/2023.

[38] Saunders, W.S.A.; De Bruin, K.; Ruiz Rivera N.; Lee, H.C. 2015. "A Comparative Study of Natural Hazard Policy in Taiwan, Mexico, New Zealand and Norway," GNS Science Report 2015/005. 94 p. DOI:10.13140/RG.2.1.2558.4166.

[39] Jeff Kingston, 2012. "Mismanaging risk and the Fukushima nuclear crisis." The Asia-Pacific Journal, March 12, 2012, Volume 10, Issue 12, Number 4, Article ID 3724. Available at Webpage: https://apjjf.org/2012/10/12/Jeff-Kingston/3724/article.html Accessed 10/2023.

[40] NEA is the Nuclear Energy Agency: "The NEA is the only intergovernmental agency which brings together a selection of countries from the Americas, Europe and the Asia-Pacific region in a non-political forum [operating] in the field of nuclear energy." NEA-OECD: Who we are. Website available at: https://www.oecd-nea.org/jcms/pl_36846/who-we-are Accessed 10/2023.

[41] Huang C., Huang J., Hsu M., 2017. "Lessons Learned from Fukushima - Applied to Emergency Preparedness in Taiwan." In: Jiang H. (eds) Proceedings of The 20th Pacific Basin Nuclear Conference. Pp. 385-397. PBNC 2016. Springer, Singapore.

programs promoted for the adoption of regulatory adaptation plans (Liou, et al., 2004), including IAEA safety standards for the application of the management system for facilities and activities,[42] among other related issues.

At the same time, it can be discussed whether participatory environmental development aligned in association with multiple technology transfer learning systems (STS) has been implemented in parallel with national or international disaster management policies, supporting territorial organizational activities which have also been recently involved with increasing economic proceedings, including multilateral correspondence for local governmental alliances and multinational industrial partnerships. Similarly in view of improving disaster risk reduction (DRR) plans in Asia, demonstrative interventions to protect essential infrastructures and to ameliorate early warning systems have been researched internationally.[43] Through contextual determinants, Taiwan's structural innovation policies facilitated in previous decades by the major political party the Kuomintang (KMT) within collaborative dimensions of centralized governmental agencies, have been redesigned in relation to the development of nuclear energy policy and its pre-established construction plans, tentatively expanding the local energy capacity with three active plants NPPs under national approval guidelines released by the Executive Yuan during KMT's party ruling decisions (Hsu, 2005).[44] Where instead since the 1980s, the Democratic Progressive Party (DPP)[45] initiated the opposed route for an anti-nuclear policy promotion

[42] IAEA Safety Standards Series No. GS-G-3.1, 2006. "Application of the management system for facilities and activities." STI/PUB/1253, 92-0-106606-6, 124 pages. International Atomic Energy Agency, Vienna, 2006.

[43] Rajib Shaw, Koichi Shiwaku, Takako Izumi, 2017. "Science and technology in disaster risk reduction in Asia." Academic Press 2017. Paperback ISBN: 9780128127117.

[44] Shu-Hsiang Hsu, 2005. "Advocacy coalitions and policy change on nuclear power utilization in Taiwan." The Social Science Journal, Volume 42, pp. 215-229.

[45] Note: In effect, national comments on Taiwan NPP plans reflect a contextual dualism, ex.: "Some Taiwanese are against nuclear power and others are for it, but when it comes to the two big political parties everyone knows that the DPP is against nuclear power and the KMT supports them." Chang Kuo-tsai, 2021. "Chiang's nuclear power falsehoods." Taipei Times, April 4, 2021. Wepage available at: https://www.taipeitimes.com/News/editorials/archives/2021/04/04/2003755043 (or) https://thoriumbaby.com/chiangs-nuclear-power-falsehoods-taipei-times/ Accessed 10/2023.

due to large civilian distrust regarding the KMT's party nuclear energy programming initiatives.[46] As recently as 2021, "all four referendum in Taiwan have failed to pass, marking a victory for the governing DPP and setback for the opposition KMT. [To the referendum question]: Do you agree that the Fourth Nuclear Power Plant should be unsealed and operated commercially to generate electricity, 4,262,151 disagree [to the NPP restart]."[47]

Over last few decades, institutional prediction analyses have confirmed complex renewable energy goals tackling development processes for the distribution of local energy capacities in Taiwan,[48] under the Renewable Energy Development Plan approved in 2001 (Tsai, and Chou, 2005).[49] In any case, the Taiwan's energy mix of solar, geothermal and ocean energies, wind power, biofuels, non-pump and storage hydropower and renewable hydrogen power[50] has led to a number of comparative policy reforms - that focus on the increase of renewable energy sources reaching a 20 percent level by 2025 while shutting down nuclear energy implementation plans[51] - with actual measures facilitated

46 Ming-Sho Ho, 2003. "The Politics of Anti-Nuclear Protest in Taiwan: A Case of Party-Dependent Movement (1980-2000)." Modern Asian Studies, Volume 37, No. 3, pp.683-708.

47 Bryan Chou, Nicholas Haggerty, 2021. "Explainer: Taiwan's 2021 Referendum Results." The New Lens (TNL) published digitally on 2021/12/18, Politics section. Webpage available at: https://international.thenewslens.com/article/160441 Accessed 10/2023.

48 Note: More recently: "Taiwanese President Tsai Ing-wen's push to have the island generate 20% of its electricity from renewable by 2025 is running into difficulties. Wind, solar, and hydro generation accounted for just 5.2 % of the island's power production in the first three quarters of 2020, [...] Tsai faces other headwinds. Localities and environmentalists are pushing back on an array of projects, and the U.S. - China trade war is creating even more demand for electricity as factories bolt back to Taiwan from China." Rik Glauert, 2020. "Taiwan's renewables push hit by big tech's appetite for power." NIKKEI Asia, Environment section. Published on 18 December, 2020. Webpage available at: https://asia.nikkei.com/Spotlight/Environment/Taiwan-s-renewables-push-hit-by-big-tech-s-appetite-for-power Accessed 10/2023.

49 W.T. Tsai, and Y.H. Chou, 2005. "Overview of Environmental Impacts, Prospects and Policies for Renewable Energy in Taiwan." Renewable and Sustainable Energy Reviews, Volume 9, No. 2, pp. 119-147.

50 IEA/IRENA Renewables Policies Database, 2013. "Statute for Renewable Energy Development Bill." IEA International Energy Agency. Website Available at: https://www.iea.org/policies/4808-statute-for-renewable-energy-develoment-bill Accessed April 2020.

51 Angelica Oung, 2021. "Rules to tie heavy electricity use to renewable power." Taipei Times, front page, Sat., Jan. 02, 2021, page 1. Website available at:

by company organizations, local planning commissions, and competent ministerial offices such as Taiwan's Ministry of Science and Technology (MOST) tied to security innovation and communication ecosystems,[52] which have been critically put in charge for the implementation of established licensing management approvals and local contractual mechanisms (Hsu, 2005). In reference to local innovation adaptive efforts, the regional political understanding about the formulation of nuclear power energy options in Taiwan has reflected composite socioeconomic backgrounds particularly reaffirmed after the martial law era in Taiwan, while converging toward the preparation of environmental safety measures associated with corresponding territorial monitoring and reporting activities;[53] comparative environmental analyses on CO2 emissions reduction trajectory (Chen, 2013)[54] have highlighted some key points about the role of nuclear power energy associated with legalization aspects of nuclear control measures, which have triggered the reformulation of public safety protection protocols, also due to nuclear waste repository management sites, pointing at a multiplication of public environment protection concerns[55] persisting at community level (Hsu, 2005; Ho, 2014).

https://www.taipeitimes.com/News/front/archives/2021/01/02/2003749789?msclkid=860de288b13c11ec8571f1fb9ca96014 Accessed 10/2023.

[52] Kirana Aisyah, 2022. "Taiwan's Ministry of Science and Technology restructures into the National Science and Technology Commission." Open Gov. Asia, published February 9, 2022. Website Available at: https://opengovasia.com/taiwans-ministry-of-science-and-technology-restructures-into-the-national-science-and-technology-commission/?msclkid=56be5a2bb13e11ecb4d829a9ffe18a24 Accessed 10/2023.

[53] Note: However, it is highlighted that: "The reality in 2019 was that Taiwan imported 98% of its energy, mostly in the form of oil and coal." Rik Glauert, 2020. "Taiwan's renewables push hit by big tech's appetite for power." NIKKEI Asia, Environment section. Published on 18 December, 2020.

[54] Y.-H. Henry Chen, 2013. "Non-nuclear, low-carbon, or both? The Case of Taiwan." Energy Economics, Volume 39, pp. 53-65.

[55] Note: About one of the legal nuclear waste compensation case in Taiwan: "the government will pay NT$2.55 billion (US$83.6 million) to Orchid Island residents to compensate them for infringing on their rights by maintaining a nuclear waste storage facility there over the past five decades. [...] The decision to position the facility to handle low - and medium-level nuclear waste from Taiwan's nuclear power plants on Orchid Island was made in 1974 and it began receiving shipments in 1982. [...] Since residents realized in the late 1980s what was actually on the site, they have feared it would contaminate the food chain and force them off the island and also led protests against nuclear power..." Focus Taiwan, by Flor Wang, Elaine Hou, Lu Tai-cheng. "Orchid Island

From a national historical perspective, nuclear policy orientations emerging in connection with international lessons learnt from catastrophic nuclear incidents such as: the Chernobyl's disaster in Ukraine[56] and Three Mile Island historic case in the US,[57] have been influenced by the formation of civilian anti-nuclear protest movements also based in Taiwan,[58] involving neighbouring areas such as South-East Asia (Ho, 2014; Hsu, 2005; Liu, 2011).[59] When Taiwan has directly addressed the state of change in nuclear policy in the post-Fukushima transition period, neighbouring partners such as South Korea and Japan itself, as specified by Alex Lee (2019),[60] have experienced national political identifications and changing management innovation approaches that have put nuclear energy programs in a critical phase, as stated by Alex Lee (2019) : "nuclear

to get NT$2.55 billion in nuclear waste compensation." Taipei, Nov. 22, 2019. Available at: https://focustaiwan.tw/politics/201911220023 Accessed 10/2023.

[56] Note: UNSCEAR, 2018 reports "[...] the increased incidence of thyroid cancer after the Chernobyl accident is a major issue and needs further investigation [...] the total number of cases of thyroid cancer registered in the period 1991-2015 in males and females, who were under 18 in 1986 (for the whole of Belarus and Ukraine and for the four most contaminated oblasts of the Russian Federation), approached 20,000. This number is almost three times higher than the number of thyroid cancer cases registered in the same cohort in the period 1991-2005." United Nations Scientific Committee on the Effects of Atomic Radiation, Chernobyl 2018 White Paper, "Evaluation of data on thyroid cancer in regions affected by the Chernobyl accident." Page 5. Available at: https://www.unscear.org/unscear/uploads/documents/publications/Chernobyl_WP_2017.pdf Accessed 10/2023.

[57] Note: In 1979 the Three Mile Island Accident was determined by technical failures that caused a meltdown of the 2nd Unit reactor. After this historic disaster crisis, nuclear energy policy attracted protests and anti-nuclear associations in the U.S. Information summarized from the History Channel Website available at: https://www.history.com/topics/1970s/three-mile-island Accessed April 2020.

[58] Note: On the Anniversary of Chernobyl: "Two environmental groups issued online statements...to mark the 34th anniversary of the Chernobyl nuclear disaster ...and call for the abolition of nuclear power in Taiwan [...] 'Can the plants still safely operate, or should they be decommissioned? Policies on the plants are a major compromise between power needs and hopes for decommissioning." Yang Mien-chieh and William Hetherington, 2020. "Anniversary of Chernobyl sees anti-nuclear appeals." Taipei Times, April 28, page 3. Available at: https://www.taipeitimes.com/News/taiwan/archives/2020/04/28/2003735431 Accessed 10/2023.

[59] Hwa-Jen Liu, 2011. "When labor and nature strike back: A double movement saga in Taiwan." Capitalism Nature Socialism, Volume 22, No. 1, pp. 22-39.

[60] Alex C. Lee, 2019. "Nuclear debates and political competition in Japan, South Korea, and Taiwan: Denuclearization or Nuclear Latency in the aftermath of Fukushima." Political Science, Corpus ID: 201338634. Webpage available at: https://www.semanticscholar.org/paper/Nuclear-Debates-and-Political-Competition-in-Japan%2C-Lee/1a8f2977a01cf5f7d2aec797e63057477c4d6575 Accessed 10/2023.

orientation is operationalized via the political behavior of domestic nuclear coalitions which include coalitions that are pro-nuclear energy, pro-nuclear weapons, anti-nuclear energy, and anti-nuclear weapons."[61] At different intervals, this process of national policy unrest that has led to large civilian protesting occurrences involving anti-nuclear mobilized stakeholders, has particularly highlighted common environment needs to improve ICT environmental information and public networking practices, eventually converging into mutual local identifications and shared communication systems. In the case of independent multiple information sources about nuclear critical issues having public resonance, connected to the use of overlapping regional technologies, a recent study[62] - reporting about post-Fukushima public perceptions emerging through social media - clarifies that South Korean users of twitter technology in the sample study processed: "continued information [...] about the nuclear issues [related to] health and environment, [...] topics were interlinked closely and represented both apprehension and concern about health threats and pollution."[63] Under public policy determinants, the inclusion of decentralized approaches for administrative controlling areas based in Taiwan, and monitored by national and local governmental bodies, has become an integral component for sustainable planning activities and local preparedness strategies, particularly aiming at assisting the local population e.g. during disaster risk crises. As collective institutional effort, the New Taipei City (NTPC) government has introduced public disaster management at the local level, in order to create a "local disaster management networks" analysed at community level.[64] In addition to this,

[61] Alex C. Lee, 2019. "Nuclear debates and political competition in Japan, South Korea, and Taiwan: Denuclearization or Nuclear Latency in the aftermath of Fukushima." Page 1.
[62] Seung-Hoi Kim, Yu-I-Ha, Meeyoung Cha, Jiyon Lee, Byoung-Jik Kim, Dong-Myung Lee, 2016. " Public discourse on environmental pollution and health in Korea: Tweets following the Fukushima nuclear accident." The Workshop of the Tenth International AAAI Conference on Web and Social Media Social Web for Environmental and Ecological Monitoring: Technical Report WS-16-20. Webpage available at: https://aaai.org/ocs/index.php/ICWSM/ICWSM16/paper/view/13219/12863 (or) https://ojs.aaai.org/index.php/ICWSM/article/view/14854/14704 Accessed 10/2023.
[63] Seung-Hoi Kim, Yu-I-Ha, Meeyoung Cha, Jiyon Lee, Byoung-Jik Kim, Dong-Myung Lee, 2016. " Public discourse on environmental pollution and health in Korea: Tweets following the Fukushima nuclear accident." Page 190.
[64] Kai-Yuan Ke, Yong-Jun Lin, Yih-Chi Tan, Tsung-Yi Pan, Li-Li Tai, and Ching-An Lee,

through fundamental concessions made about systematic deliveries of upgraded communication rescue equipment and local mapping exchange tools,[65] the local provision of structural health and community services can support multiple knowledge-related education settings and distribution environments (e.g. medical) maintaining corresponding communication standards, while implementing local environmental assessment models (referring e.g. to local agencies' ICT public tasks; local risk testing procedures; cooperative local management, and community-level planning results). Public participatory needs specified according to increasing levels of transparent information and decentralized environmental knowledge processed through territorial management models, involving the administrative departments, schools, local enterprises, volunteers, NGOs, and interested stakeholders,[66] have been interrelated with progressive institutional dialogues catalyzed on conventional protection schemes such as Taiwan disaster prevention communities adaptation plans,[67] including local safety prevention and security protection issues (Ho, 2014). The next part of this analysis focuses on a comparative overview of environmental governance studies.

3. Regional Environmental Review and Tangible Development Traits about NPPs

In this section, it is briefly reviewed the environmental participatory discourse undertaken about East-Asia Taiwan for comparative analysis interrelated to nuclear environmentalism.[68] In 2021, it is politically

2020. "Enhancing local disaster management network through developing resilient community in New Taipei City, Taiwan." International Journal of Environmental Research and Public Health, Volume 17, Issue 15, 2020. DOI: 10.3390/ijerph17155357

65 Kai-Yuan Ke, Yong-Jun Lin, Yih-Chi Tan, Tsung-Yi Pan, Li-Li Tai, and Ching-An Lee, 2020.

66 Kai-Yuan Ke, Yong-Jun Lin, Yih-Chi Tan, Tsung-Yi Pan, Li-Li Tai, and Ching-An Lee, 2020.

67 Chin-Yu He, Ching-Pin Tung, and Yong-Jun Lin, 2021. "Applying the DRCA risk template on the flood-prone disaster prevention community due to climate change." Sustainability, Volume 13, No. 2, 2021. 10.3390/su13020891

68 Note: Being either Pro or Anti Nuclear Environmentalism, the IAEA highlights that "Nuclear industries must carefully monitor and control what they release into the environment to keep the air, water, and land clean. The IAEA's Safety Standards provide for rigorous regulatory mechanisms in Member States to restrict the release of radionuclides and control any radiological impact on people and the environment."

reaffirmed that "The premier said that nuclear power plant project was suspended during the administration of former president Ma Ying-jeou (馬英九)[...], and that the disposal of nuclear waste from the nation's first and second nuclear power plants remains a problem, so it would be impossible to restart construction of the fourth plant now. [...], the Green Citizens' Action Alliance [...] said the share of non-hydro renewables in global electricity generation exceeded that of nuclear power for the first time in 2019, implying that nuclear energy is a declining industry, and that Taiwan should push its energy transition policy forward."[69] In parallel to the withdrawal from operational nuclear programs, it can be pointed out that progressive regional processes engaging national civilian environment groups, including local institutional counterparts, have basically evolved through the introduction of distinctive collaborative environmental tracks such as the 2001 Integrated Community-Based Disaster Management Program (ICBDM)[70] for local hazard mitigation guidelines (Chen, et al., 2006);[71] while there have been contingent elements regarding common environmental planning and territorial regulative conditions, when particularly focused on Taiwan, [with a reference to human health and the deployment of decentralized transparent tools supporting environmental implementation locally despite the divergent[72] formal and informal regulative orientations] (Ho, 2014; Liu, 2011). While considering modern

International Atomic Energy Agency (IAEA), 2021. "Environmental release." Website available at: https://www.iaea.org/topics/environmental-release Accessed 10/2023.

[69] Lee I-chia/Taipei Times Staff reporter, 2021. "Nuclear power not an option: Su." Taipei Times, 21 March 2021. World Nuclear Industry Status Report. Website available at: https://www.worldnuclearreport.org/Nuclear-power-not-an-option-Su.html Accessed 10/2023.

[70] Note: The (ICBDM) initiative " was launched in 2001 by the Executive Yuan to achieve the goal of strengthening community resistance[...] These programs [have] three categories: type A: disaster prevention and response groups sponsored by the fire fighting agencies; type B: disaster response and recovery actions actively undertaken by communities; type C: community-based disaster management programs." Liang-Chun Chen, Yi-Chung Liu, and Kuei-Chi Chan, 2006. "Integrated Community-Based Disaster Management Program in Taiwan: A Case Study of Shang-An Village." Natural Hazards, Volume 37, pp. 209-223.

[71] Liang-Chun Chen, Yi-Chung Liu, and Kuei-Chi Chan, 2006. "Integrated Community-Based Disaster Management Program in Taiwan: A Case Study of Shang-An Village." Natural Hazards, Vol. 37, No. 1, pp. 209-223.

[72] Simona Grano, 2015. "Environmental issues facing Taiwan." Brookings Series: Taiwan-U.S. Quarterly Analysis, November 9, 2015. Webpage available at: https://www.brookings.edu/articles/environmental-issues-facing-taiwan/ Accessed 10/2023.

adaptive expressions about local collective engagements and societal cooperative dialogues, emerging possibly in line with newly formed public regional affiliations, such as in Taiwan's collective indigenous rights-based context, the political influence played by major political parties like the KMT and the Democratic Progressive Party (DPP) has resulted in divergent regional executive approaches, based on strategic confrontational shifts; [in 2016 Taiwan president Tsai made an official speech and took up new commitments on behalf of the DPP-led government in order to promote cooperation with indigenous tribes in Taiwan, adding that legislative steps would include: 'the Indigenous Peoples Self-Government Act, the indigenous Peoples Land and See Areas Act, and the Indigenous Languages Development Act'].[73] During the same apologetic discussion in 2016, President Tsai recognized the multiple detrimental impacts that Orchid Island inhabitants had experienced due to nuclear waste policies that affected directly human health on the island while producing disempowerment for the indigenous groups.[74] Particularly, the stringent political divide existing about the implementation of nuclear-based energy planning projects, has been challenged by anti-nuclear movements protesting on comparative environmental proposals, for the construction of a fourth nuclear power plant,[75] the Lungmen NPP located in Gongliao district,[76] in New Taipei City, Taiwan (Ho, 2014; Hsu, 2005).

The actual intensification of public environmental protests taking place under the KMT's party government[77] has led to the unionisation of

[73] Office of the President Republic of China (Taiwan), 2016. "President Tsai apologizes to indigenous peoples on behalf of government." News & Activities, 2016-08-01. Website available at: https://english.president.gov.tw/NEWS/4950 Accessed 10/2023.

[74] Office of the President Republic of China (Taiwan), 2016.

[75] Note: The energy company Taiwan Power Co. stated: "Taipower said it would take at least six to seven years to start commercial operations at the plant in New Taipei City's Gongliao District. The Lungmen plant has been mothballed since July 2015 following environmental protests over the potential dangers of nuclear power.[...]" Nuclear Engineering, 2019. "Taipower rules out operation of Lungmen." Nuclear Engineering, published on 6 February, 2019. Available at Website: https://www.neimagazine.com /news/newstaipower-rules-out-operation-of-lungmen-6970272 Accessed 10/2023.

[76] Christopher Lupke, 2012. "Documenting Environmental Protest: Taiwan's Gongliao Fourth Nuclear Power Plant and the Cultural Politics of Dialogic Artifice." In : Documenting Taiwan on Film (eds) 2012 London, Routledge, Chapter 8 (28 pages).

[77] Note: In retrospective view "One observes the incoherence of the KMT in proposals by

NGOs and civilian environmental coalitions, such as "[...] the Green Citizen Action Alliance, the Taiwan Environmental Protection Union, the Taiwan Environmental Information Association, the Yanliao Anti-Nuclear Self-Help Association, [as well as] Third Force parties [...]," [78] which have been democratically opposed to further nuclear construction projects for additional local nuclear power plants NPP, supporting state's industrial innovation approaches (Hsu, 2005). In effect, after centralized power ruling decisions undertaken through stringent coordination lines, indirectly impacting on societal security formation routes and localized polluting industries innovation projects, monitored by the KMT party, formal institutional changes did occur with the arrival of the democratic party the DPP in 2014 [79] in state and local counties, [80] however getting mixed election results in 2018. The DPP's initial direction favoured a critical affirmation of democratic legitimacy representations by bringing into light local collaborative reforming provisions e.g. through constitutional reforms [81] granted for the facilitation of collective environmental debates, involving the local anti-nuclear coalitions [82] and

the party to restart the controversial Gongliao Nuclear Reactor n. 4 due to public opposition to plans by Taipower to build a new coal-fired plant in Shenao. Local residents fear that environmental assessments have not been adequately conducted by Taipower and claim that Taipower did not adequately consult with local residents before moving forward with plans to construct the plant." Brian Hioe, 2018. "KMT asserts inconsistent stance on nuclear power simply to oppose DPP." New Bloom, Radical perspectives on Taiwan and the Asia Pacific, 29/4/2018. Available at website: https://newbloommag.net/2018/04/29 /kmt-nuclear-power-stance/ Accessed 10/2023.

[78] Brian Hioe, 2018. "Annual anti-nuclear demonstration in Taipei marks seventh anniversary of Fukushima disaster." New Bloom, Environmental, Social Movements, published March, 2018. Available at Website: https://newbloommag.net/2018/03/11 /fukushima-seventh-demo/ Accessed 10/2023.

[79] Ross Darrel Feingold, , 2018. "Taiwan Election Results Are a Message to the DPP." South China Morning Post, 27 Nov., 2018. Available at website: https://www.scmp.com/ comment/insight-opinion/united-states/article/2175174/taiwan-election-results-are-message-dpp-mixing Accessed May 2020

[80] Frank Muyard, 2015. "Voting Shift in the November 2014 Local Elections in Taiwan. Strong Rebuke to Ma Ying-jeou's Government and Policies and Landslide Victory for the DPP." China Perspectives. Volume 1, pp. 55.61.

[81] Ministry of Foreign Affairs, 2016. "Progressive Leadership." MOFA-EN-105_011-|-1. Available at Website: https://www.taiwan.gov.tw/images/ufile/file20160929111258969. pdf?msclkid=e245fcbbc0cd11eca03685e0aa6a8550 Accessed 10/2023.

[82] Note: It is highlighted that "Without knowledge of local experience, it is hard to understand how anti-nuclear movements in Taiwan developed from a party-led movement to an independent one; and how communities were reconstructed when partisan politics

environmental organizations already active in local industrial pollution disputes (Hsu, 2005; Liu, 2011).

For a comparative development view, while being on a similar path to South Korea's innovation planning system, the entrepreneurial industrial representatives established in Taiwan have essentially operated according to decentralized business requirements of an industrial democracy[83] by consolidating the sectoral division capacities - across time adapted within regional production networks - and similarly reaffirming widespread technology innovation patterns focused on science and technology development (S&T) as for the case of digital governance[84] in health and food protection policies (Arnold, 1988).[85] This type of STS regional trading partnership has been established in cooperation with socioeconomic organizational partners and ministerial agencies, technically supporting the energy transition programs drafted in state-led PPP innovation plans - "[...] as a key strategy to address the climate issue as well as to enhance its energy security [...] fram[ing] the energy transition from a multilevel governance perspective to explore [...] the changing power relationships between central and local governments in implementing the transition"[86]- retroactively interlinked with Taiwan's technology diffusion mechanisms[87] monitored through exploratory

created divisions among neighbours." Shuge Wei, 2016. "Recovery from 'Betrayal': Local anti-nuclear movements and party politics in Taiwan." The Asia-Pacific Journal, Volume 14, Issue 8, Number 3, 2016. Available at website: https://apjjf.org/2016/08/Wei.html Accessed 10/2023.

83 See: Tzu-Shian Han, and Su-fen Chiu, 2000. "Industrial democracy and institutional environments: A comparison of Germany and Taiwan." Economic and Industrial Democracy, Volume 21, Issue 2, page(s): 147-182.

84 Note: As of 2021, in a post-pandemic situation in Taiwan, has been remarked: "[...] it has succeeded in leveraging information technology and citizen participation into a uniquely successful system of 'digital democracy,' most recently credited with containing COVID-19 in Taiwan." The Consilience Project, 2021. "Taiwan's digital democracy." The Consilience Project is a publication of the Civilization Research Institute (CRI), Situational Feature, 06 June 2021. Available at website: https://www.consilienceproject.org/taiwans-digital-democracy/?msclkid=43ae25c4c25d11ec8cbddc5e62ee8926 Accessed 10/2023.

85 Walter Arnold, 1988. "Science and Technology Development in Taiwan and South Korea." Asian Survey, Volume 28, No. 4, pp. 437-450.

86 Jusen Asuka, and Dan Jin, 2022. "Energy transition and energy democracy in East Asia." Springer Link, Open Access. Page 6 (vi). Available at website: https://doi.org/10.1007/978-981-19-0280-2. Accessed 10/2023.

87 Note: In summary: "[...]Taiwanese business groups did not grow to the mammoth size

development phases during 1970s and 1980s (Ho, 2014). In association with an S&T industrial affirmation, the nuclear power infrastructures NPP, in particular, were expanded only for civilian purposes; however they have increasingly led to critical regulatory and local ethnic confrontations, based on disaster risk co-management issues reviewed by public environmental organizations, and examined through leading national and international information debates,[88] which have been particularly focused on NPP accidents such as during Japan's disaster risk exposures caused by multiple tsunami-earthquakes crises in 2011; therefore the launch of concurrent civilian platforms has been followed for the inclusion of national safety reforms regarding NPP operations, as well as, the changing status of regulatory legal connotations, possibly also redefining an eventual withdrawal of these ageing structures.[89] It can be also highlighted the fact that "Taiwan has four operable nuclear power reactors, which account for around 15% of the island's electricity generation."[90]

In addition to this, further extrinsic values proximate to regional liberalization processes have driven towards the direct establishment of transnational managerial organizations,[91] particularly involved with

of their counterparts in Korea. However, within export sector, which is characterized by relatively free competition, from the 1970s on small and medium-size enterprises (SMEs) took the lead and in so doing became the main support of Taiwan's industrialization." Tamio Hattori, and Yukihito Sato, 1997. "A comparative study of development mechanisms in Korea and Taiwan: Introductory Analysis." The Developing Economies, Volume 35, No. 5, pp. 341-57; p. 9.

[88] OECD, Kimberly A. Sexton, 2015. "Crisis, criticism, change. Regulatory reform in the wake of nuclear accidents." OECD/NEA Nuclear Law Bulletin 2015 Issue 2. Available at website: https://doi.org/10.1787/nuclear_law-2015-5jm22pflfts2 Accessed 10/2023.

[89] Qunying Xiao, Huijun Liu, and Marcus W. Feldman, 2017. "How Does Trust Affect Acceptance of a Nuclear Power Plant (NPP): A Survey Among People Living with Qinshan NPP in China." PLoS One, Volume 12, No. 11. doi: 10.1371/journal.pone.0187941 Accessed 10/2023.

[90] World Nuclear Association, 2019. "Nuclear Power in Taiwan." Updated Report July 2019. Available at website: https://www.world-nuclear.org/information-library/country-profiles/others/nuclear-power-in-taiwan.aspx Accessed April 2020.

[91] Note: For (ICT) transfers: "Technology transfer experiences have also been conditioned by the configuration of national, regional and sectoral innovation systems in place in host countries. However, the policy direction governments take in facilitating knowledge transfers often varies by industry and country, and depend upon the timing of design and implementation strategies." United Nations Conference on Trade and Development (UNCTAD) 2014, "Studies in Technology Transfer." UNCTAD Current Studies on Science, Technology and Innovation. N.7. Page 1. Available at website:

sectoral innovation transfers and local practice distributions operated across East and South-east Asian neighbouring zones. In Taiwan's case securing a renewable energy transition phase has meant putting some efforts on socioeconomic sustainability plans involving technology energy industries, local households, and actual environment systems responsive to renewable energy transitions. Moreover, the specific institutional organization of centralized decision making with technical coordination roles and decentralized managerial responsibilities[92] has been reviewed through the national integration of multilateral energy companies, either directly or indirectly investing into comparable knowledge dynamic transfers and sustainable innovation associated with effective control standards of energy management systems, actualizing regional economic innovation transitions interrelated with local communities' welfare programs (Ho, 2014).

As emphasized, after Japan's critical mass earthquakes and tsunami disaster crises initially starting in March 2011, involving immediate national emergency and disaster response plans due to the nuclear power plants NNPs reactors' defaults with local management failures, occurring in the Fukushima prefecture[93] - in addition to severe socioeconomic and health consequences - there have been significant increasing cases of

https://unctad.org/system/files/official-document/dtlstict2013d7_en.pdf Accessed 10/2023.

[92] Note: About Taiwan's functional science networks: "To facilitate the development of high-technology industries in Taiwan Province of China, the Taiwanese authorities established HSIP [Hsinchu Science-based Industrial Park] in 1980 to host high-technology firms there. [...]The large-scale projects initiated by ITRI and its various spin-offs have made HSIP the centre of the information and communications technology (ICT) industries in Taiwan[...]." United Nations Conference on Trade and Development (UNCTAD) 2014. "Studies in Technology Transfer." UNCTAD Current Studies on Science, Technology and Innovation. N.7. Page 23. Available at website: https://unctad.org/system/files/official-document/dtlstict2013d7_en.pdf Accessed 10/2023.

[93] See: World Nuclear Association report 2018:"The two Fukushima plants and their siting The Daiichi (first) and Daini (second) Fukushima plants are sited about 11 km apart on the coast, Daini to the south. The recorded seismic data for both plants–some 180 km from the epicentre–shows that 550 Gal (0.56 g) was the maximum ground acceleration for Daiichi, and 254 Gal was maximum for Daini. Daiichi units 2, 3 and 5 exceeded their maximum response acceleration design basis in an East-West direction by about 20%. The recording was over 130-150 seconds. (All nuclear plants in Japan are built on rock-- ground acceleration was around 2000 Gal a few kilometres north, on sediments). Available at website: Accessed May 2020. https://www.world-nuclear.org/information-library/safety-and-security/safety-of-plants/fukushima-accident.aspx

nuclear environmental disputes in Japan as well as in other nuclear countries. Civil environmental legal disputes have been intertwined with national decision-making initiatives - which despite pre-designed environmental preparation plans set in advance for favouring local preparedness, local educational trainings, and local risk adaptation programs enhancing safety action-plans - have also resulted in growing levels of public distrust due to the NPP management programs assessed for comparative living environments.

National anti-risk preparedness plans explored in conjunction with the National Science and Technology Center for Disaster Reduction (NCDR)[94] in Taiwan[95] - like the disaster management workshop held in 2021 in Palau[96] to implement common technology-based programs aimed at reducing human vulnerability in cases of major climate exposures - have essentially testified the formal need to improve public awareness initiatives on local disaster management, also by enhancing mutual forms of communication systems[97] and by systematically advising on local

[94] National Science and Technology Center for Disaster Reduction Background Report, Available at the website: https://ncdr.nat.gov.tw/oriNCDR/Introduction.aspx?WebSiteID=873f5b27-b86d-4d5c-a356-c369768bffe9&id=43&subid=48&PageID=6 Accessed on April 2020.

[95] Note: In retrospective is highlighted that "In July 2003, the National Science and Technology Center for Disaster Reduction (NCDR), transitioned from the Program Office of the National Science and Technology Program for Hazard Mitigation (NAPHM), was officially established as a think-tank to the government by providing in-depth suggestions on natural disaster reduction. In 2014, following the restructured framework of the Executive Yuan, NCDR received a new identity, 'administrative entity,' and is now operated under the supervision of the Ministry of Science and Technology Council." NCDR Background Presentation. Webpage available at: https://ncdr.nat.gov.tw/oriNCDR/Introduction.aspx?WebSiteID=873f5b27-b86d-4d5c-a356-c369768bffe9&id=43&subid=48&PageID=6 (or) https://www.ncdr.nat.gov.tw/Page?itemid=60&mid=74 Accessed 10/2023.

[96] (NCDR) Taiwan National Science and Technology Center for Disaster Reduction, 2021. "Taiwan - Palau disaster management training workshop." Pacific Partnership 2021, U.S./Taiwan/Palau Disaster Management Workshop Koror, Palau. Published on 13/08/2021. Website Available at: https://www.ncdr.nat.gov.tw/Message/MessageView?itemid=4760&mid=93&msclkid=28f02fc2ca4f11ecadeb00491f6d2f0b Accessed 10/2023.

[97] Leo Bosner, and I-wei Jennifer Chang, 2020. "Taiwan's disaster preparedness and response: strengths, shortfalls, and paths to improvement." Global Taiwan Institute, Dossier October, 2020. Available at Website: https://globaltaiwan.org/wp-content/uploads/2020/10/GTI-Taiwans-Disaster-Preparedness-and-Response-Oct-2020-final.pdf?msclkid=441f890bca5111ec9254cb7e054a097f As of 10/2023 Authors' article

disaster risk factors [98] including temporary uncertain conditions, still critically related with national rescue efforts and coordination of internal forces,[99] involving multilateral safety missions,cyclically tested for the NPP technical managerial operations (Liu, 2011). Comparatively, multilevel government agencies collaborating in view of improving standardized procedural agreements about safety emergency for - e.g. "the full-scale exercise of the 2021 Taiwan Nuclear Emergency Exercise [...] targeted at decommissioning Chin Shan Nuclear Power Plant (NPP) for the first time" [100] - with security management procedures regarding NPPs [101] and nuclear waste disposal activities, have fundamentally

on GTI's webpage: https://globaltaiwan.org/search-results/?_sf_s=Taiwan%E2%80%99s+disaster+preparedness+and+response%3A+strengths%2C+shortfalls%2C+and+paths+to+improvement cannot be retrieved.

98 Note: For cooperation in the South-East Asia Region: "NCDR implements the program of New Southbound Countries by Smart Disaster Risk Management under Ministry of Science and Technology since 2018, to promote the disaster risk reduction experience of Taiwan to Southeast Asia and South Asia. Following the promotion of this program in Nepal, Bhutan and the Philippines, NCDR will [...] carry out the earthquake and rainfall monitoring system, data platform of disaster information network, and training programs for disaster prevention in the north of Viet Nam." National Science and Technology Center for Disaster Reduction (NCDR) Newsletters, December 2020, New Taipei City, Taiwan. "The MoU signed between NCDR and HUNRE, and will develop the cooperation on DRR technologies with Viet Nam." Available at website: https://ncdr.nat.gov.tw/Files/NewsLetter/20201230155753.pdf (or) https://www.ncdr.nat.gov.tw/Home/Index?aspxerrorpath=/Epaper/NewsLetterDownload/270%20%c2%b7%20PDF%20file Accessed 10/2023. Alternatively, it can be downloaded on Bing Search Engine using keyword: *2020 The MoU signed between NCDR and HUNRE, and will develop the cooperation on DRR technologies with Viet Nam.*

99 Leo Bosner, and I-wei Jennifer Chang, 2020.

100 Atomic Energy Council, 2021. "Well prepared for the 2021 Taiwan Nuclear Emergency Exercise during the COVID-19 pandemic." (AEC), What's New report, 29/09/2021. Available at website: https://www.aec.gov.tw/english/newsdetail/pressrelease/193.html?msclkid=411aeb78ca5311ec950be0ed0ccbc2e9 (or) https://www.nusc.gov.tw/english/newsdetail/pressrelease/194.html As of 10/2023, Title and main contents have been modified compared to the first web-link currently deleted; it opens on the homepage of (AEC) only. The second web-link retrieved from What's New: Press Release webpage archive: (2021-09-29), probably modified.

101 Note: For NPP National Response Programs, Evaluative Safety Missions have reported that: "Based on reviews of the National Report and the Stress Test reports for Chinshan, Kuosheng, and Maanshan NPPs, the independent peer review team concluded that the stress test met the criteria established by ENSREG [European Nuclear Safety Regulator's Group] and followed by the EU for the stress tests of NPPs in Europe. Building on the results of the stress test and insights from the actions being taken by other countries, the AEC [Atomic Energy Council] established clear requirements to implement enhancements.

supported local institutional counterparts, civic transnational NGOs, East Asian community-based members [102] and MNC industrial business providers, in order to favour knowledge trainings and information exchanges, specifically related to the formation of practical data-driven platforms, and integrative monitoring strategies tackling e.g. environmental justice issues, because associated to growing territorial protection concerns (Huang, et al., 2013 [103]). In 2018, under the DPP president Tsai Ing-wen's administration, a public survey published by the Taiwan Research Institute confirmed that the population maintained its distrust on NPP programs due to local nuclear waste disposal management implications.[104] See Table 1 summarizing Taiwan NPPs status through NPP safety overview according to AEC Taiwan Agency, available on webpage section: 'Nuclear Reactor Safety,' subtopic: 'NPPs of Taiwan.'

Based on the observations by the independent peer review team, it is concluded that the AEC and TPC [Taipower Company] effectively implemented a comprehensive safety review that has resulted in significant enhancements that have better prepared the operating reactors in Chinese Taipei to respond to extreme external events and severe accidents should they occur." AEC Dr. Chuen-Horng Tsai, 2013. "Independent Peer Review of the Stress Tests performed on the operating reactors in Chinese Taipei." Atomic Energy Council Report, Issued on 23 April 2013. Available at: https://www.aec.gov.tw/share/file/e_regulation/mSvbyXVrcnGTifwVgmdOKQ.pdf As of 10/2023 the link has been moved. Through search engine DuckDuckGo retrieved 'AEC' doc. pdf links (opening the AEC homepage only). This Footnote refers to: Atomic Energy Council Report, Issued on 23 April 2013, currently it cannot be retrieved. Instead from the European Nuclear Safety Regulator's Group (EU-ENSREG) could be retrieved the November 2013 Report called "EU Peer Review Report of the Taiwanese Stress Tests."Available at website for consultation: https://www.ensreg.eu/sites/default/files/EU%20Peer%20Review%20of%20the%20Taiwanese%20Stress%20Tests.pdf Accessed 10/2023.

[102] Seung-Youn Oh, 2018. "Quite Transformation from the Bottom: Emerging Transnational Networks Among Non-State Actors in Northeast Asia Community-Building." In Hayes P., Moon CI. (eds) The Future of East Asia Today. Palgrave Macmillan, Singapore.

[103] Gillan Chi-lun Huang, Tim Gray, Dereck Bell, 2013. "Environmental justice of nuclear waste policy in Taiwan: Taipower, government, and local community." Environment, Development and Sustainability, Volume 15, No. 6, DOI 10.1007/s10668-013-9461-1.

[104] Central News Agency, 2019. "Most Taiwan People Want Reduction in Fossil Fuel Power: Poll." Taiwan News, March, 11, 2019. Available on Website at: https://www.taiwannews.com.tw/en/news/3655814 Accessed on April 2020.

Table 1: Taiwan Nuclear Power Plants (AEC) Update 2020

"Chinshan"		
Thermal Power	1,840 MWt	
Electric Power	636 MWe	
Reactor Type	BWR-4	
Turbine Vendor	Westinghouse	
Containment Type	Mark-I	
	Unit 1	Unit 2
Commercial Date	12/6/1978	7/16/1979
Expiration Date	12/5/2018	7/15/2019

"Kuosheng"		
Thermal Power	3,001 MWt	
Electric Power	985 MWe	
Reactor Type	BWR-6	
Turbine Vendor	Westinghouse	
Containment Type	Mark-III	
	Unit 1	Unit 2
Commercial Date	12/28/1981	3/15/1983
Expiration Date	12/27/2021	3/14/2023

"Maanshan"		
Thermal Power	2,822 MWt	
Electric Power	951 MWe	
Reactor Type	PWR	
Turbine Vendor	General Electric	
Containment Type	Large, Dry Post-Tensioned	
	Unit 1	Unit 2
Commercial Date	7/27/1984	5/18/1985
Expiration Date	7/26/2024	5/17/2025

"Lungmen"[105]		
Thermal Power	3,926 MWt	
Electric Power	1,350 MWe	
Reactor Type	ABWR	
Turbine Vendor	Mitsubishi	
Containment Type	Reinforced Concrete Containment Vessel	
	Unit 1	Unit 2
Construction License Issued Date	3/17/1999	3/17/1999

Source: Atomic Energy Council Update 2020. Available at webpage: https://www.nusc.gov.tw/english/Nuclear-Reactor-Safety/Table-242.html Accessed 10/2023.

Through comparative understanding, it can be specified that practical policy implications deriving from national and regional institutional partnerships such as the "disaster cooperation forums between Taiwan, Japan, the United States, and the United Kingdom founded on humanitarian assistance and resilient actions in 2011"[106] have been based on the experience of an increasing awareness for disaster relief actions and local risk mitigation plans, drafted by corresponding disaster reduction agencies, [107] requiring a sustainable degree of continuity for local development activities that have already been in place, especially concerning local procedural and organizational approaches, mediating collective interests of local civilian counterparts and territorial environmental stakeholders (Huang, et al., 2013). Disaster prevention crisis units in Taiwan have been confronted with major disaster episodes such as with the impact of typhoon Morakot in southern Taiwan in 2009,

[105] Note: As stated by the World Nuclear Association on Lungmen NPP: "In February 2019 Taipower ruled out starting up the plant. It stated that it would take six to seven years to start commercial operation, and that GE would not be able to replace many of the ageing components installed 20 years ago as the company had ceased production of many of them." WNA, 2023. "Nuclear Power in Taiwan." Report updated June 2023. Webpage available at: https://www.world-nuclear.org/information-library/country-profiles/others/nuclear-power-in-taiwan.aspx Accessed 10/2023.

[106] Robert D. Eldridge, 2021. "Partners in disaster relief: Taiwan, Japan, the United Kingdom, and the United States." Global Taiwan Institute, Global Taiwan Brief, Volume 6, Issue 9. Available at website: https://globaltaiwan.org/2021/05/partners-in-disaster-relief-taiwan-japan-the-united-kingdom-and-the-united-states/ Accessed 10/2023.

[107] Teng Pei-ju, 2018. "Taiwan a model of disaster preparedness in Indo-Pacific region: AIT deputy director." Taiwan News, December 14, 2018. Available at Website: https://www.taiwannews.com.tw/en/news/3596890 Accessed on April 2020.

when it was put into question the inter-agency coordination and disaster responses for local residents.[108] In the case of distributed multilevel cooperative processes in particular, the formal consolidation of quality assessment dynamics forming at governance level, for example through: the Local Disaster Management Network for urban communities in Taipei City,[109] has entailed integrative partnerships with local environmental NGOs and other committed organizing parties, participating in local knowledge integrated exchanges [110] - involving communication management and preventive rescue plans - for the mutual inclusion of local citizens and promotion of updated information connected with complementary ICT communication and operational networks at community level.

In conjunction to participatory schemes matching with disaster relief initiatives, for the specific organization of NPP planning projects adapted in Taiwan, there is to consider that both nuclear waste industrial management process NWM - indirectly providing an improvement of disaster collaborative networks for communities[111] - and nuclear waste disposal activities NWD have been upgraded in line with territorial policies favouring the energy mix approach due to the rapid requirements of renewable energy innovation programs, evolving under the Renewable Energy Development Act 2009-2013,[112] even though "a greater percent of the electricity in Taiwan is produced from fossil fuels compared to the

[108] PreventionWeb, 2009. "Taiwan: Legislature suggests local disaster relief, prevention alliances." UNDRR, Taiwan News, 28 December 2009. Available at website: https://www.preventionweb.net/news/taiwan-legislature-suggests-local-disaster-relief-prevention-alliances Accessed 10/2023.

[109] Kai-Yuan Ke, Yong-Jun Lin, Yih-Chi Tan, Tsung-Yi Pan, Li-Li Tai, Ching-An Lee, 2020. "Enhancing local disaster management network through developing resilient community in New Taipei City, Taiwan." International Journal of Environmental Research and Public Health, Volume 17, No. 15. Doi: 10.3390/ijerph17155357.

[110] Cheng-Tong Lir Wang and Ralph Ittonen Hosoki, 2016. "From Global to Local: Transnational Linkages, Global Influences, and Taiwan's Environmental NGOs." Sociological Perspective, Volume 59, No. 3, pp. 561-581.

[111] Yung-Nane Yang, 2015. "The nuclear disaster management system in Taiwan: A case study of the third (Maanshan) nuclear power plant." Disasters (DI), Volume 40, No. 3, pp. 534-553.

[112] World Nuclear Association, 2019. "Nuclear Power in Taiwan." Updated Report. Available at Website: https://www.world-nuclear.org/information-library/country-profiles/others/nuclear-power-in-taiwan.aspx Accessed April 2020.

rest of the world."[113] Therefore by having an heavy reliance on imported energy,[114] this energy diversification process led in Taiwan has included a: "total power generated in 2017 of 270 TWh gross, nuclear providing 22.5 TWh (8%), coal 126 TWh (47%), oil 12.8 TWh (5%), gas 93 TWh (35%), hydro 8.9 TWh (1%), biofuels and waste 3.6 TWh and solar and wind 3.4 TWh."[115] Essentially, while taking into account NPP monitoring management requirements combined with NWM inspection activities of low-level radioactive waste from NPPs,[116] the resulting industrial energy assets configuration has eventually caused detrimental effects on public land systems leading in fact to the formulation of environmental protection plans, as well as safety reassessments and upgraded performances[117] (Arrigo, et al, 2006;[118] Hsu, 2005;[119] Hsu, 2015).[120] Most environmental studies which have referred to progressive affirmations of local participatory platforms supporting environmental activism in Taiwan,

[113] GPP, 2022. "The energy mix of Taiwan." Global Petrol Prices, Energy section, Available at website: https://www.globalpetrolprices.com/energy_mix.php?countryId=151 As of 10/2023 the web-link cannot be retrieved.

[114] See: Energy Security Report by: Sih Ting Jhou, and Huei-Chu Liao, 2013. "Taiwan's severe energy security challenges." Brookings, Series: Taiwan-U.S. Quarterly Analysis. Published on September 12, 2013. Available at website: https://www.brookings.edu/opinions/taiwans-severe-energy-security-challenges/ Accessed 10/2023.

[115] World Nuclear Association, 2019. "Nuclear Power in Taiwan." Updated Report Available at Website: https://www.world-nuclear.org/information-library/country-profiles/others/nuclear-power-in-taiwan.aspx Accessed April 2020.

[116] Atomic Energy Council, Taiwan Government Website Available at: https://www.aec.gov.tw/english/radwaste/index01.php Accessed April 2020.

[117] AEC-TW, 2014. "2014 AEC-NRC bilateral technical meeting." Department of Nuclear Regulation, Atomic Energy Council, R.O.C., July 1, 2014, report. Available at website: https://www.aec.gov.tw/share/file/e_law/~7m~WFyTD~HfBaUv2Rnkag__.pdf As of 10/2023, AEC/NSC Nuclear Safety Commission official website: the web-link has been moved.

[118] Linda Gail Arrigo, Gaia Puleston, 2006. "The environmental movement in Taiwan after 2000: Advances and dilemmas." pp. 165-186. In *What has changed? Taiwan before and after the change in ruling parties.* Edited by Dafydd Fell, Henning Kloter, and Chang Bi-yu. Research Unit on Taiwanese Culture and Literature, Ruhr University, Bochum: Volume 4, 2006. Harrassowitz Verlag: Wiesbaden.

[119] Shu-Hsiang Hsu, 2005. "Terminating Taiwan's fourth nuclear power plant under the Chen Shui-bian Administration." Review of Policy Research, Volume 22, No. 2, pp. 171-186.

[120] Kuang-Jung Hsu, 2015. "To regulate or not to regulate: The conundrum of Taiwan's nuclear power." Asian Perspective, Volume 39, No. 4, Special Issue: Nuclear Power in East Asia, pp. 637-665.

have outlined objective reconsiderations on NPPs public energy policies[121] associated with the DPP nuclear energy policy of phasing out nuclear power by 2025.[122] It has been specified by "the Minister of Economic Affairs Shen Jong-chin in January 2019 'there would be no extension or restarts of nuclear power plants in Taiwan due to subjective and objective conditions, as well as a strong public objection.'"[123] In addition to this, systematic strategic environmental assessments (SEA) focussed on comparative energy sectors, on radioactive waste disposal plans, and on local industrial development,[124] have prompted public attention due to an effective territorial affirmation of industrial hybrid engineering systems, combining nuclear energy and renewable energy technologies [125] operationally bounded to recurrent technical defaults, in particular emerging at local NPP's energy production sites (Arrigo, et al, 2006, Hsu, 2005, Hsu, 2015). In such process, there have been increasing environmental monitoring stages about local radiation protection levels, disaster emergency and mitigation programs, and radioactive waste technical information, [126] referring to public safety and regulative protection mechanisms. [127] To consider that "currently, there are no

[121] Note: As pointed out: "To improve the poor energy situation, some environmental groups advocate strategies for zero growth in the electricity demand rate and future energy mix comprising 100 percent renewable energy sources." Sih Ting Jhou and Huei-Chu Liao, 2013. "Taiwan's severe energy security challenges." Brookings, Series: Taiwan-U.S. Quarterly Analysis.

[122] World Nuclear Association, 2019. "Nuclear Power in Taiwan." Updated Report Available at Website: https://www.world-nuclear.org/information-library/country-profiles/others/nuclear-power-in-taiwan.aspx Accessed April 2020.

[123] WNN, 2021. "Early shutdown for Taiwanese reactor." World Nuclear News, 01, July, 2021. Available at website: https://www.world-nuclear-news.org/Articles/Early-shutdown-for-Taiwanese-reactor#:~:text=Phase-out%20policy%20Taiwan%27s%20Democratic%20Progressive%20Party%20%28DPP%29%20was,be%20decommissioned%20as%20their%2040-year%20operating%20licences%20expire. Accessed 10/2023.

[124] Ming-Lone Liou, and Yue-Hwa Yu, 2004. "Development and Implementation of Strategic Environmental Assessment in Taiwan." Environmental Impact Assessment Review, Volume 24, No. 3, pp. 337-350.

[125] Siddharth Suman, 2018. "Hybrid nuclear-renewable energy systems: A review." Journal of Cleaner Production, Volume 181, 20 April 2018, pp. 166-177.

[126] Atomic Energy Council, Taiwan Government Website Available at: https://www.aec.gov.tw/english/radwaste/index01.php Accessed April 2020.

[127] Note: In Romania's nuclear case, the IAEA report states "Law no.111/1996 republished, on the safe deployment, regulation, licensing and control of nuclear activities. Art.37. (1)The central environment protection authority shall organize, under the law, the

permanent disposal facilities in Taiwan for radioactive waste; therefore commercial radioactive waste is stored in nuclear power plants. An LLRW storage facility, equipped with an extra degree of shielding and humidity control, with a capacity of 23,000 drums was put into operation in June 1998 at Chinshan NPP. [...]"[128]

Basically it can be highlighted that national populations involved in environmental pollution disputes through contextual local environmental factors, e.g.: "Today large facilities like nuclear power plants, international airports, commercial ports, fishing harbors, industrial parks and fish farms are having a complex impact on the coastal environment. To control the pollution at the mouths of rivers in western Taiwan is a particularly pressing problem"[129] - interrelated to territorial pollution impacts (Terao, 2002),[130] which have indirectly favoured the polarization of multi-level production management directives and corresponding energy regulatory domains. In fact despite the governmental energy mix approach, renewable energy has created a diverse opposition front run by Taiwan environmental groups.[131] Recent industrial production processes have

environmental radioactivity surveillance network on the territory of Romania, providing the necessary information flow for the integrated monitoring system of the environment parameters. (4) Whenever necessary, the central environment protection authority shall notify CNCAN [National Commission for Nuclear Activities Control] and the Ministry of Administration and Interiors on its findings in the monitoring activity exercised by it, and shall collaborate with these with a view to set up the necessary measures to be taken." Alexandru Rodna, 2012. "Radiological environmental monitoring at NPP Cernavoda." IAEA/NENP - Technical Meeting on Environmental Issues in New Nuclear Power Programmes, IAEA Vienna, Austria, 20 to 23 March 2012. Page 17. Available at website: https://inis.iaea.org/collection/NCLCollectionStore/_Public/43/048/43048644.pdf Accessed 10/2023.

[128] AEC, 2020. "The inspection of low-level radioactive waste from Nuclear Power Plants." Atomic Energy Council, Radioactive Waste Management, July 06, 2020. Available at Webpage: https://www.aec.gov.tw/english/Radioactive-Waste-Management/The-Inspection-of-Low-Level-Radioactive-Waste-from-Nuclear-Power-Plants-156.html As of 2023 AEC/NSC web-link moved.

[129] Geography of Taiwan, 2001. "Taiwan's environmental problems." Website available at: http://twgeog.ntnugeog.org/en/environment/#reference Accessed 10/2023.

[130] Tadayoshi Terao, 2002. "An Institutional Analysis of Environmental Pollution Disputes in Taiwan: Cases of 'Self-Relief.'" The Developing Economies, Volume 40, No.3, pp. 284-304.

[131] Ming-sho Ho, 2020. "Why do Taiwan's environmentalists oppose renewable energy facilities?" University of Nottingham, Taiwan Studies Programme, Taiwan Insight, Special Issue: Energy and Environment in Taiwan. Available at Website: https://taiwaninsight.org/2020/07/13/why-do-taiwans-environmentalists-oppose-renewable-energy-facilities/

been comparatively assessed in regional assertive terms *de facto* dependent on the coordination of technology systems of innovation put in association with national science policies, also undertaken in view of operating in parallel to regional changing directions (Hsu, 2005), for instance "even though solar energy is a mature industry in Taiwan, the country's limited land still hinders its development. Currently, its central and southern counties, such as Kaoshiung and Pingtung, have more than 500 MW of solar power capacity on average; policies like the Green Energy Roofs project and the Photovoltaic Farming project are the driving force behind the growth."[132] As underlined, in Taiwan's case the political field represented by both major parties the KMT and the DPP has been constantly integrated with a set of distinctive programmatic objectives: "in 2017 DPP pushed through many reforms and progressive laws, including pension reform, a forward-looking infrastructure plan, transitional justice acts, [etc]"[133] - which have been related to societal ethnic divisions emerging across dominant organized historical formations; especially when it can be seen a connection with environmental legislation processes and national industrial implementations of STS case-by-case innovative arrangements (Arrigo, et al, 2006). In 2021 it was signed a collaborative bilateral agreement between Taiwan and Japan in order to upgrade a mutual partnership on the semiconductor manufacturing industry and supply-related operations and to establish a common production framework within the East Asia region.[134]

At state level, the actual creation of specialized administrative tutelage agencies facilitating public environmental protection schemes, through for instance the (TEPU) Taiwan Environmental Protection Union, or the (AEC) Taiwan Atomic Energy Council, has been mutually monitored for

Accessed 10/2023.

[132] Chris Chang, 2020. "Taiwan to boost renewable energy to 20% by 2025, introduce trillion-dollar investment." Taiwan News, 2020/02/27. Available at website: https://www.taiwannews.com.tw/en/news/3880997 Accessed 10/2023.

[133] Council of Asian Liberals and Democrats, 2019. "Democratic progressive party in Taiwan." Available at Website: http://cald.org/member-parties/democratic-progressive-party-of-taiwan/ Accessed 10/2023.

[134] Jason Pan, 2021. "DPP, LDP agree to enhance collaboration."Taipei Times, Taiwan News, December, 25th 2021. Available at website: https://www.taipeitimes.com/News/taiwan/archives/2021/12/25/2003770168 Accessed 10/2023.

legislative and regulatory correspondence concerning decentralized safety mechanisms and industrial innovation adaptive measures; TEPU's reform initiatives among others have referred to the 1994 Environmental Impact Assessment Act (EIA) and the Basic Environment Act[135] approved in 2002 (Arrigo, et al, 2006, Hsu, 2005, Hsu, 2015). In addition, due to a national phase-out nuclear policy promoted since 2016 by the DPP presidency office, it is confirmed that by 2024-5 the NPP Maanshan 1 and 2 units have to enter the decommissioning phase: "Taiwan Power Company (Taipower) has submitted an application to the Atomic Energy Council (AEC) to shut down [...] the Maanshan Nuclear Power Plant. Under Taiwan's nuclear phase-out policy, its power reactors will be decommissioned as their 40-year operating licences expire [...];"[136] the resulting energy policy reforms have included public discussions on local safety issues, land use policies, and compensation schemes, put forward by TEPU and civilian groups, meanwhile the two-unit NPP has to be decommissioned by 2025.[137] As result, the distinctive regulatory process supporting over the years a democratic referendum system has been interrelated to the development of collective environmental NGOs converging on anti-nuclear positions, including local environmental campaigns addressing the issue of no further NPP construction plans, especially for the fourth Lungmen NPP project planned in Taiwan. Public safety perceptions and emerging environmental concerns about the criticality levels of local industrial organizational plans have been reviewed cyclically in collaboration with environmentalists and KMT and DPP county representatives (Ho, 2011).[138]

[135] Taiwan Review, 2017. "Voice of the People." In Taiwan Today, published May, 01, 2017. Available at Website: https://taiwantoday.tw/news.php?unit=4,8,12,17,20&post=114985 Accessed April 2020.

[136] WNN, 2021. "Taipower applies to decommission Maanshan plant." World Nuclear News, 27 July 2021. Available at website: https://www.world-nuclear-news.org/ (or) https://www.world-nuclear-news.org/Articles/Taipower-applies-to-decommission-Maanshan-plant#:~:text=Taiwan%20Power%20Company%20has%20submitted%20an%20application%20to,the%20closure%20of%20Maanshan%20unit%202%20in%202025. Accessed 10/2023.

[137] George Liao, 2019. "An end in sight for Taiwan's third nuclear power plant." Taiwan News, 2019/09/25. Available at website: https://www.taiwannews.com.tw/en/news/3784154 Accessed 10/2023.

[138] Ming-sho Ho, 2011. "Environmental Movement in Democratizing Taiwan (1980-

For comparative assessments, the rapid introduction of environmental safety criteria and protection adaptive regulations for East Asia, mostly targeting specialized transnational productions also referring to the nuclear NPP and chemical industries, has entailed the practical affirmation of environmental knowledge programs [139] and knowledge management information transfers focussing on local capacity development through: Disaster Management planning DM and community information exchanges CIE[140] combined with science innovation transfers STS, which have been strengthened through civic grass-roots engagements and local administrative support. These different public-private DM interdependent constructions have been reviewed according to the characterization of common governmental objectives identified in Taiwan's political leaderships.

To clarify that Taiwanese industrial innovation systems have been intertwined with dynamic international trading programs merged with negotiated decision-making activities, however experienced only in more recent decades. For instance, the identification of targeted environmental opposition campaigns about the implementation of regulatory development plans concerning the fourth nuclear energy facility (NPP) Lungmen in Taiwan, as underlined, has been dependent on regional cooperation directives for local technical activities undertaken by ministerial members, changing technical monitoring committees, and citizens' representatives,[141] which have practised at local level, including

2004): A Political Opportunity Structure Perspective." In J. Broadbent V. Brockman (eds.), *East Asian Social Movements*, Nonprofit and Civil Society Studies. Springer Science Business Media, LLC 2011. https://doi.org/10.1007/978-0-387-09626-1_13.

[139] Gupta Anil, and Nair Sreeja, 2011. "Environmental knowledge for disaster risk management: Pre-conference volume." In *Environmental Knowledge for Disaster Risk Management,* (Anil K. Gupta, Sreeja S. Nair), National Institute of Disaster Management, IIPA Campus, New Delhi - 110 002.

[140] For the Health Sector (CIE) is identified as multidisciplinary approach. See: Community Information Exchanges (CIE) 211 San Diego, U.S. Webpage: https://ciesandiego.org/what-is-cie/ Accessed on May, 2021.

[141] Note: In summary: "Taiwanese citizens [have asked] that the government halts construction of the Fourth Power Plant[...] and decommission the other nuclear power plants on the island,[...] and amend the Referendum Act." Sacha Lin, 2019. "Taiwanese citizens demonstrate to end construction of the Fourth Nuclear Power Plant and amend the Referendum Act, 1988-2017." Global Nonviolent Action Database, 2019. Available at website: https://nvdatabase.swarthmore.edu/content/taiwanese-citizens-demonstrate-end-

the environmental NGOs and civilian organizations. In 2002, it is reported about Lungmen NPP management that "The inferior materials were in constructing the second to fifth layers of the pedestal which is intended to support the nuclear reactor. According to the Kaohsiung District Prosecutor's Office, inferior welding materials were used at 282 points, and an attempt was made to hide this by covering with materials that meet quality standards. The Atomic Energy Council said that about 52% of materials were replaced with 'inferior goods which are less pressure-resistant.'"[142] On a similar note, almost two decades later in 2019 it is specified that "State-run Taiwan Power Co (Taipower) on 31 January ruled out starting up the Lungmen nuclear power plant [...] The Lungmen plant has been mothballed since July 2015 following environmental protests over the potential dangers of nuclear power. Citing a legislative resolution passed last year, Taipower said it is required to remove all the fuel rods from the plant by the end of 2020."[143] Therefore, DPP governmental office has maintained a national phase-out nuclear policy scheduled for 2025-30.[144]

Political activism in centralized ruling systems as in the case of Taiwan has been confronted with multilevel procedural aggregations for functional roles and joint responsibilities, and bureaucratic collaborative configurations, involving central and local representative agencies and community stakeholders. In line with renewable energy reforms to sustain compatible technology programs and institutional research activities, a series of centralized and decentralized sponsoring plans have looked on how to increase the national energy capacity in order to reach a

construction-fourth-nuclear-power-plant-and-amend-referen Accessed 10/2023.

[142] Wise, 2002. "Taiwan: welds falsified in new scandal at Lungmen." World Information Service on Energy, (WISE), Nuclear Monitor Issue: #570, 28/06/2002. Available at website: https://www.wiseinternational.org/nuclear-monitor/570/taiwan-welds-falsified-new-scandal-lungmen Accessed 10/2023.

[143] NEI, 2019. "Taipower rules out operation in Lungmen." Nuclear Engineering International, 06 February 2019. Progressive Media International, Registered office: London, England. Available at website: https://www.neimagazine.com/news/newstaipower-rules-out-operation-of-lungmen-6970272 Accessed 10/2023.

[144] NEI, 2020. "Nuclear power to 2030: key countries." Nuclear Engineering International, Features, 08 July 2020. Available at website: https://www.neimagazine.com/features/featurenuclear-power-to-2030-key-countries-8017370/ Accessed 10/2023.

corresponding energy security policy for the next decade.[145] Instead, in the case of nuclear policy development, the continuous association of NPP national energy planning and local environmental management EIA/SEA has signalled the need to enhance a complementary local framework of institutional information networks by upgrading comparative safety mechanisms with knowledge transfers as well as creating multi-purpose sustainable initiatives, such as "Best practice and lessons learnt when using stakeholder engagement to make decisions on any changes in a NPP [...],"[146] while essentially favouring common cognitive orientations for social empowerment relations. In particular, through the effective cooperation of independent operating agencies such as DM protection bodies, industrial ICT organizations involved, and collective environmental parties, the social empowerment process can become more coherent in view of granting public safety conditions and common trusting elements (Hsu, 2005; Arrigo, et al, 2006). Participatory objective models have suggested that local preparation activities and research methods based on ICT diffusion can fully expand to the rural areas with applicable communication networks and self-learning educational approaches that tackle diverse community's needs among the engaged local participants.[147]

Significantly, STS technical governance transitions performing in parallel with democratic decision-making [148] processes entailing consensus and deliberative aims,[149] have led to further consistence on

[145] Sih Ting Jhou, and Huei-Chu Liao, 2013. "Taiwan's severe energy security challenges." BROOKINGS Series: Taiwan-U.S. Quarterly Analysis, September 12, 2013. Available at website: https://www.brookings.edu/opinions/taiwans-severe-energy-security-challenges/ Accessed 10/2023.

[146] British Office Taipei, 2015. "New energy opportunities in Taiwan." Government of the UK, World News Story, October,5, 2015. Available at webpage: https://www.gov.uk/government/news/new-energy-opportunities-in-taiwan Accessed 10/2023.

[147] Yi-Ting Huang, 2015. "Participatory design to enhance ICT learning and community attachment: A case study in rural Taiwan." Future Internet, Volume 7, No. 1, pp. 50-66. DOI:10.3390/fi7010050.

[148] Yuko Fujigaki, 2009. "STS in Japan and East Asia: Governance of Science and Technology and Public Engagement." East Asian Science, Technology and Society: An International Journal, Volume 3, No. 4, pp. 511-518.

[149] Dung-sheng Chen, and Chia-Ling Wu, 2007. "Introduction: Public participation in science and technology in East Asia." East Asian Science, Technology and Society: An International Journal, Volume 1, pp. 15-18. DOI: 10.1007/s12280-007-9005-6.

environmental organizational directions while contouring pragmatic and strategic logic, and indirectly supporting local empowerment efforts for the integration of e.g. participatory health schemes and territorial anti-pollution associated incentives, which have been redefined at normative and judicial level, also in view of formally reducing constant environmental abuses. In more recent decades, public environmental abuses due to planning and regulative limitations[150] have diminished by improving public understanding about the renewed functional formulations regarding local cooperative appropriations, evolving into local environmental and management acceptance models led in Taiwan but also in other East Asian regions.

To highlight the fact that regional environmental stakeholders have been involved with local communities as well as with national aboriginal groups in Taiwan for the formation of environmental protection plans, referring to local environmental impact assessments.[151] For instance, the local environmental disputes catalysed on the geographical siting of radioactive nuclear waste disposal facilities have increased a public demand for updated communication and information mechanisms, as well as for disaster protection knowledge networks,[152] directly monitoring the NPPs day-to-day managerial facilities.

4. Comparative Research Studies Drawing on Local Governance Learning Capabilities

For this research discussion, at this stage it is developed a descriptive analytical approach for basically comparing multidisciplinary socioeconomic regional studies. Considering specifically the nuclear policy literature, it is integrated the science technology and society STS

[150] Hsin-Huang Michael Hsiao, 1990. "The rise of environmental consciousness in Taiwan." Impact Assessment, Volume 8, No. 1-2, pp. 217-231, DOI: 10.1080/07349165.1990.9726039.

[151] Steven Crook, 2021. "Environmental impact assessment: Taiwan's Aborigines and the concept of 'country.'" Taipei Times, 24 March 2021. Available at website: https://www.taipeitimes.com/News/feat/archives/2021/03/24/2003754382 Accessed 10/2023.

[152] European Commission, 2022. "EU civil protection knowledge network." European Civil Protection and Humanitarian Aid Operations. European Union Commission, 28 April 2022. Available at website: https://civil-protection-humanitarian-aid.ec.europa.eu/what/civil-protection/eu-civil-protection-knowledge-network_en Accessed 10/2023.

paradigm,[153] in order to explain some related arguments introducing science learning direction and local environmental governance led in Taiwan - which are internationally bounded though to regional exclusion practices from environmental inter-agency learning opportunities e.g. at the UNFCCC, due to its pending status as a recognized nation for regional disputed conditions[154] still in place. To this purpose, it has been conducted the nuclear policy analysis through field reports that have been produced particularly by technical governmental agencies, national involved organizations, and international academics, focused on socio-technical knowledge diffusion practices designed through performing implementation measures and industrial innovation enabling environments - mainly referring to public multilevel integrated dynamics combined with local sectoral enterprises. In the case of nuclear energy industries in 2018 during the referendum context, Taiwanese based researchers promoted the DPP governmental policy of phasing out nuclear NPP operations by 2025.[155]

In addition, there have been into consideration societal aggregated dynamics on NPP industrial expansion programs, fundamentally related to collective levels of public participation and local institutional promotion, which overall have become more complex to understand over time. As it is observed "...The answer is that nuclear politics in Taiwan today remain tied to decades of social and political history, with attitudes about nuclear power closely associated with political identity. [...] During Taiwan's period of authoritarian rule, the right-wing Kuomintang (KMT) administered nuclear power projects [...] with disregard for local opposition and dissent."[156] This review on Taiwan's nuclear dimension

[153] See: Nasser Mansour, 2009. "Science-Technology-Society (STS): A new paradigm in science education." Bulletin of Science, Technology & Society, Volume: 29 issue: 4, pages: 287-297.

[154] Leslie Mabon, 2021. "Taiwan's status at the science-policy interface for global climate change: Why getting it right matters." University of Nottingham, Taiwan Research Hub, Taiwan Insight, 10 November 2021. Available at website: https://taiwaninsight.org/2021/11/10/taiwans-status-at-the-science-policy-interface-for-global-climate-change-why-getting-it-right-matters/ Accessed 10/2023.

[155] Andrew Silver, 2018. "Taiwan's academics urge public to vote for nuclear power shut-down." Nature, News, 09 November 2018. doi: https://doi.org/10.1038/d41586-018-07337-6.

[156] Seaver Wang, and Daniel Chen, 2021. "Could Taiwan's political left reconsider nuclear

therefore integrates comparative analyses and literature studies in order to explore the changing facets of science and technology most recent developments in industrialized ICT societies, apparently moving toward local cognitive interactions set in line with regional learning tools and knowledge innovation transfer processes. To note that multidisciplinary research emerging about environmental managerial productions and eco-technological modifying plans has remained practically quite disaggregated, particularly about local institutionalism, comparative levels of democratization, and the spread of societal utilitarian models which have been main components in the same picture (Hanna, 2010).[157]

Fundamentally, the institutional assimilation of normative accesses with science innovation paradigms which have pointed at social innovation in Taiwan, through capital-based micro-enterprises,[158] has been substantiated by the emerging societal needs enlarging ICT sectoral information as well as sustainable technology programs, involving local environmental sub-system of productions e.g. for agri-business technologies, local sustainable cooperation, and local health management practices. These qualitative normative approaches have been actualized for the purpose of reaching a common state of socioeconomic reforming objectives, e.g. on multilevel energy plans - especially with regard to necessary coordination processes operated at regional, national, and local levels.[159]

At the same time, science policy integrated by comparative knowledge innovation and technology domains, through the aggregation of compatible regulative mechanisms, has comprised public knowledge management transfers. In the case of both informal and formal common knowledge determinants, the local developing activities have been

power?" The Diplomat, Asia-Pacific section, The Debate/Opinion, 03 December, 2021. Available at website: https://thediplomat.com/2021/12/could-taiwans-political-left-reconsider-nuclear-power/ Accessed 10/2023.

[157] Nagy K. Hanna (2010), An ICT-enabled innovation and enterprise transformation. In: Hanna N. K., *Enabling Enterprise Transformation, Innovation Technology, and Knowledge Management*. Springer, New York. pp. 1-25.

[158] IEIT, 2019. "Taiwan social innovation entrepreneurship" International Entrepreneur Initiative Taiwan, Small and Medium Enterprise Administration, Ministry of Economic Affairs, Taiwan. Available at website: https://startup.sme.gov.tw/innovation As of 10/2023 the web-link had been moved.

[159] Hanna,"An ICT-enabled," 1-25.

calibrated according to the scale of regional ICT's economies, particularly with the inclusion of local innovation clusters associated with public-private industrial environments (PPP), which will be further analyzed in the following section of our narrative. However, in the case of China-Taiwan cross-strait relations the technology transfers partnerships have shifted by increasing centralized guidelines and authorization procedures to make use of innovative technologies and pursue further investments at regional level.[160]

Collective Knowledge Formation and PPP Energy Innovation Designs

Through institutional innovative interactions for effective socioeconomic adaptation, science technology and society (STS) governance networks have entailed industrial organizational changes applying to energy systems with functional performance characteristics but still within historic local communities.[161] For comparative evaluative assessments, the multilateral public-private energy partnerships PPPs have been responsive to technical managerial enhancements concerning local energy distribution designs similarly reflecting the case of nuclear energy industrial attributions. As historic preamble: the state energy company (TPC) in Taiwan founded in 1946 that runs NPP while preparing for the possibility of a 2025-30 phase out of nuclear energy, has developed hydro and thermal power plants since 1954, while investing in construction of thermal plants since 1966; between 1975 and 1985 nuclear power development and construction proceeded following further implementation between 1986 and 1993 for the supply of energy resources across the island.[162] By favoring collective distribution approaches, the changing institutional roles and comprehensive managerial

[160] Feng Ziwei, 2020. "Technology transfers from Taiwan to China now require governmental approval." Taiwan News, 27 August 2020. Available at website: https://www.taiwannews.com.tw/en/news/3995941 Accessed 10/2023.

[161] Lai, Huei-Ling, 2021. "Foregrounding the community: Geo-historical entanglements of community energy, environmental justice, and place in Taihsi Village, Taiwan." Environment and Planning E: Nature and Space, Volume 5, No. 2. https://doi.org/10.1177/25148486211000745 Accessed 10/2023.

[162] Taiwan Power Company (TPC) Website Available at: https://www.taipower.com.tw/en/index.aspx Accessed April 2020.

responsibilities for PPPs, have revealed a centralized configuration of hierarchical systems, which have been operating toward the fulfillment of multilevel programmatic expectations, leading up to a core of functions for a comparative regional affirmation of territorial knowledge transfers and transitioning innovation productions. At this stage, in order to avail a future energy security under DPP government policies "[...] gas-fired power plants would normally form a logical part of such a strategy [...]. Higher dependence on LNG imports would [eventually] result in higher long-term energy security risks, including supply disruptions and volatile oil-link prices [...]."[163]

Therefore, this national collective organizational process shifting rapidly in view of forming predictive developmental conditions directly involving nuclear energy management systems, synthesizes strategic highlights basically referring to the expanding degree of national dependent energy solutions associated with environmental justice implications. Comparatively, it can be considered that in the United States historical recurrences of environmental climate alterations have prompted the U.S. federal authorities to reconsider nuclear energy power development framed within a multilateral industrial reconfiguration, but also intertwined with international nuclear agreements and public-private PPPs for national energy trading networks operability and local planning promotion (Rosenbaum,1999).[164] As specified, there have been changing dynamics on U.S. nuclear policy and national innovation programs "[...] various factors account for the challenges facing the US nuclear industry, including the complex political, economic, scientific, and popular environment around nuclear technology and reliance on nuclear power [...]."[165] In the case of nuclear facilities decommissioning plans the U.S.

[163] Joseph Jacobelli, and Chris Rogers, 2016. "Taiwan: Energy policy and strategy challenges." Bloomberg Professional Services, Bloomberg Intelligence, January 20, 2016. Available at website: https://www.bloomberg.com/professional/blog/taiwan-energy-policy-and-strategy-challenges/ Accessed 10/2023.

[164] Walter A. Rosenbaum, 1999. "The good lessons of bad experience. Rethinking the future of commercial nuclear power." The American Behavioral Scientist, Thousand Oaks, Volume 43, No. 1, pp. 74-91.

[165] Richard Nephew, 2020. "Reconsidering US nuclear cooperation agreements." Center on Global Energy Policy (CGEP), Volume 3, Columbia Climate School, U.S. Available at website: https://www.energypolicy.columbia.edu/publications/reconsidering-us-nuclear-cooperation-agreements Accessed 10/2023.

Nuclear Regulatory Commission (NRC) regulates the licensing and processing actions required at state level.[166] In association with policy energy guidelines, the socioeconomic cooperative affirmations of transnational negotiating systems relying on technological innovation assets have essentially kept in view regional industrial assessments as well as local monitoring of risk-interface management dynamics, which have been favoured in connection with long-term regulatory environment processes.[167]

In either centralized or decentralized PPP on knowledge innovation transfers KI, the maturation of mutual environmental cooperation should rely upon the following core elements:

1. PPP international independence of KI transfer processes
2. Differentiation on sustainable planning strategies for environmental management EM
3. Deliberative quality of service distribution and local managerial transfers
4. Decentralization of PPP development transfer programs
5. States environmental interdependence through ICT monitoring responsive systems

Source: (Rosenbaum, 1999)

Following along these lines, the systematic propagation of states' regional energy initiatives supporting renewable energy projects formally processed through rule-based national development plans, has been aimed at the testing of different ICT technology strategies specified in parallel with institutional directives and environmental local provisions. In Taiwan's case for renewable energy policies, the centralized initiatives supporting local energy adaptation have involved community development and local inclusion of multiple civic groups for a sustainable

[166] See: U.S. NRC, United States Nuclear Regulatory Commission, 2019. "Decommissioning of Nuclear Facilities." Report Available at Website: https://www.nrc.gov/waste/decommissioning.html Accessed April 2020.

[167] See: Risk Interface Management refers to "Interface Management which is the systematic control of all communications that support a process operation." Available at Website: https://www.aiche.org/ccps/topics/elements-process-safety/manage-risks/ conduct-operations/interface-management Accessed May 2020.

environmental energy transition.[168] Similarly, the industrial cooperation incentives have also been stimulated in view of aggregating the complementary safety rules required for industrial energy management systems of NPP and territorial manufacturing compounds. For the formation of ICT local safety systems, the DPP government has additionally created formal paid schemes to improve local employees training periods at corporate level.[169]

This regional alignment process based on PPP has determined critical innovation transfer factors interconnected with Science and Technology (S&T) policies as well as public environmental local adaptations e.g. the anti-risk disaster awareness campaigns.[170] As in Taiwan's case, energy safeguards programs and safety preparedness schemes implemented under PPP agreements have been responsive to structural reforming environments,[171] progressively converging toward public participatory approaches for common science and technology transfers (S&T). Public modernization inductive approaches basically undertaken in view of prioritizing local knowledge management transfers have been identified according to sectoral objectives supported in multilevel ICT socioeconomic industrial affiliations (Rosenbaum, 1999; Nichols,[172]

[168] Natalie Wong, 2020. "Community energy: A way out of energy transition." Taiwan Insight, Taiwan Studies Programme, Research Centre based at the University of Nottingham. 20 July 2020. Available at webpage: https://taiwaninsight.org/2020/07/20/community-energy-a-way-out-of-energy-transition/ Accessed 10/2023.

[169] Bo-Yi Lee, 2021. "Maintaining Taiwan's global ICT industry lead by improving employees's training. " Taiwan Insight, Taiwan Studies Programme, Research Centre based at the University of Nottingham. 4 November 2021. Available at webpage: https://taiwaninsight.org/2021/11/04/maintaining-taiwans-global-ict-industry-lead-by-improving-employees-training/ Accessed 10/2023.

[170] Ministry of Foreign Affairs, Taiwan, 2016. "ICT development in Taiwan." Taipei Trade Office in the Federal Republic of Nigeria, 03 December, 2016. Available at website: https://roc-taiwan.org/ng_en/post/416.html Accessed 10/2023.

[171] Note: In connection to this process: "The government assists green industry through industrial transformation of '5+2 Industrial Innovation Plan,' which aims to transform Taiwan's manufacturing towards high value-added serve and solutions to spur domestic economic growth and industrial development." Firdevs Yuksel, 2018. "Green energy driving force for Taiwanese exports growth." Anadolu Energy Agency, Asia. Available at website: https://www.aa.com.tr/en/energy/solar/green-energy-driving-force-for-taiwanese-exports-growth/21744 Accessed 10/2023.

[172] Rodney W. Nichols, 2008. "Innovation, change, and order: Reflections on science and technology in India, China, and the United States." Technology in Society, Volume 30, No. 3-4, pp. 437-450.

2008). For example, disaster management DM and disaster risk reduction DRR accompanied through ICT technology production [173] fostering community's learning areas has emerged as additional criteria for decision-making environmental initiatives (Yang, et al., 2015).[174]

Similarly, STS governance networks have been actualized through progressive learning skills combined with practical decentralized measures facilitating the integration of public-private PPP sectoral arrangements, formulated in partnership with industrial technology organizations. For instance the enhancement of practical uses of local information and communication methodologies through ICT can facilitate responsive local action-plans in cases of DRR. [175] Furthermore, environmental adaptive mitigation models and local safety strategies tackling e.g. the nuclear energy power management periodically and the technical operational maintenance programs have been carried out through multilevel corporate energy representative groups and multiple environmental climate organizations operating in regions such as China with associated Territories, the Indian subcontinent and the United States (Nichols, 2008; Rosenbaum, 1999).

Through regional science and technology policies (STS), the inclusion of geographically-based governmental indications about security protection conditions has been strengthened across performing techno-industries and R&D assessment agencies, e.g. with "mobile information technology devices" [176] including territorial cooperative groups, interrelated with independent regional expertise commissions such as: the

[173] Yen, C.L., Loh, CH., Chen, L.C., Wei, L.Y., Lee, W.C., Ho, H.Y. 2006. "Development and implementation of disaster reduction technology in Taiwan." Natural Hazards, Volume 37, pp- 3-21. https://doi.org/10.1007/s11069-005-4652-1.

[174] Chia-Lee Yang, Benjamin J.C. Yuan, and Chi-Yo Huang, 2015. "Key Determinant Derivations for Information Technology Disaster Recovery Site Selection by the Multi-Criterion Decision Making Method." Sustainability, MDPI, Volume 7, No. 5, pp. 6149-6188.

[175] Li, W.S., Chang, C.L., Chen, K.H., Lee, Y., 2019. "How ICT changes the landscape of Disaster Risk Management." In: Murayama, Y., Velev, D., Zlateva, P. (eds.) Information Technology in Disaster Risk Reduction. Pp. 12-18. ITDRR 2017. IFIP Advances in Information and Communication Technology, Volume 516. Springer, Cham. https://doi.org/10.1007/978-3-030-18293-9_2.

[176] U.N. ESCAP, 2016. "ICT in disaster risk management initiatives in Asia and the Pacific." ESCAP Report, U.N., Thailand. Available at website: https://www.uncclearn.org /wp-content/uploads/library/ict.pdf Accessed 10/2023. page 9.

nuclear forensic working groups, consultancy bodies, and ASEAN forums [177] (Rosenbaum, 1999; Nichols, 2008). Security prevention systems have implied that the distribution of commercial technologies operated for nuclear energy power facilities' development has been encouraged in view of managing functional innovation projects within structural identified plans. At spatial level, Taiwan is prone to earthquakes and for this reason the coordination of seismic risk analyses at NPP has involved regulatory actions and partnership with the US Nuclear Regulatory Commission (NRC) due to the designs of the plants.[178] As result, this process has invariably required periodic controlling operations combined with security risk analyses industrially verified both at domestic and regional level (Rosenbaum, 1999; Nichols, 2008).

In the case of science and technology innovation programs sufficiently responding to the material increase of regional commerce requirements in newly industrialized countries NIC, like Taiwan, Singapore, Hong Kong and South Korea, the functional cooperation agencies have been demanded to provide country-to-country institutional collaborative learning methodologies, e.g. with international exchanges contributing to nuclear safety communications and regulatory reviews able to form responsive environments, [179] depending on statutory roles and international relations maintained across regions. Such systemic cooperative attempts to improve nuclear safety networking activities have also entailed public engagements and local preparation forums increasing public understanding when critically aligned with regulative adaptive implications of multilateral industrial PPP transfers.

One of the motives for regional collaboration integrating PPP industrial projects at the local level, through e.g. Taiwan's Act for

[177] Wayne Mei, 2012. "U.S.-Taiwan Nuclear Forensics Experts Meeting." Office of Nonproliferation and International Security (NIS), Working Presentation available at website: https://www.aec.gov.tw/webpage/control/emergency/files/index_01_1_5-4_03.pdf Accessed April 2020.

[178] Nuclear Engineering International, 2009. "Seismic safety under scrutiny in Taiwan." Institute of Nuclear Energy Research, Atomic Energy Council, 29 May 2009. Available at website: https://www.neimagazine.com/features/featureseismic-safety-under-scrutiny-in-taiwan/ Accessed 10/2023.

[179] David Dalton, 2011. "Taiwan calls for more cooperation on safety." NUCNET, The Independent Nuclear News Agency, 2 August 2011. Available at websites: https://www.nucnet.org/news/taiwan-calls-for-more-cooperation-on-safety Accessed 10/2023.

Promotion of Private Participation in Infrastructure Projects incorporating among others: environmental pollution prevention facilities[180] - has been related to an extensive acceleration of recurrent ICT distribution patterns indicating common knowledge and educational transfers[181] as well as public learning accesses to science and technology development, which overall have determined territorial adaptation plans, including industrial organizational changes. Additionally, progressive institutional remodeling in multilevel governance networks has been materially absorbed into supportive local partnerships, maintaining a specific attention on issues like:

1. Development of Local ICT Knowledge Centres
2. National ICT Provisions for Educational Bodies & Risk Emergency Agencies
3. Local Cooperation of STS socio-industrial transnational institutions
4. Territorial ICT Associations with International Private Corporate Management, and
5. ICT Information Exchanges and Electronic Communication Services of Sectoral Units

Distributive ICT innovation factors have concurrently redefined technical responsive flows of transnational knowledge exchanges, interlinked with Smart City projects[182] that can relate to changing aspects of regional innovation production systems (Nichols, 2008). Comparatively, competitive East Asian neighbouring partners have manifested aggregated governance approaches about the possible identification of practical local sustainability measures undertaken in relation to environmental dynamic

[180] Working Group of the R.O.C. Laws and Regulations Database, Ministry of Justice. Government Website Open Information Announcement. Available at website: https://law.moj.gov.tw/ENG/LawClass/LawAll.aspx?pcode=D0070062 Accessed April 2020.

[181] Sarvi, Jouko E., Balaji, Venkataraman, and Pillay, Hitendra, 2015. "Public-private partnerships in information and communication technology for education." Asian Development Bank (ADB), Philippines. Papers and Briefs, ADB Briefs, ISBN:978-92-9257-236-5 (Print).

[182] Caribbean News Global, 2021. "Smart City Taiwan: A hub for digital solutions to new heights - Part 1." CNG Media, October 27, 2021. Available at website: https://www.caribbeannewsglobal.com/smart-city-taiwan-a-hub-for-digital-solutions-to-new-heights-part-1/ (or) https://foodindustrynetwork.com/smart-city-taiwan-a-hub-for-digital-solutions-to-new-heights-part-1/ Accessed 10/2023.

processes, which have led to the adoption of common ecological adaptation policies combining different PPP modelling approaches operated in regional commerce supported networks (Rayner,[183] 2012; Chi,[184] et al., 2015); it is put into relevance that "At every level of governance - international, national, provincial and municipal - public-private partnerships are empowering public entities to meet their sustainability objectives while also benefiting business."[185] In view of implementing collaborative innovation with performance criteria in industry and science research projects, the national improvement of environmental protection technologies (EPT)[186] operated in Taiwan, has been interlinked to targeted environmental pollution issues: "Environmental protection programs [combined with] national science technology development programs, and [...] technology consultation conferences [have included] sustainable development and prospective environmental technology research and development [for] technical regulations, disaster prevention, disaster relief, disaster response systems, environmental inspection and international EPT cooperation."[187]

Instead about the S&T case, the effective constitution of multilevel governing partnerships recommending public policies formulated on comparable delivery processes of STS managerial systems, has also meant importing responsive technical dispositions to changing scenarios due to the rapid diffusion of environmental hybrid designs associated with legal provisional engagements (Rayner, 2012; Chi, et al., 2015). However, the specific consistency of STS technical identifications that have been

[183] Steve Rayner, 2012. "Uncomfortable knowledge: the social construction of ignorance in science and environmental policy discourses." Economy and Society, Volume 41, No. 1, pp. 107-125.

[184] Cheryl S.F. Chi, Inkeri Ruuska, Jianhua Xu, 2015. "Environmental impact assessment of infrastructure projects: a governance perspective." Journal of Environmental Planning and Management, Volume 59, No. 3, pp. 393-413. DOI: 10.1080/09640568.2015.1013623.

[185] Mike Hower, 2015. " 5 public-private partnerships pushing the sustainability envelope." GreenBiz, March 4, 2015. Available at website: https://www.greenbiz.com/article/5-public-private-partnerships-pushing-sustainability-envelope Accessed 10/2023.

[186] EPA Taiwan R.O.C., 2021. "Research and development of environmental protection technologies." Environmental Protection Administration, Executive Yuan, R.O.C. (Taiwan). Information available at: https://www.epa.gov.tw/eng/619CCA3475CFC5E0 (or) https://www.moenv.gov.tw/EN/7668B5A92350AB53 Accessed 10/2023.

[187] EPA Taiwan R.O.C., 2021. "Research and development of environmental protection technologies."

defined in accordance with local managerial characterizations, has been monitored in parallel with local participating stakeholders who have been publicly active through transnational or national engaging discussion forums - about environmental, health, and scientific approaches[188] - while enhancing proximity to information knowledge platforms and common deliberative learning objectives for educational projects (Rayner, 2012). As another example, governmental anti-pollution industrial campaigns can be analyzed through the affirmation of environmental regulatory information which has been rationalized in view of an increasing complexity of productive networks and local PPP organizational arrangements, tackling environmental impact assessments EIA as well as monitoring and evaluation programs confirmed locally (Chi, et al., 2015).

Additionally, environmental assessment programs EIA have been quite controversial in terms of territorial management impacts because of an informal and formal capacity of implementing national project activities, which have evolved under different circumstances, especially when responding to distinctive technical and procedural planning of structural innovation processes requiring qualitative protocols and systematization of EIA[189] results (Chi, et al., 2015). As consequence, the coordination of systematic resource based-actions reviewed by institutional counterparts administering with industrial managerial partners for the distribution of territorial regulatory mechanisms can be better operated according to programmatic levels of ICT networked information services maintaining a local diffusion. Interchangeably, common ICT knowledge networks have been essentially stratified in relation to science and environmental adaptation planning set in association with territorial action plans and EIA cyclical reviews,[190] which have been dependent on the consistency of technical sustainable

[188] Nasser Mansour, 2009. "Science-Technology-Society (STS). A new paradigm in science education." Bulletin of Science, Technology & Society, Volume 29, No. 4, pp. 287-297.
[189] Tetsuya Kamijo, 2022. "How to enhance EIA systems in developing countries: A quantitative literature review." Environment, Development and Sustainability, Volume 24. https://doi.org/10.1007/s10668-021-02029-0.
[190] Lohani, B.N., J.W. Evans, H. Ludwig, R.R. Everitt, R. A. Carpenter, and S.L. Tu, 1997. "Environmental Impact Assessment for developing countries in Asia. (Volume 1)." Overview. 356 pp. Asian Development Bank (ADB) report.

assessments, particularly when country-based and materially available (Chi, et al., 2015; Rayner, 2012). Within Asian institutional conditions shifting toward adaptive local conservation and environmental protection plans under EIA methodologies, it is pointed out that "many institutions are concerned with pollution prevention and the protection of air and water quality. Others are concerned with conservation, protected areas, and the protection of biodiversity. Still others, including EIA institutions, regulate, enforce, and coordinate resource use and development activities."[191]

In the case of East Asian knowledge innovation processes, the managerial assimilation with comparative roles and responsibilities connected to a hierarchical devolution of national ruling decisions, have been configured through consistent public legitimacy access conditions, which have indirectly permeated into societal implementing proceedings, [192] resulting in distinctive organizational performances (Funabashi, [193] 2011). At policy environment level, the incremental introduction of different upgraded management and planning models referred, for instance, to nuclear waste facilities operations and land

[191] Lohani, B., J.W. Evans, H. Ludwig, R.R. Everitt, Richard A. Carpenter, and S.L. Tu, 1997. (ADB), page 27 (xxiii).

[192] Note: In the case of Climate Adaptation plans: "In a number of SEA countries, the level of knowledge and awareness on climate change impacts, mitigation and adaptation measures are low among local officials and insufficient to prompt them to formulate proactive and anticipatory action agendas. However, many local governments have been traditionally responding to climate change extreme events like flooding, storm surges, and typhoons in their own areas. [...] Based on a study of four provinces in the Philippines,..., local government actions in disaster preparedness included the creation, enhancement or the strict implementation of coastal laws, land regulations, coastal management and disaster programmes. In Vietnam, the provincial government of Thu Thien-Hue Province forged a three-year project partnership beginning 2004 with the Canadian Centre for International Studies and Cooperation (CECI),..., on a programme that focused on strengthening capacity to plan and implement community based anticipatory adaptation strategies through disaster preparedness and integration of risk reduction and mitigation with local development planning [...]." Bernadette R. Resurreccion, Edsel E. Sajor, and Elizabeth Fajber, 2008. "Climate Adaptation in Asia: Knowledge gaps and research issues in South East Asia." Full Report of the South East Asia Team, ISET-International and ISET-Nepal. Page 25. Available at website: https://www.preventionweb.net/ files/ 8126_ClimateAdaptationSEASept081.pdf Accessed 10/2023.

[193] Harutoshi Funabashi, 2011. "The duality of social systems and the environmental movement in Japan." Pp. 37-61. Book edition: Jeffrey Broadbent, Vicky Brockman, 2011. "East Asian Social Movements. Power, protest, and change in a dynamic region." Nonprofit and Civil Society Studies, Springer Science+Business Media.

mitigation activities, has been analyzed in relationship with valuable expectations of corresponding knowledge-based societies emerging with a comparative understanding about disaster risk perception attitudes and local environmental acceptance participation (Brunnengraber[194] et al., 2015).

Regional science and political experts focusing on Japan's science innovation model or the European Union states' international trading integration, have highlighted comparative aspects about the development of technology hybrid management systems[195] combined with changing conditions of managerial operating programs correlated to local territorial organizations, which have been associated to environmental resource-based rules. As such, the concurrent succession of mutual decision-making agreements involving international or national member parties has basically contributed to affirmative identifications of regional knowledge productions PPPs, locally adapted within systematic modifying interventions based on e.g. common renewable energy maintenance systems, supporting cross-development activities [196]. Essentially, normative performing systems and organizational knowledge innovation, particularly pointing at local environmental related dynamics, have been analyzed in relationship with material explorations on environmental management and data assessment tools, intertwined with local environmental risk factors that are interrelated to the emergence of critical disaster risk exposures.

Effectively, the cohabitation of interdependent organizational ecosystems has facilitated functional estimations and progressive understanding referring to industrial management risks and local communities' participatory expectations, as well as, common direct confrontations e.g. about the case of nuclear energy facilities'

[194] Achim Brunnengraber, Maria Rosaria Di Nucci, Ana Maria Isidoro Losada, Lutz Mez, Miranda A. Schreurs (Eds.), 2015. "Nuclear waste governance. An international comparison." Freie Universitat Berlin, Germany. Springer VS Edition.
[195] Clark Miller, 2001. "Hybrid Management: Boundary Organizations, Science Policy, and Environmental Governance in the Climate Regime." Science, Technology, & Human Values, Volume 26, No. 4, pp. 478-500.
[196] Wen-Cheng Hu, Jui-Chu Lin, Chien-Te Fan, Chien-An Lien, Shih-Ming Chung, 2016. "A Booming Green Business for Taiwan's Climate Perspective." Renewable and Sustainable Energy Reviews, Volume 59, pp. 876-886.

administrative supervision, combined with concurrent multilevel managerial siting activities (Hasegawa,[197] 2011; Brunnengraber, et al., 2015).

Concerning the environmental regulatory sphere, governance protection models have been planned in view of facilitating local risk reduction and local management adaptation programs, assessed within regional or national distribution systems more recently reaffirmed in East and South-east Asia. In essence, cooperative monitoring schemes provided in supra-national and national governance systems have been evaluated through sector-based environmental mutual negotiations supporting international projects' arrangements such as: the International E-Waste Management Network (IEMN)[198] - which has been put into place in order to solve, for instance, civic conflicts forming on local land settlement issues; or otherwise in cases of local environmental pollution disputes maintained across different territories. About the EPA/IEMN " the United States Environmental Protection Agency (U.S. EPA) and the Taiwan Environmental Protection Administration (Taiwan EPA) have collaborated through the *International Environmental Partnership* since 2011 to build global capacity for the environmentally sound management of waste electrical and electronic equipment (WEEE) [...]."[199] Due to the systematic managerial accountability, formal calls have also been made for more transparency on environmental management relations, especially in view of national environmental crises interrelated with challenging industrial pollution impacts (Hasegawa, 2011).

Consequentially, the possible aggregation of local participatory approaches connected to the case of nuclear hazardous waste storage sites and environmental pollution implications has been amplified through

[197] Koichi Hasegawa, 2011. "A comparative study of social movements for a post-nuclear energy era in Japan and the USA." Pp. 63-79. Book edition: Jeffrey Broadbent, Vicky Brockman, 2011. "East Asian social movements. Power, protest, and change in a dynamic region." Nonprofit and Civil Society Studies, Springer Science+Business Media.

[198] EPA U.S. Environmental Protection Agency. International Cooperation Cases. Available at Website: https://www.epa.gov/international-cooperation/international-e-waste-management-network-iemn Accessed May 2020.

[199] EPA, 2021. "International E-Waste management network (IEMN)." EPA United States, Environmental Protection Agency, International Cooperation news. Available at website: https://www.epa.gov/international-cooperation/international-e-waste-management-network-iemn Accessed 10/2023.

specific energy security cooperation agreements,[200] reviewed in order to bring organizational change in vertically integrated technology-based functional ecosystems. As a matter of fact, the promotion of democratic participation attributes about the nuclear energy managerial acquisitions with incremental transparency principles[201] has been adapted according to societal environmental interactions, involving civilian associations and local strategic stakeholders, similarly mobilized in nuclear power states projecting on common renewable energy distribution processes, such as in Japan and the United States (Hasegawa, 2011).

At the same time, structural STS trends on communication accessibility initiatives pointing at participatory political environments promoted in cases of public knowledge innovation transfers, interrelated with national energy reforms[202] have also been reviewed in terms of local ethical issues and environmental justice targets. This type of exploration about local ethics and comparable ideological meanings have been discussed by newly generation of people referring to the recognition of primary local needs in environmental justice programs. The adoption of ethical principles is mandated in sustainable socioeconomic programs that should be able to combine regional decision-making strategies defined

[200] David von Hippel, Tatsujiro Suzuki, Tadahiro Katsuta, Jungmin Kang, Alexander Dmitriev, Jim Falk, and Peter Hayes. Report of the East Asia Science and Security Project, 2010. "Future Regional Nuclear Fuel Cycle Cooperation in East Asia: Energy Security Costs and Benefits." Nautilus Institute for Security and Sustainability, Available at Website: http://nautilus.wpengine.netdna-cdn.com/wp-content/uploads/2012/01/EASS_Report_6-2010_rev.pdf Accessed April 2020. (or) https://nautilus.org/wp-content/uploads/2012/01/EASS_Report_6-2010_rev.pdf Accessed 10/2023.

[201] Bachner K.M., 2016. "Transparency in civilian nuclear endeavors." U.S. Department of Energy, Office of Science, NA-24, NA-241. Available at website: https://www.bnl.gov/isd/documents/93395.pdf (or) https://www.osti.gov/biblio/1303006 Accessed 10/2023.

[202] Note: In the case of energy innovation process "the Taiwanese government further promoted energy transition, encouraged citizen participation in energy policy, and also subsidised community solar panel installation in 2013. Later, in 2018, the DPP government implemented a White Paper for Energy Transition, with the notion of community energy being highlighted. It concluded that during the energy transition, the roles of social force should not be neglected." Natalie Wong, 2020. "Community energy: a way out of energy transition." Energy, Environment, Society, Taiwan Insight, 20 July, 2020. Online magazine available at website: https://taiwaninsight.org/2020/07/20/community-energy-a-way-out-of-energy-transition/ Accessed 10/2023.

multilaterally and across multilevel regulatory areas.[203] Eventually, the unrestricted environmental objectives have involved public programming tools addressing localized changing configurations at municipal levels,[204] with local centre partners investing on participatory risk protection activities related to the case of nuclear power plants management, particularly referring to the technical maintenance procedures associated with local waste disposal monitoring operations, which have been located in e.g. the U.S., in Canada, or in Japan (Hasegawa, 2011; Brunnengraber, et al., 2015). As underlined, there is to consider that a historical inheritance of practical organizational choices has been designed through functional distributed transfers cyclically arranged within pertinent long-term aggregated policies and comparable institutional frameworks, which have been regimented by international and regional organizational ruling systems.

Comparative safety planning factors identified in regional security regimes have then put into light different regulatory formations of functional cooperative powers as for the ASEAN[205] security community established across the Asia-Pacific region. For instance, in Thailand, Singapore and the Philippines incremental urbanization processes have increased the quantity of solid waste with a potential for recurrent municipal crisis management contexts foreseen for the long-term.[206] In the case of PPP public-private energy policy schemes, community's cooperation for development of nuclear waste management policies, has meant an inclusion of public knowledge transfers implemented in view of configuring territorial safety plans, as well as, local environmental anti-risk protection measures. Overall, regional energy security and safety environment initiatives have been distributed across multinational

[203] Daniel A. Vallero, 2006. "Lessons learned: A case approach to environmental problems." In *Paradigms Lost*, Learning from Environmental Mistakes, Mishaps and Misdeeds. Pp. 13-54. eBook ISBN: 9780080457963.

[204] Michael Borrelli, 2018. "The nuclear waste management organization." In Magazine, Management, Sustainability, published in Municipal World, November 2018. Website available at: https://www.municipalworld.com/feature-story/nuclear-waste-management-organization/ Accessed 10/2023.

[205] ASEAN: Association of Southeast Asian Nations.

[206] NTUS, 2018. "Solving the waste management problem in ASEAN." Team Re:volution, Nanyang Technological University Singapore, ASEAN Report. Available at website: https://aseandse.org/uploads/asset/Bp5TJ2Fc4g.pdf Accessed 10/2023.

Fukushima." *Political Science*, Corpus ID: 201338634. Available at webpage: https://www.semanticscholar.org/paper/Nuclear-Debates-and-Political-Competition-in-Japan%2C-Lee/1a8f2977a01cf5f7d2aec797e63057477c4d6575 (or) https://escholarship.org/content/qt5q09b5xs/qt5q09b5xs_noSplash_e8ae895ab24f6612ee8e9cf4af6bc00c.pdf Last Accessed 10/2023.

- Lee, B.Y. (2021). "Maintaining Taiwan's global ICT industry lead by improving employees's training. " *Taiwan Insight*, Taiwan Studies Programme, Research Centre based at the University of Nottingham. 4 November 2021. Available at webpage: https://taiwaninsight.org/2021/11/04/maintaining-taiwans-global-ict-industry-lead-by-improving-employees-training/ Last Accessed 10/2023.
- Lee, I.C., Taipei Times Staff reporter, (2021). "Nuclear power not an option: Su." *Taipei Times*, 21 March 2021. World Nuclear Industry Status Report. Available at website: https://www.worldnuclearreport.org/Nuclear-power-not-an-option-Su.html Last Accessed 10/2023.
- Lee, Y.J. (2013). "Planning of creative Taipei." *Proceedings of International Symposium on City Planning 2013*, Taipei, Taiwan. Available at website: http://wwwnew.cpij.or.jp/com/iac/sympo/13/ISCP2013-40.pdf Last Accessed 11/2023.
- Lee, Y.J. Tung, C.M. and Lin, S.C. (2018). "Attitudes to Climate Change, Perceptions of Disaster Risk, and Mitigation and Adaptation Behavior in Yunlin County, Taiwan." *Environmental Science and Pollution Research*, Volume 26, No. 30, pp. 30603-30613.
- Li, W.S. Chang, C.L. Chen, K.H. and Lee, Y. (2019). "How ICT changes the landscape of Disaster Risk Management." In: Murayama, Y., Velev, D., Zlateva, P. (eds.) *Information Technology in Disaster Risk Reduction*. Pp. 12-18. ITDRR 2017. IFIP Advances in Information and Communication Technology, Volume 516. Springer, Cham. https://doi.org/10.1007/978-3-030-18293-9_2.
- Liao, G. (2019). "An end in sight for Taiwan's third nuclear power plant." *Taiwan News*, 2019/09/25. Available at website: https://www.taiwannews.com.tw/en/news/3784154 Last Accessed 10/2023.
- Lin, C.K. (2021). "Debate over nuclear power is not over yet." *Taipei Times*, Tuesday, December 8. Available at website: https://taipeitimes.com/News/editorials/archives/2021/12/28/2003770303 Last Accessed 10/2023.
- Lin, C.N. (2021). "Resumption of Fourth Nuclear Power Plant rejected." *Taipei Times*, Taiwan news section, 19 December 2021. Available at website: https://www.taipeitimes.com/News/taiwan/archives/2021/12/19/2003769851 Last Accessed 11/2023.
- Lin, S. (2019). "Taiwanese citizens demonstrate to end construction of the Fourth Nuclear Power Plant and amend the Referendum Act, 1988-2017." *Global Nonviolent Action Database*, 2019. Available at website: https://nvdatabase.swarthmore.edu/content/taiwanese-citizens-demonstrate-

end-construction-fourth-nuclear-power-plant-and-amend-referen Last Accessed 10/2023.

- Lin, W.I. (2015). "Community development in Taiwan." *Encyclopedia of Social Work*. National Association of Social Workers Press and Oxford University Press. https://doi.org/10.1093/acrefore/9780199975839.013.1179 Last Accessed 11/2023.
- Liou, M.L. and Yu, Y. H. (2004). "Development and implementation of Strategic Environmental Assessment in Taiwan." *Environmental Impact Assessment Review*, Volume 24, No. 3, pp. 337-350.
- Liu, H.J. (2011). "When labor and nature strike back: A double movement saga in Taiwan." *Capitalism Nature Socialism*, Volume 22, No. 1, pp. 22-39.
- Liu, M. C. (2015). "Manufacturing servitization and revitalizing industrial clusters: A case study of Taiwan's LIIEP." *Journal of the Asia Pacific Economy*, Volume 20, No. 3, pp. 423-443.
- Lohani, B.N. Evans, J.W. Ludwig, H. Everitt, R.R. Carpenter, R.A. and Tu, S.L. (1997). "Environmental Impact Assessment for developing countries in Asia. (Volume 1)." *Overview*. 356 pp. Asian Development Bank (ADB) report.
- Lowery, S. and Vhugen, D. (2016). "Land tenure and energy infrastructure." USAID, *LandLinks*, March 15, 2016. Available at website: https://www.land-links.org/issue-brief/land-tenure-and-energy-infrastructure/ Last Accessed 10/2023.
- Lupke, C. (2012). "Documenting Environmental Protest: Taiwan's Gongliao Fourth Nuclear Power Plant and the Cultural Politics of Dialogic Artifice." In : *Documenting Taiwan on Film* (eds) 2012 London, Routledge, Chapter 8 (28 pages).
- Lyons, D. (2009). "The two-headed dragon: Environmental policy and progress under rising democracy in Taiwan." *East Asia*, Volume 26, pp. 57-76.

M

- Mabon, L. (2021). "Taiwan's status at the science-policy interface for global climate change: Why getting it right matters." University of Nottingham, Taiwan Research Hub, *Taiwan Insight*, 10 November 2021. Available at website: https://taiwaninsight.org/2021/11/10/taiwans-status-at-the-science-policy-interface-for-global-climate-change-why-getting-it-right-matters/ Last Accessed 10/2023.
- Maillard, P. and Brunet, P. (2017). "Urban environmental monitoring (UEM): A demonstration project pooling corporate expertise for smarter cities implemented in Nice Plaine du Var." *The Journal of Field of Action*, Field of Actions Science Reports, Special Issue 16, 2017: Smart Cities at the Crossroads. Open Edition Journals.
- Mansour, N. (2009). "Science-Technology-Society (STS). A new paradigm in science education." *Bulletin of Science, Technology & Society*, Volume 29, No. 4, pp. 287-297.
- McKinsey Global Institute, (2020). "Climate risk and response in Asia." Report on: *The Future of Asia: Climate risk and response in Asia*, (ii). Available at

webpage: https://www.mckinsey.com/~/media/McKinsey/Featured%20 Insights/Asia%20Pacific/Climate%20risk%20and%20response%20in%20Asia%20Research%20preview/Climate-risk-and-response-in-Asia-Future-of-Asia-research-preview-v3.pdf?msclkid=09f3f56baa3811ec8b2079a4972c4613 Last Accessed 10/2023.

- Mei, W. (2012). "U.S.-Taiwan Nuclear Forensics Experts Meeting." *Office of Nonproliferation and International Security (NIS)*, Working Presentation. Available at website: https://www.aec.gov.tw/webpage/control/emergency /files/index_01_1_5-4_03.pdf Last Accessed April 2020.
- Miller, C. (2001). "Hybrid Management: Boundary Organizations, Science Policy, and Environmental Governance in the Climate Regime." *Science, Technology, & Human Values*, Volume 26, No. 4, pp. 478-500.
- Minagawa, Y. (2013). "Management of humanitarian supply chains in times of disaster." In Y. Monden (ed.) *Management of Enterprise Crises in Japan*, Singapore: World Scientific Publishing Co., chapter 9, pp. 149-163.
- Ministry of Agriculture, COA, (2012). "Planning for disaster prevention and response in rural areas." *Council of Agriculture*, Executive Yuan, R.O.C., MOA Annual Report. Available at website: https://eng.coa.gov.tw/ws.php? id=2504029 Last Accessed 10/2023.
- Ministry of Foreign Affairs, (2016). "Progressive Leadership." MOFA-EN-105_011-|-1. Available at website: https://www.taiwan.gov.tw/images/ ufile/file20160929111258969.pdf?msclkid=e245fcbbc0cd11eca03685e0aa6a8550 Last Accessed 10/2023.
- Ministry of Foreign Affairs, Taiwan, (2016). "ICT development in Taiwan." *Taipei Trade Office in the Federal Republic of Nigeria*, 03 December, 2016. Available at website: https://roc-taiwan.org/ng_en/post/416.html Last Accessed 10/2023.
- Moore, M.T. 2018. "Nuclear Plant closures bring economic pain to cities and towns." *Stateline* news article, 5th September, 2018. The Pew Charitable Trusts. Available at website: https://www.pewtrusts.org/it/research-and-analysis/blogs/stateline/2018/09/05/nuclear-plant-closures-bring-economic-pain-to-cities-and-towns (or) https://stateline.org/2018/09/05/nuclear-plant-closures-bring-economic-pain-to-cities-and-towns/ Last Accessed 11/2023.
- Muyard, F. (2015). "Voting Shift in the November 2014 Local Elections in Taiwan. Strong Rebuke to Ma Ying-jeou's Government and Policies and Landslide Victory for the DPP." *China Perspectives*. Volume 1, pp. 55-61.

N

- NBR podcast series *Asia Insight* features interviews, (2021). "Lessons Learned. Disaster management perspectives from Japan and Taiwan." *Podcast from Nontraditional Security Challenges in South Asia*. November 5th, 2021. Available at webpage: https://www.nbr.org/publication/lessons-learned-disaster-management-perspectives-from-japan-and-taiwan/ Last Accessed 10/2023.

- (NCDR) Taiwan National Science and Technology Center for Disaster Reduction, (2021). "Taiwan - Palau disaster management training workshop." *Pacific Partnership 2021*, U.S./Taiwan/Palau Disaster Management Workshop Koror, Palau. Published on 13/08/2021. Available at website: https://www.ncdr.nat.gov.tw/Message/MessageView?itemid=4760&mid=93&msclkid=28f02fc2ca4f11ecadeb00491f6d2f0b Last Accessed 10/2023.
- NEI, (2019). "Taipower rules out operation in Lungmen." *Nuclear Engineering International*, 06 February 2019. Progressive Media International, Registered office: London, England. Available at website: https://www.neimagazine.com/news/newstaipower-rules-out-operation-of-lungmen-6970272 Last Accessed 10/2023.
- NEI, (2020). "Nuclear power to 2030: key countries." *Nuclear Engineering International*, Features, 08 July 2020. Available at website: https://www.neimagazine.com/features/featurenuclear-power-to-2030-key-countries-8017370/ Last Accessed 10/2023.
- Nephew, R. (2020). "Reconsidering US nuclear cooperation agreements." *Center on Global Energy Policy (CGEP)*, Volume 3, Columbia Climate School, U.S. Available at website: https://www.energypolicy.columbia.edu/publications/reconsidering-us-nuclear-cooperation-agreements Last Accessed 10/2023.
- Nichols, R.W. (2008). "Innovation, change, and order: Reflections on science and technology in India, China, and the United States." *Technology in Society*, Volume 30, No. 3-4, pp. 437-450.
- NIST, National Institute of Standards and Technology, (2021). "Integrating science & technology with disaster response." *Science for Disaster Reduction Interagency Coordination Group*, 01 June, 2021. Available at website: https://www.nist.gov/news-events/news/2021/06/integrating-science-technology-disaster-response Accessed 11/2023.
- NTUS, (2018). "Solving the waste management problem in ASEAN." *Team Re:volution*, Nanyang Technological University Singapore, ASEAN Report. Available at website: https://aseandse.org/uploads/asset/Bp5TJ2Fc4g.pdf Last Accessed 10/2023.
- National Resilience Programme (NRP), (2021). "Decentralization of disaster risk management in Bangladesh." Briefing paper, NRP, Department of Disaster Management Ministry of Disaster Management and Relief, Bangladesh report. Available at website: https://nrpbd.net/wp-content/uploads/2022/08/Report-on-Decentralized-DRR.pdf Last Accessed 11/2023.
- Nuclear Engineering International, (2009). "Seismic safety under scrutiny in Taiwan." *Institute of Nuclear Energy Research*, Atomic Energy Council, 29 May 2009. Available at website: https://www.neimagazine.com/features/featureseismic-safety-under-scrutiny-in-taiwan/ Last Accessed 10/2023.
- Nuclear Engineering, (2019). "Taipower rules out operation of Lungmen." *Nuclear Engineering*, published on 6 February, 2019. Available at Website:

https://www.neimagazine.com/news/newstaipower-rules-out-operation-of-lungmen-6970272 Last Accessed 10/2023.

O

- OECD, Sexton, K.A. (2015). "Crisis, criticism, change. Regulatory reform in the wake of nuclear accidents." *OECD/NEA Nuclear Law Bulletin,* 2015, Issue 2. Available at website: https://doi.org/10.1787/nuclear_law-2015-5jm22pflfts2 Last Accessed 10/2023.
- Office of the President Republic of China (Taiwan), (2016). "President Tsai apologizes to indigenous peoples on behalf of government." *News & Activities*, 2016-08-01. Available at website: https://english.president.gov.tw/NEWS/4950 Last Accessed 10/2023.
- Oh, S.Y. (2018). "Quite Transformation from the Bottom: Emerging Transnational Networks Among Non-State Actors in Northeast Asia Community-Building." In Hayes P., Moon CI. (eds) *The Future of East Asia Today*. Palgrave Macmillan, Singapore.
- Onaga, L. Schieder, C.S. Buhrman, K. Jacoby, J.M. Juraku, K. Slater, D.H. *et al.* (2021). "Sources of Disaster: A roundtable discussion on new epistemic perspectives in Post-3.11 Japan." *East Asian Science, Technology and Society: An International Journal*, Volume 15, 2021 - Issue 4, pp. 482 - 496. https://doi.org/10.1080/18752160.2021.1997015.
- Oung, A. (2021). "Rules to tie heavy electricity use to renewable power." *Taipei Times*, front page, Sat., Jan. 02, 2021. Available at website: https://www.taipeitimes.com/News/front/archives/2021/01/02/2003749789?msclkid=860de288b13c11ec8571f1fb9ca96014 Last Accessed 10/2023.

P

- Pan, J. (2021). "DPP, LDP agree to enhance collaboration." *Taipei Times*, Taiwan News, December, 25th 2021. Available at website: https://www.taipeitimes.com/News/taiwan/archives/2021/12/25/2003770168 Last Accessed 10/2023.
- Park, S.C. (2012). "Competitiveness of East Asian science cities: discourse on their status as global or local innovative clusters." *Artificial Intelligence & Society (AI & Soc)*, Volume 27, pp. 451-464. Springer editions.
- Parker, B. (2018). "Taiwan's 2025 energy goals demand an 'Energy 'Czar.'" *The New Lens*, TNL Media Group, Politics, 19 June, 2018. Available at website: https://international.thenewslens.com/article/98126 Last Accessed 11/2023.
- Peimani, H. (2012). "Prospects for nuclear energy in Asia." NBR, *The National Bureau of Asian Research*, Paper from the Pacific Energy Summit, March 20, 2012. Available at website: https://www.nbr.org/publication/prospects-for-nuclear-energy-in-asia/ Last Accessed 10/2023.
- Peir, J. J. (2011). "Power Uprate Effect on Thermal Effluent of Nuclear Power Plants in Taiwan." In: Pavel V. Tsvetkov, 2011. *Nuclear Power - Operation, Safety and Environment*. ISBN: 978-953-307-507-5.DOI: 10.5772/987.

Available at website: https://www.intechopen.com/books/nuclear-power-operation-safety-and-environment/power-uprate-effect-on-thermal-effluent-of-nuclear-power-plants-in-taiwan Last Accessed May 2020.
- PreventionWeb, (2009). "Taiwan: Legislature suggests local disaster relief, prevention alliances." *UNDRR, Taiwan News*, 28 December 2009. Available at website: https://www.preventionweb.net/news/taiwan-legislature-suggests-local-disaster-relief-prevention-alliances Last Accessed 10/2023.

R

- Rayner, S. (2012). "Uncomfortable knowledge: the social construction of ignorance in science and environmental policy discourses." *Economy and Society*, Volume 41, No. 1, pp. 107-125.
- Reynolds, B. (2016). "Understanding Risk Accumulations in Taiwan's Science Parks." *Moody's RMS Report.* Available at website: https://www.rms.com/blog/2016/12/19/understanding-risk-accumulations-in-taiwans-science-parks. Last Accessed April 2020.
- Rosenbaum, W.A. (1999). "The good lessons of bad experience. Rethinking the future of commercial nuclear power." *The American Behavioral Scientist*, Thousand Oaks, Volume 43, No. 1, pp. 74-91.

S

- Sarvi, J.E. Balaji, V. and Pillay, H. (2015). "Public-private partnerships in information and communication technology for education." Asian Development Bank (ADB), Philippines. *Papers and Briefs, ADB Briefs*, ISBN:978-92-9257-236-5 (Print).
- Saunders, W.S.A. De Bruin, K. Ruiz Rivera N. and Lee, H.C. (2015). "A Comparative Study of Natural Hazard Policy in Taiwan, Mexico, New Zealand and Norway," *GNS Science Report* 2015/005. 94 p. DOI:10.13140/RG.2.1.2558.4166.
- Shaw, R. Shiwaku, K. and Izumi, T. (2017). "Science and technology in disaster risk reduction in Asia." *Academic Press 2017*. Paperback ISBN: 9780128127117.
- Shellenberger, M. (2018). "Pro-Nuclear Activists Win Landslide Electoral Victory in Taiwan." *Forbes*, 24th November, 2018, Energy Section, Available at website: https://www.forbes.com/sites/michaelshellenberger/2018/11/24/pro-nuclear-activists-win-landslide-electoral-victory-in-taiwan/#77e9977329a0 Last Accessed May 2020.
- Silver, A. (2018). "Taiwan's academics urge public to vote for nuclear power shut-down." *Nature*, News, 09 November 2018. doi: https://doi.org/10.1038 /d415 86-018-07337-6.
- Staff writer, with CNA, 2018. "Eric Chu urges selection of safe nuclear disposal site." *Taipei Times*, 08 December, 2018. Available at website: https://www.taipeitimes.com/News/taiwan/archives/2018/12/08/200370572 5 Last Accessed 11/2023.

- Sua, Y. (2015). "Bridging the Blue-Green Divide: The role of environmental NGOs in tackling environmental problems in Taiwan." *Pomona Senior Theses* Paper 133. Available at website: http://scholarship.claremont.edu/pomona_theses/133 Last Accessed 11/2023.
- Suman, S. (2018). "Hybrid nuclear-renewable energy systems: A review." *Journal of Cleaner Production*, Volume 181, 20 April 2018, pp. 166-177.
- Svalova, V. (2018). "Monitoring and risk management for landslide hazard in Taiwan." *IAEG/AEG Annual Meeting Proceedings*, San Francisco, California, 2018 - Volume 1, pp. 193-199.
- Synergy Media Specialists, (2018). "Transforming Taiwan: Innovative industries and new partnerships." Taiwan Report 2018, *The Japan Times*, 10 October, 2018. Available at website: https://www.japantimes.co.jp/country-report/2018/10/10/taiwan-report-2018/transforming-taiwan-innovative-industries-new-partnerships/ Last Accessed 11/2023.

T

- Taipei City Disaster Prevention Info website, 2021. "ECO characteristics." EOC Introduction, Available at website: https://eocen.gov.taipei/News_Content.aspx?n=7D02D558266270B6&sms=CD353E13515129EB&s=9148DE518AEA3F64 Last Accessed 11/2023.
- Taipei City Government, (2021). "Mayor encourages industries to help boost Taiwan's ICT capabilities." *Department of Information Technology*, 23 November, 2021, City News Webpage, available at website: https://english.gov.taipei/News_Content.aspx?n=A11F01CFC9F58C83&sms=DFFA119D1FD5602C&s=F87BCF9D64E905E3 Last Accessed 11/2023.
- Taipower Energy Company, (2020). "Ancillary service trading platform public briefing Taipower: Will be launched in Q1 of next year to boost up green energy development." *Taipower*, News & Events, 17 June, 2020. Available at website: https://www.taipower.com.tw/en/news_info.aspx?id=54&chk=d833ae1b-ff29-41ee-925c-c076ec535e47&mid=4412 Last Accessed 11/2023.
- Taipower Energy Company, (2022). "First Nuclear Power Plant decommissioning plan." Taipower, Information Disclosure, Plan Description. Available at website: https://www.taipower.com.tw/en/page.aspx?mid=4506 Last Accessed 11/2023.
- Taiwan Adaptation Platform, TAP, Legislation and Policy, (2022). Environmental Protection Administration, Executive Yuan, R.O.C. (Taiwan). Available at webpage: https://adapt.epa.gov.tw/eng/TCCIP-1-D_en.html As of 11/2023, web-link moved. (or) https://adapt.moenv.gov.tw/eng/TCCIP-1-D_en.html Last Accessed 11/2023.
- Taiwan MOST governmental report, (2021). "National science and technology development plan. (2021-2024)." May 21, 2021. *Yuan Tai-Ke-Letter No. 1100009078*. Webpage available at: https://www.most.gov.tw/most/attachments/36977724-a4cd-42f3-bcd1-6e50e98b648e As of 2023 the

website changed to: https://www.nstc.gov.tw/nstc/attachments/fd10ecfa-f319-44fe-8058-f379d3de22c2 Last Accessed 10/2023.

- Taiwan Review, (2017). "Voice of the People." In *Taiwan Today*, published May, 01, 2017. Available at website: https://taiwantoday.tw/news.php?unit=4,8,12,17,20&post=114985 Last Accessed April 2020.
- Taiwan Today, (2011). "Taiwan's nuclear power plants clear safety checks." *Eco-Business*, News, Energy, May 31, 2011. Available at website: https://www.eco-business.com/news/taiwans-nuclear-power-plants-clear-safety-checks/ Last Accessed 11/2023.
- Teng, P.J. (2018). "Taiwan a model of disaster preparedness in Indo-Pacific region: AIT deputy director." *Taiwan News*, December 14, 2018. Available at website: https://www.taiwannews.com.tw/en/news/3596890 Last Accessed on April 2020.
- Teng, P.J. (2020). "Taiwan Election: Tsai Ing-wen Wins Second Presidential Term, Beating Beijing-friendly Rival." *Hong Kong Free Press HKFP*, 11th January 2020. Available at website: https://hongkongfp.com/2020/01/11/breaking-taiwan-election-tsai-ing-wen-wins-second-presidential-term-beating-beijing-friendly-rival/ Last Accessed May 2020.
- Terao, T. (2002). "An Institutional Analysis of Environmental Pollution Disputes in Taiwan: Cases of 'Self-Relief.'" *The Developing Economies*, Volume 40, No. 3, pp. 284-304.
- Terao, T. (2007). "Democratization, Decentralization and Environmental Policy in Taiwan: Political economy of environmental policy formation and implementation." In: Terao, T., Otsuka, K. (eds) *Development of Environmental Policy in Japan and Asian Countries*. IDE-JETRO Series. Palgrave Macmillan, London. https://doi.org/10.1057/9780230624931_10.
- Tsai, J. S. and Chi, C.S.F. (2010). "Dysfunction of governmental emergency management system for natural disaster management – A case study of Taiwan Xiaolin village." *Working Paper Proceedings*; The Engineering Project Organization Conference, South Lake Tahoe, CA, United States. (or) The Engineering Project Organization Journal (June 2011), Volume 1, pp. 107-119.
- Tsai, W.T. and Chou, Y.H. (2005). "Overview of Environmental Impacts, Prospects and Policies for Renewable Energy in Taiwan." *Renewable and Sustainable Energy Reviews*, Volume 9, No. 2, pp. 119-147.
- TSMC 2012 Corporate Social Responsibility Report, (2013). "TSMC's Climate Change Management Structure." *Taiwan Semiconductor Manufacturing Company (TMSC)* Report. Available at website: https://esg.tsmc.com/download/file/2013_tsmc_csr/english/pdf/e_8_3.pdf Last Accessed 10/2023.
- Tso, Y.E. and McEntire, D.A. (2011). "Emergency Management in Taiwan: Learning from Past and Current Experiences." *FEMA* report available at website: https://training.fema.gov/hiedu/downloads/compemmgmtbookproject/comparative%20em%20book%20-%20em%20in%20taiwan.pdf Accessed May 2020. (or) https://dokumen.tips/documents/emergency-

management-in-taiwan-learning-from-past-emergency-management-in-taiwan.html?page=1 Last Accessed 11/2023.
- Turpin, T. (2011). "Planning partnerships and policy performance: National governance for innovation policy." Background Paper III; In "Proceedings and papers presented at the Asia-Pacific Forum on Strengthening the Governance of National Innovation Systems (NIS) for Senior Policy-Makers." Asian and Pacific Centre for Transfer of Technology of the Economic and Social Commission for Asia and the Pacific (APCTT - ESCAP), New Delhi, India, 2011.
- Turton, M. (2021). "Notes from central Taiwan: How to resolve Taiwan's nuclear fuel waste problem." *Taipei Times*, March 22, 2021. Available at website: https://www.taipeitimes.com/News/feat/archives/2021/03/22/2003754255 Last Accessed 11/2023.

U

- U.N. ESCAP, (2016). "ICT in disaster risk management initiatives in Asia and the Pacific." *ESCAP Report,* U.N., Thailand. Available at website: https://www.uncclearn.org/wp-content/uploads/library/ict.pdf Last Accessed 10/2023.

V

- Vallero, D.A. (2006). "Lessons learned: A case approach to environmental problems." In *Paradigms Lost*, Learning from Environmental Mistakes, Mishaps and Misdeeds. Pp. 13-54. eBook ISBN: 9780080457963.
- Vidal, J. (2012). "Sellafield: 'It Was All Contaminated: Milk, Chickens, the Golf Course." *The Guardian*, 11 March, 2012. Available at website: https://www.theguardian.com/environment/2012/mar/11/sellafield-stories-book-nuclear-accident Last Accessed May 2020.

W

- Walters, J. and Agencies, (2016). "Taiwan Earthquake: Death Toll Rises with Dozens Trapped in Toppled Building." *The Guardian*, 7 February, 2016. Available at website: https://www.theguardian.com/world/2016/feb/05/earthquake-hits-tainan-southern-taiwan-causing-at-least-one-partial-building-collapse Last Accessed May 2020.
- Wang, C.T.L. and Hosoki, R.I. (2016). "From Global to Local: Transnational Linkages, Global Influences, and Taiwan's Environmental NGOs." *Sociological Perspective*, Volume 59, No. 3, pp. 561-581.
- Wang, S. and Chen, D. (2021). "Could Taiwan's political left reconsider nuclear power?" The Diplomat, Asia-Pacific section, The Debate/Opinion, 03 December, 2021. Available at website: https://thediplomat.com/2021/12/could-taiwans-political-left-reconsider-nuclear-power/ Last Accessed 10/2023.

- Wang, T.J. and Liu, S.Y. (2010). "Shaping and Exploiting Technological Opportunities: The Case of Technology in Taiwan." *Renewable Energy*, Volume 35, No. 2, pp. 360-367.
- Wang T.J. (2019). "Indigenous peoples and the politics of the environment in Taiwan." *Lecture SOAS Centre of Taiwan Studies*; 30 January 2019. In: *Taiwan Contemporary Peoples.* 1st Edition. Routledge. ISBN: 9781003093176. Available at website: https://www.taylorfrancis.com/chapters/edit/10.4324/9781003093176-13/indigenous-peoples-politics-environment-taiwan-wang-ting-jieh Last Accessed 11/2023.
- Wang, Q. Chen, X. and Yi-chong, X. 2013. "Accident Like the Fukushima Unlikely in a Country with Effective Nuclear Regulation: Literature Review and Proposed Guidelines." *Renewable and Sustainable Energy Reviews*, Volume 17, pp. 126-146.
- (van der) Wees, G. (2020). "President Tsai and the DPP win an overwhelming victory: a strong rejection of China's encroachment." *Taiwan Insight Magazine*, 15 January 2020. Available at website: https://taiwaninsight.org/2020/01/15/president-tsai-and-the-dpp-win-an-overwhelming-victory-a-strong-rejection-of-chinas-encroachment/ Last Accessed 11/2023.
- WISE, (2002). "Taiwan: welds falsified in new scandal at Lungmen." World Information Service on Energy, (WISE), *Nuclear Monitor,* Issue: #570, 28/06/2002. Available at website: https://www.wiseinternational.org/nuclear-monitor/570/taiwan-welds-falsified-new-scandal-lungmen Last Accessed 10/2023.
- WNN, (2021). "Early shutdown for Taiwanese reactor." World Nuclear News, 01, July, 2021. Available at website: https://www.world-nuclear-news.org/Articles/Early-shutdown-for-Taiwanese-reactor#:~:text=Phase-out%20policy%20Taiwan%27s%20Democratic%20Progressive%20Party%20%28DPP%29%20was,be%20decommissioned%20as%20their%2040-year%20operating%20licences%20expire. Last Accessed 10/2023.
- WNN, (2021). "Taipower applies to decommission Maanshan plant." World Nuclear News, 27 July 2021. Available at website: https://www.world-nuclear-news.org/ (or) https://www.world-nuclear-news.org/Articles/Taipower-applies-to-decommission-Maanshan-plant#:~:text=Taiwan%20Power%20Company%20has%20submitted%20an%20application%20to,the%20closure%20of%20Maanshan%20unit%202%20in%202025. Last Accessed 10/2023.
- Woetzel, J. and Wang, B., *et al.*, (2021). "Reskilling China: Transforming the world's largest workforce into lifelong learners." *McKinsey Global Institute*, Report, 12 January 2021. Available at website: https://www.mckinsey.com/featured-insights/china/reskilling-china-transforming-the-worlds-largest-workforce-into-lifelong-learners Last Accessed 11/2023.
- Wong, N. (2020). "Community energy: A way out of energy transition." *Taiwan Insight*, Taiwan Studies Programme, Research Centre based at the University of Nottingham. 20 July 2020. Available at webpage:

https://taiwaninsight.org/2020/07/20/community-energy-a-way-out-of-energy-transition/ Last Accessed 10/2023.
- World Nuclear Association, (2019). "Nuclear Power in Taiwan." *WNA Updated Report*, July 2019. Available at website: https://www.world-nuclear.org/information-library/country-profiles/others/nuclear-power-in-taiwan.aspx Last Accessed April 2020.
- Working Group of the R.O.C. Laws and Regulations Database, Ministry of Justice. *Government Website Open Information Announcement*. Available at website: https://law.moj.gov.tw/ENG/LawClass/LawAll.aspx?pcode=D0070062 Last Accessed April 2020.
- Wu, H.Y. Chen, C.H. Wang, C.C. Su, J. and Kao, E. (2018). "Environmental groups protest restarting nuclear reactor." *The China Post*, February 6, 2018. Available at webpage: https://chinapost.nownews.com/20180206-224581 As of 10/2023 this link has been disabled. The article can be read here: https://focustaiwan.tw/politics/201802050015 CNA Archive. Last Accessed 10/2023.
- Wu, S. (2022). "Taiwan to invest in green energy, smart grids to reach net-zero emissions goal." *Reuters News Agency*, Environment, April 22, 2022. Available at website: https://www.reuters.com/business/environment/taiwan-invest-green-energy-smart-grids-reach-net-zero-emissions-goal-2022-04-22/ Last Accessed 10/2023.
- Wu, S.S. (2014). "A possible nuclear disaster in Taiwan: An international crisis in East Asia." *Australian Institute of International Affairs*, Australian Outlook, 06 August 2014. Available at website: https://www.internationalaffairs.org.au/australianoutlook/a-possible-nuclear-disaster-in-taiwan-an-international-crisis-in-east-asia/ Last Accessed 11/2023.
- Wu, Y.C. (2013). "Seismic hazard and performance for operating NPPs in Taiwan." *European Nuclear Safety Regulation Group (ENSREG) Review Meeting*. Institute of Nuclear Energy Research report. Available at webpage: https://www.ensreg.eu/sites/default/files/2013%2009%2024%2002_SHA%20and%20Performance%20for%20NPPs%20in%20Taiwan_1020924.PDF Last Accessed 10/2023.

X

- Xiao, Q. Liu, H. and Feldman, M.W. (2017). "How Does Trust Affect Acceptance of a Nuclear Power Plant (NPP): A Survey Among People Living with Qinshan NPP in China." *PLoS One*, Volume 12, No. 11. doi: 10.1371/journal.pone.0187941 Last Accessed 10/2023.

Y

- Yang, C.L. Yuan, B.J.C. and Huang, C. Y. (2015). "Key Determinant Derivations for Information Technology Disaster Recovery Site Selection by the Multi-Criterion Decision Making Method." *Sustainability*, MDPI, Volume 7, No. 5, pp. 6149-6188.

- Yang, Y.N. (2015). "The nuclear disaster management system in Taiwan: A case study of the third (Maanshan) nuclear power plant." *Disasters (DI)*, Volume 40, No. 3, pp. 534-553.
- Yan-chih, M. (2013). "President, KMT lawmakers discuss nuclear safety." *Taipei Times*, Taiwan News, 23 February 2013, page 3. Available website at: https://www.taipeitimes.com/News/taiwan/archives/2013/02/23/2003555506 Last Accessed 11/2023.
- Yen, C.L. Loh, C.H. Chen, L.C. Wei, L.Y. Lee, W.C. and Ho, H.Y. (2006). "Development and implementation of disaster reduction technology in Taiwan." *Natural Hazards*, Volume 37, pp- 3-21. https://doi.org/10.1007/s11069-005-4652-1.

Z

- Zarsky, L. and Hunter, J. (1997). "Environmental Cooperation at APEC: The first five years." *APSNet Special Reports*, March 31, 1997. Available website at: https://nautilus.org/apsnet/environmental-cooperation-at-apec-the-first-five-years-2/ Last Accessed April 2020.
- Zheng, S. and Tiong, R.L.K. (2010). "First public-private partnership application in Taiwan's wastewater treatment sector: Case Study of the Nanzih BOT Wastewater Treatment project." *Journal of Construction Engineering and Management,* Volume 136, Issue 8. https://doi.org/10.1061/(ASCE)CO.1943-7862.0000196.
- Ziwei, F. (2020). "Technology transfers from Taiwan to China now require governmental approval." *Taiwan News*, 27 August 2020. Available website at: https://www.taiwannews.com.tw/en/news/3995941 Last Accessed 10/2023.

Suggested Literature

B

- Bosner, L. and I-wei Jennifer Chang, 2020. "Taiwan's disaster preparedness and response: Strengths, shortfalls, and paths to improvement." Global Taiwan Institute, October 2020. Webpage available at: https://globaltaiwan.org/wp-content/uploads/2020/10/GTI-Taiwans-Disaster-Preparedness-and-Response-Oct-2020-final.pdf?mc_cid=518eb59a56&mc_eid=ad991f7720 Last Accessed 10/2023.

C

- Chang K.T., 2021. "Chiang's nuclear power falsehoods." Taipei Times, April 4, 2021. Wepage available at: https://www.taipeitimes.com/News/editorials/archives/2021/04/04/2003755043 (or) https://thoriumbaby.com/chiangs-nuclear-power-falsehoods-taipei-times/ Last Accessed 10/2023.
- The Consilience Project, 2021. "Taiwan's digital democracy." The Consilience Project is a publication of the Civilization Research Institute (CRI), Situational Feature, 06 June 2021. Available at Website: https://www.consilienceproject.org/taiwans-digital-democracy/?msclkid=43ae25c4c25d11ec8cbddc5e62ee8926 Last Accessed 10/2023.

D

- Department of Natural Sciences and Sustainable Development, Ministry of Science and Technology, 08/2021. "International experts and scholars gathered in Taipei for the Belmont Forum 10th Anniversary & Annual Plenary Meeting." MOST news & events section. Webpage available at: https://www.nstc.gov.tw/folksonomy/detail?subSite=&l=en&article_uid=11b7814d-8bcc-4030-a75a-38e59604517b&menu_id=eb9eb136-4319-40d6-abd3-0788bea0d3a8&content_type=P&view_mode=listView#:~:text=This%20year%20coincides%20with%20the%2010th%20Anniversary%20of,center%20and%20Apex%20Building%20in%20the%20NTU%20campus. Last Accessed 10/2023.
- Dorman, B., and Tyler James Olsen, 2019. "The ASEAN Way out? Toward cooperative environmental governance in Southeast Asia." E-International Relations, August 10, 2019. Available online at: https://www.e-ir.info/2019/08/10/the-asean-way-out-toward-cooperative-environmental-

governance-in-southeast-asia/ Last Accessed 11/2023.

E

- Energy Security Report by: Sih Ting Jhou, and Huei-Chu Liao, 2013. "Taiwan's severe energy security challenges." Brookings, Series: Taiwan-U.S. Quarterly Analysis. Published on September 12, 2013. Available at website: https://www.brookings.edu/opinions/taiwans-severe-energy-security-challenges/ Last Accessed 10/2023.

F

- Freschi, N., 2018. "Taiwan's Nuclear Dilemma." *The Diplomat,* March 14, 2018. Available at webpage: https://thediplomat.com/2018/03/taiwans-nuclear-dilemma/ Last Accessed 10/2023.
- The Fukushima Nuclear Accident and Crisis Management – Lessons for Japan-U.S. Alliance Cooperation - Final report of the SPF Research Project on "Assessment: Japan-US Response to the Fukushima Crisis." Sasakawa Peace Foundation. September, 2012. Webpage available at: https://www.spf.org/en/_jpus_media/img/investigation/book_fukushima.pdf Last Accessed 10/2023.

G

- Glauert, R., 2020. "Taiwan's renewables push hit by big tech's appetite for power." NIKKEI Asia, Environment section. Published on 18 December, 2020. Webpage available at: https://asia.nikkei.com/Spotlight/Environment/Taiwan-s-renewables-push-hit-by-big-tech-s-appetite-for-power Last Accessed 10/2023.

H

- Han, T.S., and Su-fen Chiu, 2000. "Industrial democracy and institutional environments: A comparison of Germany and Taiwan." *Economic and Industrial Democracy*, Volume 21, Issue 2, page(s): 147-182.
- Hattori, T., and Yukihito Sato, 1997. "A comparative study of development mechanisms in Korea and Taiwan: Introductory Analysis." The Developing Economies, Volume 35, No. 5, pp. 341-57.
- Hioe, B., 2018. "KMT asserts inconsistent stance on nuclear power simply to oppose DPP." New Bloom, Radical perspectives on Taiwan and the Asia Pacific, 29/4/2018. Available at website: https://newbloommag.net/2018/04/29/kmt-nuclear-power-stance/ Last Accessed 10/2023.
- Hsiang Y., and Elizabeth Hsu, 2021. "Nuclear power plant referendum set to take place in August." Focus Taiwan CNA English News, 22 January, 2021. Available online at: https://focustaiwan.tw/politics/202101220020 Last Accessed 11/2023.

I

- International Atomic Energy Agency (IAEA), 2021. "Environmental release." Website available at: https://www.iaea.org/topics/environmental-release Last Accessed 10/2023.
- Isdijoso, B., 2021. "PPPs in Indonesia are gaining momentum - these 5 steps were key." World Bank Blogs, World Bank Group, 2021. Available online at: https://blogs.worldbank.org/ppps/ppps-indonesia-are-gaining-momentum-these-5-steps-were-key Last Accessed 11/2023.

K

- Knowlton, R. G., Cochran John C., Arnold Bill Walter, Jow Hong-Nian, Mattie Patrick D, Schelling Frank Joseph)2007. "Taiwan industrial cooperation program technology transfer for low-level radioactive waste final disposal - phase I." United States Department of Energy Office of Scientific and Technical Information. Available at webpages: https://doi.org/10.2172/900849. (or) https://www.osti.gov/servlets/purl/900849. Last Accessed 10/2023.

M

- Mansour, N., 2009. "Science-Technology-Society (STS): A new paradigm in science education." *Bulletin of Science, Technology & Society*, Volume: 29 issue: 4, pages: 287-297.

- Mien-chieh Y., and William Hetherington, 2020. "Anniversary of Chernobyl sees anti-nuclear appeals." Taipei Times, April 28, Available at website: https://www.taipeitimes.com/News/taiwan/archives/2020/04/28/2003735431 Last Accessed 11/2023.

N

- National Science and Technology Center for Disaster Reduction (NCDR) Newsletters, December 2020, New Taipei City, Taiwan. "The MoU signed between NCDR and HUNRE, and will develop the cooperation on DRR technologies with Viet Nam." Available at website: https://www.ncdr.nat.gov.tw/Home/Index?aspxerrorpath=/Epaper/NewsLetterDownload/270%20%c2%b7%20PDF%20file Last Accessed 10/2023.
- Nuclear Engineering International magazine, 2013. "EU completes peer review of Taiwanese nuclear plant safety." Published on 12/11/2013. Available at webpage: https://www.neimagazine.com/news/newseu-completes-peer-review-of-tianwanese-nuclear-plant-safety Last Accessed 10/2023.

R

- Resurreccion, B.R., Edsel E. Sajor, and Elizabeth Fajber, 2008. "Climate Adaptation in Asia: Knowledge gaps and research issues in South East Asia." Full Report of the South East Asia Team, ISET-International and ISET-Nepal.

Page 25. Available at website: https://www.preventionweb.net/files/8126_ClimateAdaptationSEASept081.pdf Accessed 10/2023.

- Risk Interface Management refers to "Interface Management which is the systematic control of all communications that support a process operation." Available at website: https://www.aiche.org/ccps/topics/elements-process-safety/manage-risks/conduct-operations/interface-management Last Accessed May 2020.
- Rodna, A., 2012. "Radiological environmental monitoring at NPP Cernavoda.." IAEA/NENP - Technical Meeting on Environmental Issues in New Nuclear Power Programmes, IAEA Vienna, Austria, 20 to 23 March 2012. Page 17. Available at website: https://inis.iaea.org/collection/NCLCollectionStore/_Public/43/048/43048644.pdf Last Accessed 10/2023.

S

- Shi P., Ye, T., Wang, Y, N., Okada, *et al.,* 2020. "Disaster Risk Science: A Geographical Perspective and a Research Framework." *International Journal of Disaster Risk Science*, Volume 11, pp. 426-440 (2020).

T

-Taipei Times, section: Taiwan News. Yang Chun-hui and Jonathan Chin, "Fourth Nuclear Plant activation 'no option': Tsai." Published March 19, 2021. Available at webpage: https://www.taipeitimes.com/News/taiwan/archives/2021/03/19/2003754116 Last Accessed 10/2023.
- Taiwan National Science and Technology Center for Disaster Reduction (NCDR) Background Presentation Webpage Available at website: https://www.ncdr.nat.gov.tw/Page?itemid=60&mid=74 Last Accessed 10/2023.
- Taiwan Power Company, 2013. "EU Stress Test for KS NPP - Licensee Report. (Rev. 1c)." Available at website: http://www.ensreg.eu/sites/default/files/TPC%20Utilitity%20Report%20of%20EU%20Stress%20Test%20for%20KSNPP_May%202013.pdf Last Accessed 11/2023.
- Taiwan Trade Office, 2016. "Focus on environmental protection in Taiwan." Taipei Trade Office in the Federal Republic of Nigeria, 2016. Available at website: https://www.taiwanembassy.org/ng_en/post/368.html Last Accessed 11/2023.
- Tan, Q. Peter Kien-hong Yu, and Wen-chun Chen, 1996. "Local Politics in Taiwan. Democratic Consolidation." *Asian Survey,* Volume 36, No. 5, pp. 483-494.
- Tobishima Engineering and Construction Corporation, 2021. "Expert in Disaster Prevention Technology." Available at webpage: https://www.tobishima.co.jp/english/business/ Last Accessed 10/2023.

U

- United Nations Conference on Trade and Development (UNCTAD) 2014. "Studies in Technology Transfer." UNCTAD Current Studies on Science, Technology and Innovation. N.7. Available at website: https://unctad.org/system/files/official-document/dtlstict2013d7_en.pdf Last Accessed 10/2023.
- United Nations Scientific Committee on the Effects of Atomic Radiation (UNSCEAR), Chernobyl 2018 White Paper, "Evaluation of data on thyroid cancer in regions affected by the Chernobyl accident." Available at website: https://www.unscear.org/unscear/uploads/documents/publications/Chernobyl_WP_2017.pdf Last Accessed 10/2023.
- USAID, 2011. "Introduction to Disaster Risk Reduction." Full Report available at website: https://www.preventionweb.net/files/26081_kp1concepdisasterrisk1.pdf Last Accessed 10/2023.
- U.S. NRC, United States Nuclear Regulatory Commission, 2019. "Decommissioning of Nuclear Facilities." Report. Available at website: https://www.nrc.gov/waste/decommissioning.html Last Accessed April 2020.

W

- Wang, F., Elaine Hou, Lu Tai-cheng. In Focus Taiwan. "Orchid Island to get NT$2.55 billion in nuclear waste compensation." Taipei, Nov. 22, 2019. Available at website: https://focustaiwan.tw/politics/201911220023 Last Accessed 10/2023.
- Wang, L.J., 2014. "Cultural difference, national identity and cultural policy in Taiwan." In: Lee, HK, Lim, L. (eds) *Cultural Policies in East Asia*. Pp. 35-52. Palgrave Macmillan, London.
- Wei, S., 2016. "Recovery from 'Betrayal': Local anti-nuclear movements and party politics in Taiwan." The Asia-Pacific Journal,Volume 14, Issue 8, Number 3, 2016. Available at website: https://apjjf.org/2016/08/Wei.html Last Accessed 10/2023.
- World Nuclear News, 2022. "Finland sets out nuclear waste plans." WNN, Waste & Recycling section, 02 March 2022. Webpage available at: https://www.world-nuclear-news.org/Articles/Finland-sets-out-nuclear-waste-plans Last Accessed 10/2023.
- World Nuclear News, 2019. "Taiwan government maintains nuclear phase-out." WNN, Nuclear Policies, 01 February 2019. Available online at: https://www.world-nuclear-news.org/Articles/Taiwan-government-maintains-nuclear-phase-out Last Accessed 11/2023.
- Wu Y.Y., and Hwong-Wen Ma, 2019. "Challenges for integrating strategic environmental assessment to enhance environmental thinking: A case study of Taiwan energy policy." *Sustainability*, Volume 11, No. 3, pp.609. Available at website: https://www.mdpi.com/2071-1050/11/3/609 Last

Accessed 10/2023.

Y

- Yuksel, F., 2018. "Green energy driving force for Taiwanese exports growth." Anadolu Energy Agency, Asia. Available at website: https://www.aa.com.tr/en/energy/solar/green-energy-driving-force-for-taiwanese-exports-growth/21744 Last Accessed 10/2023.

Public Nuclear Agendas Applied to Japan in Post-Disaster Crises

Overview

This monograph provides a brief comparative study through a selection of regional literature research in order to better understand a dual context of Japan and Taiwan that reflects post-Fukushima monitoring compliance strategies, for nuclear safety. This dual analysis has combined a structural overview about public policy contexts and national regulative issues, related to technology industries and organizational management directions. As an introductory section centred on Japan's governance impacts, it has been framed a conceptual overview about environmental impact assessments EIA and nuclear policy. This discussion delves into comparative local safety risk aspects emerging in connection with post Fukushima-related institutional reporting processes. Fundamentally, this review addresses comparative affirmative agendas of the post-Fukushima assessment period. This discourse also involves the public-private PPP under common management guidelines, as well as environmental regulatory planning. Overall, this reporting activity confirms that local industrial configurations have remained an essential mediation ground for promoting comparative understanding and collaborative environmental programs. In conclusion, the reflection made is that at country-level still persists a permanent lack of alternative distribution programs based on Science and Technology energy transfers that also increase contextual hindrances, which might impact on complex environmental regulatory dimensions, for instance affecting an evolving status of local communities entrusting a normative process currently pointed at national NPP energy innovation implementation and PPP collaboration dynamics. Thus, the regional organizational protocols of STS changing societies can determine comprehensive objectives that in any case will be difficult to fulfil at a complete industrial scale.

1.1 Introductory Notes on Nuclear Energy Governance in Japan

In this comparative review, it will be discussed the political and economic transitioning relationships that have taken shape in the case of the industrial nuclear emergency at the Fukushima Daiichi nuclear power plant in Japan 2011.[347] In order to widen theoretical assessments, it has been followed an interdisciplinary approach that is based on the concept of local knowledge transferring processes.[348]

At governmental level, structural changing processes have been interrelated to the formation of collaborative environmental strategies able to indicate specified local regulative provisions, in particular, about local environmental assessment dynamics and regional decision-making activities. Regional industrial changes and local knowledge dynamics have been analyzed in connection with fundamental public assessment criteria that can specify, for instance, a material degree of effectiveness of governmental interventions,[349] which have been associated with sustainable energy programs and environmental protection systems.

[347] Note: This accident has occurred: "Following a major earthquake, a 15-metre tsunami disabled the power supply and cooling of three Fukushima Daiichi reactors, causing a nuclear accident beginning on 11 March 2011. All three cores largely melted in the first three days...All four Fukushima Daiichi reactors were written off due to damage in the accident – 2719MWe net. " WNA, 2023 Updated Contents. "Fukushima Daiichi Accident." reported on: World Nuclear Association website, available online at: https://www.world-nuclear.org/information-library/safety-and-security/safety-of-plants/fukushima-daiichi-accident.aspx - Accessed 07/2023.

[348] See: OECD study project "Assessing the impacts of the policy mix for knowledge transfer between industry and science."/ "2017-18 project implemented by the Working Party on Innovation and Technology Policy (TIP) under the auspices of the OECD Committee for Science and Technological Policy (CSTP)." OECD reference websites available at: (1) https://www.oecd.org/sti/inno/working-group-on-innovation-and-technology-policy.htm#:~:text=The%20core%20objective%20of%20the%20TIP%20is%20to,foster%20the%20creation%20of%20science%20and%20technology-based%20firms. (2) https://stip.oecd.org/knowledge-transfer/case-studies - Accessed 07/2023.

[349] Note: In 2021, it is reported that: "The government wants to achieve a 46% emissions reduction by 2030 compared with 2013 levels. Japan currently produces a large portion of its power through coal and natural gas, neither of which are sourced domestically and many nuclear power facilities remain shuttered since the incident at a plant following the 2011

Using this analytic context, it has been independently reviewed the nuclear industrial policy of Japan through country-based studies, while considering at the same time constructive technology and societies issues, referring in particular to: nuclear waste technology status, scientific development transfers, and science technology and innovation (STI) networks, which have been regularly configured in socio-democratic environments, in view of regional sustainable development goals (SDG)[350] of changing societies. What can be identified as point of discussion in this review it has been the inclusive combination of comparative science and energy planning systems, coordinated according to upgraded national procedures [351] that have been renewed in connection with an administrative interplay of correspondent assertive actions. In fact, interdependent aligned actions have been structured within the public and private boundaries of science, technology and societies (STS), based on

Great East Japan Earthquake." Andy Colthorpe, October 25, 2021. "Japan's policymakers approve higher 2030 renewable energy target." PVTECH News, Markets & Finance, Policy. Webpage available at: https://www.pv-tech.org/japans-policymakers-approve-higher-2030-renewable-energy-target/ Accessed 08/2023.

[350] Note: In terms of SDGs mirrored at local level: "Each year since 2018, the national government has designated about 30 municipalities as 'SDGs Future Cities'...Each candidate SDGs Future City decides its priority goals and formulates an action plan that is reviewed from social, economic and environmental perspectives. About 10 of these municipalities are selected as 'SDGs Models of Local Governments' and are provided subsidies for cross-sectional initiatives that can potentially be rolled out to other areas...Various measures have been taken to foster STI utilization for local SDGs." Report of (JST) Japan Science and Technology Agency, April 2021. "Mobilizing Science, Technology and Innovation for SDGs. Japanese Actions in STI for SDGs." Page 22. Webpage available at: https://www.jst.go.jp/sdgs/en/pdf/sti_for_sdgs_report_en_apr_2021.pdf Accessed 08/2023.

[351] Note: In a 2018 report, the Government of Japan focuses on energy policy by validating that "it is important to increase transparency over the energy policy planning process and obtain public trust in the policy...GOJ will maximize the openness of the policymaking process through advisory councils, meeting of experts and the like and enhance their transparency...GOJ will strengthen communication to conduct the dialogue with all layers of society. For various challenges related to energy including nuclear power, *the fact that the substance is highly technical and complicated is a factor that impedes understanding.* Therefore, GOJ will seek to promote further understanding by careful dialogue and two-way communication instead of merely conveying information on a one-way street." Japan's Agency for Natural Resources and Energy, Government of Japan (GOJ) report, 2018. "Strategic Energy Plan." July 2018. Page 114. Webpage available at: https://www.enecho.meti.go.jp/en/category/others/basic_plan/5th/pdf/strategic_energy_plan.pdf Accessed 08/2023.

local knowledge transfers and technical distribution plans involving the managerial processing organizations.

More specifically, this functional analysis discusses on centralized bargaining powers' relationships that have evolved in connection with local municipalities, national energy security centers, and public networking bureaus thorough multi-layered systems. Such complex regulatory systems have been characterized by environmental preservation policies validated in terms of local development and technical operable measures, which have been adopted for the case of nuclear energy distribution systems of (NPP).

Through comparative views, the energy technology of local planning systems and managerial implementation of local impact assessments (EIA) in Japanese municipalities[352] have been associated with configured decision-making activities that have contributed to re-establish cross-countries environmental adaptive programs. Essentially, in view of developing instrumental renewable energy innovation plans, the public-private partnerships PPP have provided technical knowledge tools and systemic regulatory contributions as well as cooperative rebuilding mechanisms, which have been studied in relation with environmental standardized practice models adopted in comparative law perspective.[353] For study purposes, this initial review examines nuclear governance adaptation and prospective local environmental issues that have referred to the formal implementation of Environmental Impact Assessments

[352] Kiyohiko Suzuki, 2019. "Environmental impact assessment of renewable energy in Japan." Environmental Impact Assessment Division, Ministry of the Environment, Japan. Webpage available at: https://www.nedo.go.jp/content/100899753.pdf Accessed 08/23.

[353] Note: In Japan's case, the legal environment procedural laws relate to "the Basic Act on Environment...[it] requires the Japanese government to establish a Basic Environment Plan, a comprehensive plan for the promotion of environmental protection (Article 15 of the Act). The Act further requires the government to establish environmental standards for air, water, soil and noise, and to adopt protective measures when engaging in projects that may impact the environment (Article 16 of the Act). The Act also provides ground for environmental impact assessments [EIA] (Article 20 of the Act), the adoption of regulatory measures (Article 21 of the Act) and 'economic' measures to dissuade polluting activities (Article 22 of the Act)." Akira Nagasaki, 2021. "Environmental Law 2021. Japan." Chambers and Partners, November 30, 2021. Website available at: https://practiceguides.chambers.com/ practice-guides/comparison/711/9875/15767-15769-15771-15774-15776-15779-15782-15785-15788-15793-15796-15798-15801-15803-15807-15811-15814 Accessed 08/2023.

(EIAs).[354] In order to be able to identify both differences and commonalities emerging in terms of environmental risk assessment models and national environmental protocols, there is to consider that the national implementation of local environmental aims and regional managerial objectives has remained a central issue in governance.[355] The reason being that the emergence of regulatory practice in the nuclear management field has possibly led toward the formation of multilateral activities that have been increased at domestic and international level. Depending on the variability of governmental regulatory purposes,[356] the

[354] Note: As comparative EIA assessment in an NPP case: "Fortum (Power and Heat Oy) [...]has initiated an Environmental Impact Assessment procedure (EIA procedure) for the Loviisa nuclear power plant. The procedure will assess the environmental impacts of a potential extension of the operation of the power plant or, alternatively, the decommissioning of the power plant, as well as the environmental impacts of the final disposal facility for low- and intermediate-level waste." Eurasia Review, News & Analysis, 2020. " Fortum begins environmental impact assessment procedure for Loviisa Nuclear Power Plant." ER 13-08-2020. Website:https://www.eurasiareview.com/13082020-fortum-begins-environmental-impact-assessment-procedure-for-loviisa-nuclear-power-plant/ Accessed 09/2020.

[355] Note: As of 2021, TEPCO Energy Agency reports that: "[…] the Government of Japan held 'Meetings for Hearing Opinions' to hear the opinions of the stakeholders and solicited opinions from the general public. The comments submitted raised…concerns about the impact of discharge of ALPS [Advanced Liquid Processing System] treated water into the sea in the surrounding environment. Based on these studies and comments, the Government of Japan announced its 'Basic Policy on handling of ALPS treated water at the Tokyo Electric Power Company Holdings' Fukushima Daiichi Nuclear Power Station,' during the meeting of the Ministerial Council regarding Decommissioning/Contaminated Water/Treated Water on April 13, 2021. In this Basic Policy, the Government of Japan selected handling of the ALPS treated water by discharge into the sea, conditional on ensuring safety as to this method of discharge." Tokyo Electric Power Company Holdings (TEPCO), 2021. "Radiological Impact Assessment Report Regarding the Discharge of ALPS Treated Water into the Sea (design stage)." TEPCO report, November 2021. Page 5. Webpage available: https://www.tepco.co.jp/en/hd/newsroom/press/archives/2021/pdf/211117e0102.pdf Accessed 08/2023.

[356] Note: The reforming initiatives for nuclear regulation in Japan's case faced a national re-organization because: "[...] The previous bureaucratic alignment facilitated 'regulatory capture' by the nuclear power industry, resulting in substandard and weakly enforced rules to ensure safety. The primary agency in charge of regulation, the Nuclear and Industrial Safety Agency (NISA) was routinely overpowered by the industry interests represented in the Ministry of Economy Trade and Industry (METI) that housed it while also holding responsibility for promoting the nuclear power industry. Another problem that the Fukushima accident exposed was the poorly defined responsibilities of other agencies that had a role in developing regulation and in managing accident scenarios." Charles D. Ferguson, and Mark Jansson, 2013. "Regulating Japanese nuclear power in the wake of the Fukushima Daiichi Accident." Federation of American Scientists (FAS), FAS Issue Brief,

national evaluation procedures based on the selection of multilevel environmental agendas have integrated industrial technology programs in more progressive ways. The national documentation activity focused on technical industrial assessments has been strategically arranged according to different planning stages, systematically undertaken in view of adapting to local changing dynamics occurring in the case of public and private partnerships PPPs.[357]

A critical attention has been put on the domestic organizational dimension as well as on local information service provision. Because, there is to consider that local operating conditions have become instrumental in order to understand the institutional role of EIAs interrelated with functional programmatic aspects of PPP, including the preparation of public civic rules. The further identification of common territorial rules regarding the affirmation of managerial energy projects, developed through comparative environmental assessments, has been associated with single states' regulatory capacity when put into practice.[358] Following this line of understanding, there have been interdependent causal factors about the development of PPPs, strategically designed in view of framing common regulatory practices.[359]

When comparing local states' intervention policies established in connection with different national performance criteria, the environmental local programs have been associated with national provisions operated through EIAs, for instance. Public assessment and mediation tools have reflected common participatory practices which in essence have become

May 2013. Page 1. Webpage available at: https://uploads.fas.org/2013/05/Regulating_Japanese_Nuclear_13May131.pdf Accessed 08/2023.

[357] Note: For project management activities of NPPs: "In Japan, private electric power suppliers undertake construction of the nuclear energy plants and serve as the owners and operators of the nuclear energy plant units. Electric power suppliers manage entire construction projects, with construction work and manufacturing of equipment and facilities done by the companies that constructed the plants." International Atomic Energy Agency, 2020. "Country Nuclear Power Profiles. Japan." (IAEA) Country Energy Overview. Webpage available at: https://cnpp.iaea.org/countryprofiles/Japan/Japan.htm Accessed 08/2023.

[358] J. Pope et al., 2013; A.J. Sinclair et al., 2008; H. Runhaar et al., 2010; I. Polonen et al., 2011.

[359] Jenny Pope, Alan Bond, Angus Morrison-Saunders, Francois Retief, 2013. "Advancing the theory and practice of impact assessment: Setting the research agenda." Environmental Impact Assessment Review, Volume 41, July, pp. 1-9.

functional in terms of public guidance models that can be identified in view of sustaining collaborative societal linkages, for instance, related to Canada's nuclear energy case for Northern America.[360] In EIA reviews, the Japanese government defined a revision of the EIA act in 2012 with major elements amending the previous act, such as: [1] "[...] Obligation to hold a public session at the stage of the assessment method determination; [2] obligation for the publication of the documents prepared by the project proponents (environmental assessment documents) via Internet; [...] [3] enabling direct submission of opinion from the designated cities to the project proponents."[361] As an institutional path, the interdependent process also resulting in common transnational adaptations within open learning plans for local environmental assessments[362] has provided flexible and consistent regional organizational approaches related with the structural territorial contexts, involving multilevel planning activities and decision-making processes. How? For instance: the EIA mandates and regulations in Japan's case have tended to overlap and in order to avoid coincidental procedures the EIA Law has addressed EIA systems at local governmental level in order to reduce the additional overlapping procedures.[363] In correspondence to this operational setting, regional local development and industrial management innovation have been theoretically lined up for the possible inclusion of public learning models and environmental participation activities.[364] As underlined by environmental experts as F. Krupp about the "Fourth Wave of

[360] A. John Sinclair, Alan Diduck, Patricia Fitzpatrick, 2008. "Conceptualizing learning for sustainability through environmental assessment: critical reflections on 15 years of research." Environmental Impact Assessment Review, Volume 28, Issue 7, October, pp. 415-428. https://doi.org/10.1016/j.eiar.2007.11.001

[361] Japan, Ministry of the Environment, 2013. "Environmental impact assessment in Japan." Environmental Impact Assessment Network Report, page 2: Revision of the Environmental Impact Assessment Act. Available at website: http://assess.env.go.jp /5_global/OutlineofEnvironmentalImpact_inJapan/index.html and http://assess.env.go.jp/files/1_seido/pamph_e.pdf and http://assess.env.go.jp/files/5_ global/OutlineofEnvironmentalImpact_pdf/e_02.pdf Accessed 08/2023.

[362] A. J. Sinclair et al., 2008.

[363] Environmental Impact Assessment Division, online 2022. "Environmental impact assessment in Japan." Ministry of the Environment, Government of Japan, National Report, page 16. Available at website: https://www.env.go.jp/en/policy/assess/pamph.pdf Accessed 08/2023.

[364] J. Pope et al., 2013.

environmental innovation: It's a revolution in environmental progress driven by innovation and technology that gives people the power to take action. It has the power to transform how we solve environmental problems, helping us scale the solutions we need to stabilize the climate, reverse overfishing, and protect public health and endangered species."[365]

Regional comparative reviews coming from development policy scholars have approached the environmental governance models in connection with cognitive dynamics of environmental territorial project assessments promoted in terms of structural adaptation activities that can remain dependent on material determinism, as well as, on technical procedural understanding, connected with practical technology implications and local innovation impacts. Through common deliberative aims, the identification of critical assumptions that have specifically referred to: practical local knowledge on societal environmental issues ex. the Japan Air Pollution Reduction policies,[366] or to local participatory elements such as: public knowledge acquisitions, systematic upgraded information, transparent procedural transfers - have essentially highlighted comparative increasing levels of structural decentralized changes combined with national innovation and intervention policies, revisiting environmental management directions, civilian local activism programs, and coherent regulatory implementation measures.[367]

2.1 Formalized Environmental Adaptive Designs

From an organizational perspective, the interconnection of political mediators on PPP transfers with private contractors, public officials, and involved civilian stakeholders has allowed the diffusion of local operational levels of technology and knowledge transfers. The JICA

[365] Fred Krupp, 2018. "Harnessing the fourth wave of environmentalism." The Fourth Wave of Environmental Innovation, EDF Environmental Defense Fund, 21 March, 2018. Available at website: https://medium.com/the-fourth-wave/harnessing-the-fourth-wave-of-environmentalism-c71afa14eb11 Accessed 08/2023.

[366] Junko Edahiro, 2009. "A brief history of the environmental movement in Japan (part I)." JFS, Japan for Sustainability, Newsletter No. 82, July 21, 2009. Available at website: https://www.japanfs.org/en/news/archives/news_id029180.html Accessed 08/2023.

[367] Hens Runhaar, Piety R. Runhaar, Tammo Oegema, 2010. "Food for thought: Conditions for discourse reflection in the light of environmental assessment." Environmental Impact Assessment Review, Volume 30, No. 6, pp. 339-346.

office[368] has implemented PPP regional partnerships both in East and Southeast Asia concerning sustainability for infrastructures, logistics innovation, or financial schemes: Private-Sector Investment Finance PSIF, is based on JICA's programmatic guidelines on a "collaboration program with the private sector for disseminating Japanese technology for the social and economic development of developing countries, [established in] 2013."[369] Through the use of multiple learning approaches that have been undertaken in order to achieve the necessary formal stages of local constructive commitments, have also received support environmental management projects involving local effective planning within PPP regional contexts, as in the case of resource-based energy development[370] programs.[371] Nonetheless, the EIAs have been analyzed in association with the changing requirements of local regulatory administrations adopting systemic practice tools, which have been operated according to multiple distributive sets of local mutual arrangements that are defined in relation with local environmental protection policies. Across Japanese municipalities, it has been reviewed the relationship between ecological efficiency targets and socioeconomic growth through different analyses including the LCIA life-cycle impact assessment that identifies essential impact parameters for comprehensive national evaluations.[372] The EIAs have also been subjected to systemic regional assessment practices and local managerial compliance conditions. Effectively, environmental local governance when based on institutional economic and policy objectives has stimulated different programmatic feedbacks, especially when assessed in connection with attentive local ecology legislation and social

[368] JICA Annual Report, 2018. "Public-private partnerships and partnership with Japanese private sector." Japan International Cooperation Agency, Cooperation with Partners, Available at website: https://www.jica.go.jp/english/publications/reports/annual/2018/c8h0vm0000dxws0g-att/2018_20.pdf Accessed 08/2023.

[369] JICA Annual Report, 2018. Page 51.

[370] Runhaar, et al., 2010.

[371] Ismo Polonen, Pekka Hokkanen, Kimmo Jalava, 2011. "The effectiveness of the Finnish EIA system – What works, what doesn't, and what could be improved?" Environmental Impact Assessment Review, Volume 31, No. 2, pp. 120-128.

[372] Junya Yamasaki, Toshiharu Ikaga, Norihiro Itsubo, 2019. "Eco-efficiency assessment of Japanese Municipalities based on environmental impacts and gross regional product." Sustainability, Volume 11, No. 15, pp. 4045; https://doi.org/10.3390/su11154045 Accessed 08/2023.

participative tools, grounded on a practical local dimension that reflects common environmental distributive causes e.g. the Finnish case about public evaluation procedures of EIAs.[373]

Overall, the descriptive concepts introduced in this book propose an illustration of environmental practice cases that emerged in the post-Fukushima Japan's nuclear context, associated with nuclear national policy and corresponding organizational dynamics specifically expressed through PPP comprehensive regional adaptation plans tackling ex: disaster management and resilient infrastructural designs.[374] Potential descriptive indications developed in this review can provide a theoretical basis on Japan's security through intra-disciplinary formulations particularly focused on comparative environmental risk protection efforts, as well as, on risk management in local performing systems, technically involved in cross-countries environmental territorial impacts, reported through quantitative and qualitative governance analyses. For instance, in view of PPP renovation projects and public consensus the "local governments are the implementation entities for about 80 percent of PPP projects in Japan [...]"[375]

From a comparative advantage standpoint, regional normative flexibility combined with local practical implications, affecting the institutional integration of managerial performing systems, can be responsive to different types of domestic public-private preparatory assessments that have been expanded for supporting an inter-operational environmental regulatory dimension. At governmental level, the sectoral definitions related with either direct or indirect preparation of environmental emergency measures and information contingency procedures have been specified in connection with the standardization of

[373] I. Polonen et al., 2011.

[374] The World Bank, 2017. "Resilient infrastructure public-private partnerships (PPPs): Contracts and procurement. The case of Japan." World Bank DRM Hub, Tokyo, International Bank for Reconstruction and Development, Report, Available at website: https://thedocs.worldbank.org/en/doc/221901515466795175-0090022018/original/ResilientInfrastructurePPPsContractsandProcurementJapanCase.pdf Accessed 08/2023.

[375] The World Bank, 2017. "Resilient infrastructure public-private partnerships (PPPs)." Page 25.

common knowledge provisions.[376] However, there is to consider that this type of complementary knowledge transfer and local learning process has been difficult to align for the case of post-crisis disaster situations referring e.g. to strategic management crises of nuclear energy plants and nuclear waste disposal operations, based on environmental planning conditions.[377] However, national academic experts and humanitarians have pointed at the "importance of 'localization' and 'local knowledge' tending to define constructive dynamics on disaster management led across Asia in particular.[378]

To this, the comprehensive regulatory field of democratic local interactions and national deliberative conditions, has provided methodological cognitive inputs, facilitating the integration of local environmental assessments, through (SIA) social impact assessments. The EIAs have been aggregated in terms of comparative technical definitions, which have necessarily pointed at complex structural and managerial energy issues, including local compliance efforts and a systematic flow of common interactions involving regional representative entities, ex: distributed municipalities in Japan. So that, the comparative knowledge transfers for common aggregated developing areas involving participatory interactions have been put in association with EIAs networks and territorial mechanisms ex. defined in Japan's Enforcement Regulation of the EIA Act.[379] Both theoretical and practical combinations of dual PPP organizational models have led to the diffusion of societal learning rules confronted with regional assessment processes, that can facilitate

[376] Christophe Roux-Dufort, Emmanuel Metais, 1999. "Building core competencies in crisis management through organizational learning: The case of the French Nuclear Power Producer." Technological Forecasting and Social Change, Volume 60, No. 2, pp. 113-127.
[377] Roux-Dufort *et al.*, 1999.
[378] ANU, Japan Institute, 2021. "Local knowledge as the basis of disaster management in Asia." Australian National University, ANU College of Asia & the Pacific, Public Event, 20 October 2021. Available at website: https://japaninstitute.anu.edu.au/events/local-knowledge-basis-disaster-management-asia
Accessed 08/2023.
[379] Japan Government, 1998. "Enforcement regulation of the environmental impact assessment act." Order of the Prime Minister's Office N. 37 of June 12, 1998. Available at website:
http://assess.env.go.jp/files/5_global/Enforcement%20Regulation%20of%20the%20EIA%20Act.pdf Accessed 08/2023.

environmental local adaptation for transnational societies, independently investing on regulatory Science, Technology, and Society (STS) targets framed more in terms of local adaptive governance and local practice tools. [380] About EIA conducted in Japan, the environmental policy ministerial office has published an EIA report 2012 on EIA mandatory law for power plant designs including nuclear energy facilities summarized in table 1.[381]

Table 1

Excerpt of "Environmental Impact Assessment Law" in Japan for "Power Plant Projects"

"Japan Energy Power Plant"	"Projects Subject to the (EIA) Law"	
"Projects 5."	"Class-1 project (EIA is always required)"	"Class-2 project (The necessity of EIA is judged by project)"
"Hydraulic power plant Thermal power plant Geothermal power plant Nuclear power plant"	"Output:30,000Kw or over Output:150,000Kw or over Output:10,000Kw or over All"	"Output:22,500Kw-30,000Kw Output:112,500Kw-150,000Kw Output: 7,500kw-10,000kw" -

Source: "Environmental Impact Assessment in Japan" Environmental Policy Bureau, Ministry of the Environment, Government of Japan, 2012 Report. Quote: "Project proponents implement EIA themselves." Japan 2012 Report, p. 5. Available at website: http://www.env.go.jp/en/policy/assess/pamph.pdf Accessed 11/2023.

380 Glucker *et al,* 2013; Chanchitpricha *et al.*, 2013; Runhaar *et al.*, 2013; Rozema *et al.*, 2012.

381 Note: To add about the environmental law and practice in Japan: "regarding the use of renewable energy, the Act on Purchase of Renewable Energy Sourced Electricity by Electric Utilities was enacted and a feed-in tariff scheme (FIT scheme) for renewable energy started on 1 July 2012. Under the Act, electrical power suppliers must purchase electricity from renewable energy sources (solar PV, wind power, hydraulic power, geothermal and biomass) at a fixed price for a government-guaranteed period, unless electrical power suppliers can establish that they have justifiable reasons for not doing so as described in the Act." Online report: Hideaki Ozawa, Shogo Umeda, Nishimura & Asashi, 2015. "Environmental law and practice in Japan: overview." Thomson Reuters, Practical Law, Available at website: https://uk.practicallaw.thomsonreuters.com/6-502-8920?contextData=(sc.Default)&transitionType=Default&firstPage=true Accessed 01/2021.

3.1 Risk Management Implementation for Comparable Participation Initiatives

In relation to given processes of public participation and policy-making which have been intertwined with projects performance status and local governmental activities, common environmental protection approaches have been integrated for territorial policy proceedings. In analogous ecosystems, Japanese municipalities have been the subject of Eco-efficiency assessments based on industry production and environmental risks affecting proximate communities, and beyond.[382] Effectively, national associated explorations made about societal cognitive relations which tend to reflect the common local participatory attributions have been particularly emphasized in the case of EIAs. This process has been versatile in view of proposing comparative descriptive theories which have referred to '*space for participation*,' and '*political safeguards measures*,' in order to provide specific indications about the level of national responses given on local environmental planning and collaborative public-private institutional designs, cyclically lined up for the potential aggregation of citizens' operable and interdependent spaces.[383] Then, the environmental public debates stimulating public regulators' initiatives and participant stakeholders' orientations have remained quite central for the preparation of specific qualitative or quantitative environmental assessments EIA, able to promote normative accesses to science planning programs and national innovation platforms assisting on comparative ecological learning spheres.[384] At administrative level, there are "various national laws provid[ing] specific regulations that, together with the general policy declared in the BEL [The Basic Environment Law of 1993], form the Japanese environmental law system

[382] Junya Yamasaki, Toshiharu Ikaga, Norihiro Itsubo, 2020. "Eco-efficiency assessment by industry for Japanese municipalities nationwide based on gross regional product and environmental damage." Journal of Environmental Engineering (Japan), Volume 85, No. 776, pp. 745-755.

[383] Jaap G. Rozema, Alan J. Bond, Matthew Cashmore, Jason Chilvers, 2012. "An investigation of environmental and sustainability discourses associated with the substantive purposes of environmental assessment." Environmental Impact Assessment Review, Volume 33, No. 1, pp. 80-90.

[384] Rozema *et al.*, 2012.

[...] Japanese environmental policy is also realised through various local ordinances and regulations enacted by each local government."[385]

At the same time, it can be considered that the specific diffusion of societal concomitant domains that refer to the inclusivity of local participatory environments; the instrumentality of environmental policy choices, and the sustainability of local environmental impacts, can favour contextual government approaches for local environmental learning with contributing attributions. In addition, the possible determination of regulatory decisions with local attributed practices can better specify what we know about effective information transition practices, handled in connection with local environmental distribution tools. It is affirmed that in Japan's hierarchical system "government authorities are required to proactively make public certain environment-related information, including publishing environmental policies and plans under the BEL and notifying the public about environmental standards and pollution measurement results under certain laws [...]." [386] Similarly, another regulatory aspect to consider is about how best to interact with the public sector when it promotes public innovation knowledge measures and local environmental practices sustaining the decentralized levels of multi-governance research areas, tackling local environmental impacts' protection plans with corresponding objective activities. [387] As highlighted, the multilevel societal affirmation of local democracies has emerged according to different categorizations of intra-sectoral development conditions, reaffirmed in correspondence to structural decision-making models and technical EIAs reviews that have included national information networks, such as the Open Data initiative promoted

[385] Hajime Kanagawa, 2022. "Environmental policy and its enforcement." Environment & Climate Change Laws and Regulations Japan 2022, ICLG report, 23 March, 2022. Available at website: 1. https://iclg.com/practice-areas/environment-and-climate-change-laws-and-regulations/japan and 2. https://www.mccannfitzgerald.com/uploads/International_Comparative_Legal_Guide_-_Environment__Climate_Change_Law_2022.pdf Accessed 08/2023. *The n. 2. web-link also refers to the author H. Kanagawa but the article cannot be directly retrieved on the ICGL website.*

[386] Hajime Kanagawa, 2022. "Environmental policy and its enforcement."

[387] Hens Runhaar, Frank van Laerhoven, Peter Driessen, Jos Arts, 2013. "Environmental assessment in The Netherlands: Effectively governing environmental protection? A discourse analysis." Environmental Impact Assessment Review, Volume 39, pp. 13-25.

by local administrations in Japan.[388] Put it in a perspective focus, local distribution networks have primarily assimilated environmental learning platforms which can be responsive to national and local regulatory applications, eventually promoting action-planning interfaces.

Regional policy scholars have clearly remarked the fact that national and local knowledge identifications have been aligned with integrated environmental performances and local planning systems able to improve resilient regulatory attributes related to continuity[389] of action-plans pursued at territorial level. For instance, in Japan's coastal zones[390] systematic local ecological measures can provide objective knowledge interactions with effective decentralized responses favoring distinctive PPP management adaptive[391] spheres of multilateral decision-making bodies, as well as, of local participatory groups.[392] Similarly, environmental procedural effectiveness associated with local strategic development has basically remained instrumental to public policy programs constantly implemented in view of achieving common programmatic objectives at field level - ex: plastic waste management[393]

[388] Akio Yoshida, Tetsuo Noda, and Masami Honda, 2020. "Regional binding in information networks of open data promotion in local governments of Japan." In: Baghdadi, Y., Harfouche, A., Musso, M., (eds) ICT for an Inclusive World. Lecture Notes in Information Systems and Organisation, book series, (LNISO, Volume 35). Pp. 105-111- Springer, Cham. https://doi.org/10.1007/978-3-030-34269-2_8

[389] Masahiko Haraguchi, 2020. "How can a municipal government continue operations during megadisasters? An analysis of preparedness using complex adaptive systems." Disaster Prevention and Management, Volume 29, No. 5, pp. 779-792.

[390] Julius Ibukun Agboola, 2011. "The changing socio-ecology of Japan's Ishikawa coast." Our World, United Nations University, 26 October, 2011. Available at website: https://ourworld.unu.edu/en/the-changing-socio-ecology-of-japans-ishikawa-coast Accessed 08/2023.

[391] To note: " The Intergovernmental Panel on Climate Change (IPCC) Fourth Assessment Report identifies the need to make social-ecological systems more resilient by building 'adaptive capacity.'" Julius Ibukun Agboola, 2011.

[392] Chaunjit Chanchitpricha, Alan Bond, 2013. "Conceptualising the effectiveness of impact assessment processes." Environmental Impact Assessment Review, Volume 43, pp. 65-72.

[393] Elliot Silverberg, Elizabeth Smith, 2019. "Does Japan have a global environmental strategy?" The Diplomat, 06 November, 2019. Available at website: https://thediplomat.com/2019/11/does-japan-have-a-global-environmental-strategy/ Accessed 08/2023.

- combined with environmental integrated goals pointing at regional learning recognitions.[394]

In essence, the national implementation of local collaborative decisions and environmental collective choices has been shaped in the form of territorial sustainable processes, which are recognized at both normative and legalistic levels.[395] For the revitalization of contaminated areas in Japan's Fukushima sites,[396] the decontamination process - including 'special decontamination areas' summarized in table 2 - has been carried out at municipal level in order to fit with a national planning status of proceedings to reduce local radiation risks and improve risk management and contextual living conditions for long-term goals.[397]

Table 2

"Special Decontamination Areas (SDA)" completed by 2017

"Municipality"	**"Residential area"**	**"Farmland"**	**"Forest"**	**"Road"**	**"Evacuation order was lifted on"**
	"Number of implementated houses"	**"Implemented area ha"**	**"Implemented area ha"**	**"Implemented area ha"**	
Minami soma	4,500	1,700ha	1,300ha	270ha	July 12, 2016
Namie	5,600	1,400ha	390ha	210ha	March 31, 2017
Tomioka	6,000	750ha	510ha	170ha	April 1, 2017
Iitate	2,000	2,100ha	1,500ha	330ha	March 31, 2017
Futaba	97	100ha	6.2ha	8.4ha	March 4, 2020
Kawamata	360	600ha	510ha	71ha	March 31, 2017

394 Chanchitpricha *et al*, 2013.

395 Anne N. Glucker, Peter P.J. Driessen, Arend Kolhoff, Hens A.C. Runhaar, 2013. "Public participation in environmental impact assessment: why, who, and how?" Environmental Impact Assessment Review, Volume 43, pp. 104-111.

396 Ministry of the Environment, 2020. "Environmental Remediation. Results and Effects of Decontamination." Government of Japan MOE report, available at website: http://josen.env.go.jp/en/decontamination/ Accessed 08/2023.

397 Ministry of the Environment, 2020. "Environmental Remediation. Results and Effects of Decontamination."

Katsurao	460	570ha	660ha	95ha	June 12, 2016
Okuma	180	170ha	160ha	31ha	April 10, 2019
Kawauchi	160	130ha	200ha	38ha	"Former Preparation Areas for lift of Evacuation Order : October 1, 2014 Former Habitation Restricted Areas: June 14, 2016"
Naraha	2,600	830ha	470ha	170ha	September 5, 2015
Tamura	140	140ha	190ha	29ha	April 1, 2014
Total Number	22,000	8,500ha	5,800ha	1,400ha	N/A

Source: Full Table MOE Japan. Ministry of the Environment, 2020. "Environmental Remediation. Results and Effects of Decontamination." Available at website: http://josen.env.go.jp/en/decontamination/ Accessed 11/2023.

To this, it can be emphasized that environmental policy participation and environmental integrative practices have become responsive through the material inclusion of procedural and operational understanding, which have been responsive to progressive organizational frameworks of intra-regional countries, ex. urban infrastructures and commitment to a net-zero GHG emissions. [398] However, it can be assumed that democratic participation in politics has also changed because of instrumental decision-making determinants forming at contextual level that can be ambivalent at times, particularly in relation to comparative advisory and local

[398] City of Kyoto, 2018. "Becoming a net-zero emissions city through transformative changes in lifestyle, work-style and urban infrastructure." (KEAA) Kyoto Environmental Activities Association, ICLEI - Local Governments for Sustainability, Japan Office, (RIHN) Research Institute for Humanity and Nature, National Report, 10 December 2017. Available at website: http://copjapan.env.go.jp/talanoa/assets/pdfs/stories/en/20181101-009.pdf Accessed 08/2023.

information spheres, which have been arranged according to single countries' environment-based assessment analyses EIAs, that have been periodically modified.[399] For instance, critical processes on radioactive wastes treatment have been debated in Japan, influencing people on nuclear energy continuity with NNP production sites.[400]

Therefore, it can be considered that collective environment perspectives about EIA have been associated with deliberative learning processes indicating also the periodic level of national regulatory attention. In this case, local learning interactions have been widened in order to favour the empowerment of local territorial parties integrated with public deliberative processes and organic functional aspects involving, for instance, quantitative environmental assessment provisions that have been addressed in regard to regional populations located in large geographical areas. The environmental learning and practices provided through citizens' networks have put forward best practice approaches undertaken ex. by the KIKO Network based in Japan that includes both NGOs and citizens' networks working on climate change issues[401] as: "[...] the Energy savings law, The Climate Change Countermeasure Plan, The Basic Energy Plan, and the Japan Business Federation Voluntary Action Plan."[402]

At the same time, the territorial identification of knowledge transfer frameworks related to information, and communication technology (ICTs) tools, operated for environmental assessment analyses, has been linked to comparative local knowledge innovation initiatives tackling: ex. environment management and businesses infrastructure using ICTs[403] -

[399] Glucker et al., 2013.
[400] John McCloy, 2019. "6 key environmental issues in Japan you should know." Green Coast, 19 September 2019. Available at website: https://greencoast.org/environmental-issues-in-japan/ and https://greencoast.org/author/john-mccloy/page/7/ Accessed 08/2023.
[401] Japan Ministry of the Environment, 2000. "Detailed description of best practices - Japan No. 14." G8 Environmental Futures Forum 2000 on "Domestic Best Practices Addressing Climate Change, report. Available at website: https://www.env.go.jp/earth/g8_2000/ forum/g8bp/detail/japan/japan14.html Accessed 08/2023.
[402] Yun Tzu (Allison) Lin, 2021. "Best climate practice Japan: Kiko Network." Climate Scorecard, Japan News Brief and Action Alert, 12 May, 2021. Available at website: https://www.climatescorecard.org/2021/05/best-climate-practice-japan-kiko-network/ Accessed 08/2023.
[403] Japan Ministry of the Environment, 2012. "Advancement of environmental management and use of environmental information. Building infrastructures to promote

while involving public information domains, interrelated with science policy organizations within knowledge-based societies. Effectively, deliberative constitutional models granting public participation in democratic systems have become a critical learning ground, incorporating technical local knowledge in association with environmental monitoring systems intertwined e.g. with nuclear power industry and renewable energy power maintenance facilities. In essence, public cognitive affirmations and local participatory interactions have involved a common environmental awareness directed at the constitution of industrial innovating characteristics, which have been highlighted for the nuclear energy sector established, for instance, in East Asian countries. For the actualization of a green energy mix, in Japan has been framed a conceptual plan called: the Fukushima Innovation Coast concept focusing on hydrogen production and wind energy power.[404]

For comparable reasons, it can be underlined that environmental governance has been assessed by incrementing a particular focus on local renewable energy policies of selected countries, including STS local development cases. In fact, the aggregation of comparative STS management practices tackling regional adaptation and knowledge transfer processes for the rehabilitation of complex ecosystems,[405] has been substantiated in association with constitutive learning patterns identified at the national level. In addition, there has been in view the prioritization for environmental adaptation initiatives which have remained interrelated with the need of better defining national emergency active plans - ex. through an institutional adherence agreed internationally on so-called: "Nature-based Solutions (NbS) [...] tackling the triple crisis of biodiversity loss, climate change and pollution, [...] disaster risk reduction [...] for sustainable development;"[406] especially in the case of

green economy." Government of Japan MOE, report, March 2012. Available at website: https://www.env.go.jp/content/900453304.pdf Accessed 08/2023.

[404] Japan Ministry of the Environment, 2018. "The Basic Environment Plan." MOE, Japan Cabinet Decision on April 17, 2018, Report. Available at website: https://www.env.go.jp/content/000042331.pdf Accessed 08/2023.

[405] Japan Ministry of the Environment, 2018. "The Basic Environment Plan."

[406] G7 Germany, 2022. "G7 climate, energy and environment ministers' communiqué." Japan MOE, Berlin, 27 May 2022, Report. Page 4. Available at website: https://www.env.go.jp/content/000039438.pdf Accessed 08/2023.

nuclear energy organizational models, operated through PPP with public agencies' operational interventions managed in accordance with technical safety standards, as well as, public safety perceptions.[407] As such, it is pointed out: "The G7 underline that the highest standards of nuclear safety and security are important to all countries and their respective publics."[408]

Basically, comparative environmental policies that have been established in view of addressing local adaptive changes connected with structural conditions of renewable energy programs, have emerged in association with common EIA safety paradigms, including specific procedures and security elements supported through national or local sponsored public policies. Nonetheless, territorial planning policies can as well entail fundamental drawbacks when it comes to discern transitional multi-purpose energy aims shifting from national environmental risk assessments to structural local reliability issues that overall have been operated in relation to multiple comparative STS networks and local developmental conditions.

For EIA international procedures, in the case of China, table 3 synthesizes main comparative standards identified in the report on China EIA procedures.

[407] Vlado Vivoda, 2012. "Japan's energy security predicament post-Fukushima." Energy Policy, Volume 46, pp. 135-143.
[408] G7 Germany, 2022. Page 32.

Table 3

"Chinese EIA system vs. International EIA procedures"

"IFC (International Finance Cooperation) Performance Standards"	**"China's EIA System"**
1. "Assessment and Management of Environmental and Social Risks and Impacts"	"Technical Guidelines for Environmental Risk Assessment on Projects (HJT/169-2004 in place HJ 169-2018). China has formulated technical guidelines for risk assessment under its EIA system. Chinese environmental impact statements have a separate section called Environmental Risk Analysis and Mitigation Strategy for assessing the latent risks exposed by construction projects and proposing relevant mitigation measures."
3. "Resource Efficiency and Pollution Preservation ➢ Avoid or minimize pollution ➢ Reduce emissions that contribute to climate change"	"China has put the Three Synchronization system in place order to put a stop to new pollution and ecological destruction. The system requires that the environmental conservation facilities required in the course of construction projects are designed, built, and utilized alongside the main construction. These environmental conservation facilities primarily refer to those presented in the EIA statements. China also announced its National Strategy on Adaptation to Climate Change at the end of 2013 with the aim of increasing its capacity to respond to climate change. The strategy emphasizes the need to incorporate climate change adaptation requirements in all of the nation's economic and social development processes. However, climate change adaptation requirements are not built into the EIA system for construction projects at present. Most of the requirements and countermeasures for climate change adaptation are limited to a few key infrastructure projects being put forward by the government or to the policy or planning level."

4. "Community Health, Safety, and Security ➢ Avoid or minimize risks to and impacts on health and safety of the local community during both routine and non-routine circumstances ➢ Ensure that the safeguarding of personnel and property is carried out in a legitimate manner that avoids or minimizes risks to the community's safety and security." [...]	"Content related to the health, safety, and security of the local community can be found in three sections of the EIA statement: social and environmental impacts, environmental risk assessment, and public participation. In addition, when compiling EIA statements, China requires that construction units take into account overall community development plans and other development plans in order to minimize adverse impacts on the environment and the community." [...]

Source: a) Summarized text - table design, In: "(6) China comparison with international EIA procedures." Japan Ministry of the Environment, China Report 2020, linked to MOE direct website available at: https://www.env.go.jp/search/search_result.html?cx=003400915082829768606%3Awiib6pxwlwc&ie=UTF-8&q=EIA+safety&sa=+ ; b) China's EIA Report, pages 1-2. Available at webpage: http://assess.env.go.jp/files/5_global/AsiaCountries/6.China%20comparison%20with%20international%20EIA%20procedures.pdf Accessed 11/2023.

4.1 Local Disaster Risk Aspects

This EIA overview is part of the introductory analysis introduced in this work. At this stage, the discussion delves into the exploration of comparative safety risk aspects related to the nuclear energy domain. Basically, the international literature produced about thematic areas of energy security and national safety regulation issues, confronted with post-disaster public risk perception analyses, has pointed at an increasing interdependence of systemic industrial interrelations. Interdependent production strategies have been related to local knowledge transfers and information diffusion processes advanced in connection with the nuclear power industry, and regional management systems operating through supporting energy policies, which are drafted in view of comparative changing environments.[409] In order to integrate businesses environments

[409] Sara K. Yeo, Michael A. Cacciatore, Dominique Brossard, Dietram A. Scheufele, Kristin Runge, Leona Y. Su, Jiyoun Kim, Michael Xenos, Elizabeth A. Corley, 2013. "Partisan amplification of risk: American perceptions of nuclear energy risk in the wake of

and environmental focused initiatives for national civil societies in Japan, it is underlined the sustainability as well as responsiveness criteria in order to proceed with local distributive resources and energy security programs.[410] In terms of local territorial reviews, parallel comparative regional studies have examined post-disaster industrial local risks, and pre/post public recovery cases, which have been specified for the necessity to understand an increasing regional polarization of multilateral energy production operations, carried out in correspondence with national regulatory frameworks. In the case of low-carbon societies, it is advised to promote and ameliorate 'Voluntary Action Plans of Industry'[411] as well as progressive implementation of industry voluntary programmes matching the efforts of a low-carbon development entailing monitoring and evaluative production cycles.[412] In addition, national representative institutions have been scrutinizing common managerial indications in order to assess effectively the development of multinational technology innovation projects compared with local planning schemes while, at the same time, mediating public acceptance levels for local correspondence that has been required in reference with nuclear power processing plants and managerial maintenance systems. Decentralized administrations as in Japan's case can lead local residents on convergent ground about ex. land conservation measures, due to defined roles and responsibilities, as specified: "Local governments establish and implement the Local Government Action Plan, Administration and Projects, in regards to their own administration and projects based on the Plan for Global Warming Countermeasures."[413]

the Fukushima Daiichi disaster." Energy Policy, Volume 67, pp. 727-736. https://doi.org/10.1016/j.enpol.2013.11.061

[410] Japan Ministry of the Environment, 2012. "Environmental reporting guidelines." MOE, Government of Japan, Report. Available at website: https://www.env.go.jp/en/policy/economy/erg2012.pdf Accessed 08/2023.

[411] Government of Japan, December 2017. "Japan's third biennial report under the United Nations Framework Convention on Climate Change." Governmental Report, December 2017. Available at website: https://www.env.go.jp/content/900446224.pdf Accessed 08/2023.

[412] Government of Japan, December 2017. "Japan's third biennial report under the United Nations Framework Convention on Climate Change."

[413] Government of Japan, December 2017. "Japan's third biennial report under the United Nations Framework Convention on Climate Change." Page 95.

In such terms, either statutory conservative designs or progressive ideological orientations which have emerged about public knowledge transfers and information diffusion programs have been politically stratified. Especially when taking into account corresponding common levels of public participation. For instance, environmental mobilization campaigns have been associated with societal groups' interactions that have supported local communities' mutual knowledge exchanges and development practice spheres;[414] to consider that an overlapping material distribution of multiple information sources has been widespread through worldwide media alternatives in order to reach larger audiences.[415]

In the case of environmental participatory determinants, the community alert systems assisted by prevention/recovery measures for local emergency practices that are adopted at governance level have entailed complex environmental integration procedures, tackling long-term alternative community-based approaches. Systematic environment practices have also become functional to industrial innovation diffusion and to states' structural organization mechanisms, implementing internal and external territorial controlling measures. Through a comparative overview about PPP organizational performances regarding the nuclear industrial energy domains for selected STS cases involving ex. international cooperation for 'low carbon societies' - it has led to the initiation of an 'International Research Network for Low Carbon Societies (LCS -RNet)':[416] they have been specified within national normative frameworks including public agencies' local reporting activities. Legitimate national platforms have particularly looked into managerial safety models and decision-making transfers, essentially operated in line

[414] Note: Citizens civil actions conducted in Japan include "[...] a group of 15,000 Fukushima citizens [which] sought criminal prosecution of the state and Tepco for the nuclear disaster as early as 2012. [...] In its September 2019 verdict, the Tokyo District Court concluded that there was insufficient evidence to convict them. The case is now pending on appeal with little chance of a reversed verdict." Paul Jobin, 2020. "The Fukushima nuclear disaster and civil actions as a social movement." The Asia-Pacific Journal, Vol. 18, Issue 9, Number 1, Article ID 5392.

[415] Yeo *et al.*, 2013.

[416] Ministry of the Environment, Japan, 2009. "International research network for low carbon societies (LCS-RNet)." Clean Asia Initiative, MOE, International Cooperation Office, Short Report. Available at website: https://www.env.go.jp/earth/coop/coop/english/cai/pdf/lcs-rnet_e.pdf Accessed 08/2023.

with local managerial systems intertwined with nuclear power plants' energy productions, and waste disposal maintenance operations. Over the years, due to the Tohoku earthquake and tsunami in 2011, with NPP critical accidents registered in the Fukushima Prefecture, municipalities have been directly involved in decontamination efforts, additionally "In municipalities where decontamination has been completed as planned, monitoring will be implemented as necessary in the decontaminated areas."[417]

In relation with environmental compliance studies highlighting the national implementation mechanisms that refer to local planning approaches for contingent emergency measures, this review tends to focus on public environmental reports, advising on national systematic conditions for local information diffusion procedures, based on technical compliance issues, related to radioactive chemical and hazardous waste with local pollution exposures.[418] In view of Climate Change PPP monitoring networks, the sharing of information on public platforms can improve progressive understanding on knowledge management areas connected to ecosystems sustainability.[419] Based on the selection of environmental comparative studies clarifying some aspects about regional nuclear energy compliance, this research specifically examines the post-Fukushima nuclear crisis impact and respective transition periods, mainly because it has been linked to correspondent national and municipal emergency planning strategies, assessed in connection with cooperative organizational levels of integrated local practical measures for communities involved.[420] At public level, technical emergency

[417] Ministry of the Environment, Japan, 2014. "Initiatives for restoration of the environment." Annual Report on the Environment, the Sound Material-Cycle Society, and Biodiversity in Japan. Page 17. Available at website:https://www.env.go.jp/content/900457394.pdf Accessed 08/2023.

[418] U.S. Department of Energy report, 2000. "Waste Isolation Pilot Plant Biennial Environmental Compliance Report." DOE/WIPP 99-2171 ; U.S. DOE Carlsbad Area Office, New Mexico, United States.

[419] Ministry of the Environment, Japan, 2017. "Evolving sustainable energy policy in Nagano Prefecture, Japan: The path towards a 100% renewable energy region." MOE, Nagano, March 2018, Report. Available at website: http://copjapan.env.go.jp/talanoa/assets/pdfs/stories/en/20180601-001.pdf Accessed 08/2023.

[420] Environment Canada report. Environmental Emergencies Program, 1999. "National Environmental Emergencies Contingency Plan." Environmental Emergencies Branch.

compliance strategies have been developed in order to provide specific contingent preparedness activities and try to restore responsive emergency measures, adopted locally. In particular, the regional identification of community rights-based approaches has come as well into place due to regulatory environmental commitments made on participatory resilience aspects.[421] In the review of the U.S. embassy and MOE Japan 2013, about reporting observations and commentary on the Fukushima Daiichi reactors, it is recalled the need to "[...] enabling local communities to have strong roles in forming decontamination plans and in siting waste storage facilities [...]."[422]

At the same time, the combination of disciplinary and normative management procedures of environmental reporting agencies has reflected the concurrent status of local monitoring activities undertaken in view of supported ecological case projects. Therefore, environmental compliance mechanisms converging into local integrated approaches have been complemented by recurrent practical assessments and cognitive determinants, including complementary recovery and emergency programs, following on multilateral strategies undertaken at community level.[423] With respect to radiation protection environmental conditions, intertwined with local interdependent actions, the report of U.S. embassy and MOE Japan 2013, suggests "[...] [to] include community/stakeholder involvement process [...] to ensure that local considerations are incorporated into radiation protection processes [...]."[424]

Canada; Quebec K1A 0H3. Available at website: https://publications.gc.ca/collections/collection_2017/eccc/En40-584-1999-eng.pdf Accessed 11/2023

[421] U.S. Department of Energy report, 2006 "Waste Isolation Pilot Plant Biennial Compliance Report." Washington Regulatory and Environmental Services. DOE/WIPP 06-2171; U.S. DOE - Office of Environmental Management (EM).Carlsbad Field Office, New Mexico, United States.

[422] Ministry of the Environment, Japan, 2013. "Observations and commentary on remediation of the lands off-site from the Fukushima Daiichi reactors." Report of the United States Embassy Science Fellows Support to the Government MOE of Japan, EPA/600/R-13/135, page 9. Available at website: http://josen.env.go.jp/en/documents/pdf/workshop_july_17-18_2013_04.pdf Accessed 08/2023.

[423] DOE/WIIP, 2006.

[424] Ministry of the Environment, Japan, 2013. "Observations and commentary on remediation of the lands off-site from the Fukushima Daiichi reactors." Page 11.

In connection to local emergency planning exercises, public management guidelines on respective functional roles and social responsibility aspects, including technical local requirements identified in the case of nuclear industrial facilities and waste disposal operational activities, have been tied to specific information protocols and national controlling proceedings, which are locally implemented, while indirectly causing the aggregation of common local representatives, environment groups, governmental technical divisions, and municipal authorities, collectively ensuring territorial learning exchanges.[425] For instance, due to the 2011 NPP crisis, voluntary decontamination plans were set up in Japan, it was also established the 'Act on Special Measures for the Reconstruction and Revitalization of Fukushima'[426] through which "[...] each of the municipalities transitioned to doing decontamination based on their decontamination implementation plan [...] the municipalities understood the importance of discussions with residents and consensus formation, and in each stage [...] they held repeated dialogue with residents and therefore obtained their understanding and cooperation. [...] due to differences in the contamination situation and population, the size of the urban areas, etc. in each municipality, the decontamination implementation plan also had different content for each municipality."[427] Broadly referring to environmental impact assessments EIA and energy compliance systems within PPP, involving technical knowledge determinants identified for regional distribution areas, this research considers selected descriptive factors based on the post-Fukushima nuclear policy phase that has been taken into account for this discussion.

[425] DOE/WIIP, 2006.

[426] Ministry of the Environment, Japan, 2018. "Decontamination projects for radioactive contamination discharged by Tokyo Electric Power Company Fukushima Daiichi Nuclear Power Station Accident." Editorial Committee for the Paper on Decontamination Projects, MOE. Page 6 (ii). Available at website: http://josen.env.go.jp/en/policy_document/pdf/decontamination_report1807_01.pdf Accessed 08/2023.

[427] Ministry of the Environment, Japan, 2018. "Decontamination projects for radioactive contamination discharged by Tokyo Electric Power Company Fukushima Daiichi Nuclear Power Station Accident." Page 28.

Comparative Exploratory Factors

Post-Fukushima Environment Monitoring Networks:
For this policy review, it is considered that EIA decision making process has been implemented in connection with PPP public-private knowledge exchanges based on the ICT methodological practices. Procedural compliance efforts have therefore been analyzed in relation to comparative effective levels of common information management systems. In Japan's environmental disaster case, a concerted reporting process has been possibly framed according to the following characteristics:

- PPP Knowledge-based Energy Compliance Plans
- Regulatory EIA Control Mechanisms on Nuclear Waste/Hazards Exposures
- Qualitative Planning about Post-recovery Community Measures on Nuclear Waste/Hazards Exposures
- National Emergency Protocols on Nuclear Waste/Hazards Exposures
- Multilateral Coordination Process of Operational Emergency Facilities
- National Information Provision about Emergency Mitigation Policies
- R&D Commissions about Local Knowledge-based IT Exchanges

(Source: Washington Regulatory and Environmental Services. *Waste Isolation Pilot Plant Biennial Environmental Compliance Report.* United States: N. p., 2006. DOE/WIPP 06-2171; U.S. DOE Carlsbad Field Office, New Mexico, United States. Web. doi:10.2172/925568).

The science policy literature that has been produced in this case about the identification of socio-technical innovation transfers and local knowledge diffusion conditions, associated with public agencies regulatory assessment models, has often referred to different degrees of a national programmatic complexity, emerging about distinctive managerial sectoral processes, also integrating industrial innovation representations that have evolved at regional local level. According to objective innovation spheres retracing local sustainability, the integrated environmental assessments IEAs[428] run at the local level have included

[428] APEIS-IEA, 2004. "Technical Summary. IEA, Integrated Environmental Assessment." Asia-Pacific Environmental Innovation Strategy Project, Report. Available at website: https://www.env.go.jp/en/earth/ecoasia/APEIS/iea/pdf/TS_IEA.pdf Accessed 08/2023.

monitoring and information dissemination for local pollution,[429] for example. In comparative science innovation studies, regional innovation policy scholars have retraced socio-technical systemic interconnections that have been formed in dynamic local innovation systems, which have been implemented at institutional level. Functional progressive analyses formulated about comparative science policy cases produced since the 2000s time-frame, have indirectly pictured socio-technical changing systems with local integration management theories, ex. adaptation and mitigation planning set by Japan.[430] At sectoral level, progressive managerial innovation inputs favoring different STS operational assets - e.g. in the service adaptation industries[431] - have fundamentally influenced local levels of societal adaptations multiplying on a regional industrial scale.[432]

According to the territorial diffusion of technological changing systems and environmental policy measures, there has been a particular attention devoted to better understanding the connection of states to sectoral innovations of ICT transformation industries such as: ICT monitoring environmental infrastructures,[433] associated with institutional coordination guidelines, and corresponding societal feedbacks. Science policy and comparative ICT knowledge transfers, in this sense, have become integral part of institutional developmental approaches explored through comparative socio-technical reviews.[434]

429 APEIS-IEA, 2004. "Technical Summary. IEA, Integrated Environmental Assessment."

430 Ministry of Environment, Japan, 2019. "Japan's assistance initiatives to address climate change. Responding to needs of the developing countries." MOE, Report, Global Environment Bureau, Japan. Available at website: https://www.env.go.jp/content/900505739.pdf Accessed 08/2023.

431 Ministry of the Environment, Japan, 2017. "Evolving sustainable energy policy in Nagano Prefecture, Japan: The path towards a 100% renewable energy region."

432 Frank W. Geels, 2004. "From sectoral systems of innovation to socio-technical systems: Insights about dynamics and change from sociology and institutional theory." Research Policy, Volume 33, No. 6-7, pp. 897-920.

433 IGES, 2018. "Japan's initiative towards expansion of environmental infrastructure ." Clean Asia Initiative Newsletter [CAI], Volume 17, March 2018. Edited by the Institute for Global Environmental Strategies. Available at website: https://www.env.go.jp/earth/coop/coop/english/cai/pdf/newsletter_e_vol17.pdf Accessed 08/2023.

434 Frank W. Geels, 2004.

5.1 The PPP Knowledge-based Energy Compliance Plans

In a prospective view, it can be found through Geels's study[435] that the affirmation of extrinsic factors about progressive innovation characteristics has been evolving in relation with sectoral local development. Comparative policy analysts have highlighted the presence of complex societal interactions emerging across institutional intra-sectoral processes, which have indirectly involved innovation knowledge transfers, translated in line with technological production systems. For instance, energy consumption patterns can reflect educational choices for the efficient distribution of urban/rural services.[436] In this case, the applicable PPP management conditions that have been operable in combination with knowledge innovation plans and technical production domains - e.g. implementing the Circulating and Ecological Sphere[437] (CES)[438] - have been functional to intra-sectoral production systems. In connection with societal local groups, the representative stakeholders have acquired specialized levels of common comprehensive knowledge specified through social networking relations, which however have been bounded to defined structural processes.[439]

[435] Frank W. Geels, 2004.
[436] Shuichi Ashina, 2009. "Model analysis for low carbon society (1) Japan's case." National Institute for Environmental Studies. The 18th Asia-Pacific Seminar on Climate Change "Building an Architecture of an Effective Future Regime." 2-3 March 2009, Vietnam. Full Report. Available at website: https://www.env.go.jp/en/earth/ap-net/documents/seminar/ 18th/0-2_NIES_Mr.ShuichiAshina.pdf Accessed 08/2023.
[437] Note: "[...] the Government of Japan in its Fifth Basic Environment Plan 2018 proposed the concept of the Circulating and Ecological Sphere (CES) [...][it] provides a framework for a new paradigm in sustainable development bringing together existing approaches, namely, rural-urban linkages, ecosystem-based solutions, decarbonisation, and resource circulation [...]." Ortiz-Moya, F., Kataoka, Y., Saito, O., *et al.,* 2021. "Sustainable transitions towards a resilient and decentralised future: Japan's Circulating and Ecological Sphere (CES)." Sustainability Science, Volume 16, pp. 1717-1729.
[438] Ministry of the Environment, Japan, 2019. "Toward sustainable transformation in the post-COVID-19 Era - Circulating and Ecological Sphere (CES) and Societal Innovation." Exhibition, Virtual Japan Pavilion - Innovation for 2050 net-zero - Available at website: http://copjapan.env.go.jp/cop/virtualjapanpavilion2021/en/exhibition/lifestyle.html Accessed 08/2023.
[439] Frank W. Geels, 2004.

What has been revisited in this part of the project, it is the association of conceptual explicitations made about so-defined multilateral 'cross-learning processes' also referred to nuclear safety protection, and to public-private PPP compliance advocacy modes, which have emerged from single countries' organizational control mechanisms. For instance, it is emphasized the role that municipalities can have on nuclear informative issues concerning local populations, as local decision-making activity can be identified for respective territorial programs involving citizens' participation as for the case of radioactive waste management.[440] Essentially, the public management sphere of socio-technical (ST) industrial interactions defining technical compliance issues and local operational innovation has been arranged according to different managerial performance systems, including the nuclear civil facilities and waste disposal activities, integrating multilevel local knowledge determinants. Nuclear energy development has in fact included national and international collaboration with public-private managerial interactions that point at environmental protection schemes, introducing technological advances but at the same time systemic efficiency in terms of national growth and applicable cooperative performances.[441]

In terms of national governance rules, public comparative scholars have critically emphasized constructive regional dynamics of multilevel coordination agencies carrying out national decision-making plans that have been committed to redefine functional development areas about renewable energy infrastructural configurations[442] for identified reliable innovation targets addressing the case-based scenarios of nuclear local construction plants.[443] In a sustainable dimension, the functional identification of common operational energy plans adapted for regional

440 GMF, website. "Welcome to GMF website." Group of European Municipalities with Nuclear Facilities, declaration summary available at website: https://gmfeurope.org/about-us/ Accessed 08/2023.

441 The Government of Japan, 2019. "The long-term strategy under the Paris Agreement." Cabinet decision, June 11, 2019. Report available at website: https://www.env.go.jp/press/111913.pdf Accessed 08/2023.

442 Government of Japan, 2019. "The long-term strategy under the Paris Agreement."

443 See: A. Adamantiades, I. Kessides, 2009. "Nuclear power for sustainable development: Current status and future prospects." Energy Policy, Volume 37, No. 12, pp. 5149-5166; William Walker, 2000. "Entrapment in large technology systems: institutional commitment and power relations." Research Policy, Volume 29, No. 7-8, pp. 833-846.

diversification programs, has been configured in relation to national structural capacities assessed through local institutional organizations. At the same time, the accelerated elaboration of industrial risk analyses and environmental risk avoidance practices has progressively specified the local sectoral impacts associated with societal environment determinants such as: public social health, public local safety and public territorial acceptance. Therefore, establishing a corresponding capacity for local adaptation becomes a democratic investment undertaken recently by federal agencies and local municipalities interested on active networking exchanges as well as knowledge integrated projects that can implement cohesive methods to increase environmental sustainability at community level.[444]

In view of national disaster emergency cases related to industrial hazards and civil nuclear accidents, as the Fukushima accidents occurring in Japan 2011 – it can be observed that single country's disaster crisis responsive platforms, reflecting respective agencies reporting systems, at regulatory, environmental, and industry level, have offered controversial perspectives about the diffusion of public emergency management programs undertaken across distinctive time-periods, in order to contain potential post-crisis events, which have involved local follow-ups based on search and rescue services, local planning adaptation and societal impact assessments.[445] Based on regional STS accounts, institutional strategic interactions converging toward multilevel energy innovation diversified policies, including nuclear power plants development, have revealed a so-called social hybrid conjunction as reference to participatory emancipation environments. Experimental protection schemes in Japan have become a unionized trend for local stakeholders, competent administrations and science bodies putting common efforts to reach

[444] Adelphi, 2018. "Networking communities: How municipalities can learn from each other and increase their capacity for adaptation." Adelphi independent think tank based in Germany, web-page article. Available at website: https://www.adelphi.de/en/project/networking-communities-how-municipalities-can-learn-each-other-and-increase-their-capacity Accessed 08/2023.

[445] T.N. Srinivasan, T.S. Gopi Rethinaraj, 2013. "Fukushima and thereafter: Reassessment of risks of nuclear power." Energy Policy, Volume 52, pp. 726-736; Masahiko Aoki, Geoffrey Rothwell, 2013. "A comparative institutional analysis of the Fukushima nuclear disaster: Lessons and policy implications." Energy Policy, Volume 53, pp. 240-247.

cooperative environment agreements.[446] But at the same time, STS technical maintenance operations associated with public decisional systems have effectively required dynamic production adjustments, including local organizational changes reflecting common guidance protocols and national energy diversification plans.[447] For such reasons, effective monitoring evaluative systems observing the Earthquake and Tsunami impacts on the natural ecosystems have been listed among main priorities by the government of Japan in more recent years.[448]

In terms of environmental sustainability perspectives, the formation of PPP public-private science technology interfaces promoted at governmental level and favoring sustainable STS cooperative management exchanges between nuclear industry partners and participant stakeholders, has been a challenging matter in terms of theoretical and empirical approaches. Because the sectoral industrial knowledge determined through local compliance factors can also be associated with common levels of STS local innovation transfers scrutinized in view of environmental assessment processes. In comparative chemical pollution cases in Japan, innovative technical approaches led by the private sector have engaged local administrations, local communities as well as centralized entities to improve health and living conditions and reduce environmental degradation at the local level.[449]

5.2 Japan Regulatory EIA Control Mechanisms

Institutional comparative analyses considered in this paper have addressed the comparative affirmation of public regulatory undertakings concerning the case of STS diffusion systems intertwined with PPP nuclear energy transition developed in association with civil nuclear

[446] Ministry of the Environment, Japan, 2011. "Building healthy and satisfied local communities." Reconstruction from the Disaster, Section 1. Chapter 3. Annual Report on the Environment, the Sound Material-Cycle Society and the Biodiversity in Japan 2012. Available at website: https://www.env.go.jp/content/900457371.pdf Accessed 08/2023.

[447] T.N. Srinivasan, et al., 2013. Aoki, et al., 2013.

[448] Ministry of the Environment, Japan, 2011. "Building healthy and satisfied local communities."

[449] Ministry of the Environment, Japan, 2011. "To achieve a green growth nation to lead the world." Section 1. Green Economy and Green Innovation, Chapter 4. Annual Report on the Environment, the Sound Material-Cycle Society and the Biodiversity in Japan 2011. Available at website: https://www.env.go.jp/content/900457372.pdf Accessed 08/2023.

configurations and territorial management guidelines, drafted during the post-Fukushima assessment period. It is highlighted that "[...] In order to reduce nuclear dependency [in Japan] [...] energy security and global warming measures should be satisfied simultaneously [...] The options should provide all possible measures to ensure nuclear risk management [...]"[450] In ample terms, regulatory environmental planning has been contextualized through national or local interactions of multilevel entities and local citizens' groups involved in national industry risk analyses and local environmental risk assessments such as: federal states' representatives, local administration units, and local environmental stakeholders, including knowledge-based industry partners, promoting regional networking frameworks.[451]

To this situation, functional concurrent agreements formulated in conjunction with renewable energy governmental directives, incorporating technical standardization measures, have involved the formation of transnational cooperation activities, undertaken by regional governmental bodies promoting the implementation of local knowledge and science-based integrated energy systems.[452] For instance, in the case of regional risk impact assessments and environmental facilitation plans, supported in different autonomous territories like Canada and Taiwan, the institutional collaborative programs have delivered comparative local deliberative concessions regarding institutional territorial statements,

[450] Ministry of the Environment, Japan, 2011. " To achieve a green growth nation to lead the world." Section 1, Green Economy and Green Innovation, Report, Chapter 4, page 99. Available at website: https://www.env.go.jp/content/900457372.pdf Accessed 08/2023.

[451] Ministry of the Environment, Japan, 2015. "Submission by Japan to the UN Framework Convention on Climate Change Communication on Japan's undertakings in adaptation." MOE Japan Report, November 27, 2015. Available at website: https://www.env.go.jp/en/earth/cc/submission151127.pdf Accessed 08/2023.

[452] See: a. William J. Kinsella, Ashley R. Kelly, Meagan Kittle Autry, 2013. "Risk, Regulation, and Rhetorical Boundaries: Claims and challenges surrounding a purported nuclear renaissance." Communication Monographs, Volume 80, No. 3, pp. 278-301; b. M.V. Ramana, 2013. "Shifting strategies and precarious progress: Nuclear waste management in Canada." Energy Policy,Volume 61, pp. 196-206; c. Ying-Feng Chen, Yungnane Yang, 2012. "Taming the nuclear dragon? The prospect and potential of cross-Strait cooperation on nuclear security." Journal of Asian Public Policy, Volume 5, No. 2, pp. 155-167; d. Pius Krutli, Michael Stauffacher, Thomas Flueler, Roland W. Scholz, 2010. "Functional-dynamic public participation in technological decision-making: site selection processes of nuclear waste repositories." Journal of Risk Research, Volume 13, No. 7, pp. 861-875.

national environmental public hearings, and public regulatory designs, among other options. At an international level, the Bali Action Plan 2007[453] with negotiated concessions established among all parties to the UNFCCC introduced technical Working Groups to tackle environmental development targets related to global warming in complex ecosystems. At the same time, configured local options when analysed together in multi-stage changing conditions have not necessarily provided convergent empowerment processes transferred at societal level. Having also in view that local environmental sustainability issues correlated with territorial coordination plans as well as transnational regulatory activities have integrated the operability of technical maintenance services preserving energy safety programs and technology financial assets run at the regional level.

Concerning complementary levels of managerial risk safety modes, the institutional comparative relations have been upgraded through sub-regional conformations of stratified structural networks. In environmental socioeconomic literature studies centred on public moral ethics, public environmental conflicts, participatory networking initiatives, and social disputes about nuclear power facilities management, the comparative regulatory dynamics have been emphasized in a more comprehensive term. In fact, the correspondent juxtaposition related to safety environmental protocols including public policy measures managed at local level, has been the subject of investigative interpretations formulated, in particular, about the formal involvement of central regulatory authorities engaged in nuclear decision-making processes.[454] Some of these measures have been drafted in the aftermath of national disaster crises due to large earthquakes occurring in Japan 2011, and the ministry of the environment particularly on nuclear power specified the need for "1. Separation of the administration of the responsible for the nuclear safety and regulation from

[453] Ministry of the Environment, Japan, 2008. "Towards a low carbon society and a sound material-cycle society." MOE Annual Report on the Environment and the Sound Material-Cycle Society in Japan 2008. Available at website: https://www.env.go.jp/content/900457288.pdf Accessed 08/2023.

[454] John S. Ash, 2011. "Radiation or Riots: Risk perception in nuclear power decision making and deliberative approaches to resolving stakeholder conflict." Politics & Policy, Volume 39, No. 3, pp. 317-344.

the Ministry of Economic, Trade and Industry which has an objective to promote nuclear power plants. 2. Efforts to restore trust in the nuclear regulatory administration and enhancement of its functions."[455]

Across comparative regions, the United Kingdom, Taiwan, and Canada, have implemented the configuration of structural regulatory plans tackling in particular the local management activities run at nuclear waste disposal sites. Such strategic shifts have reached a stage of programmatic fragmentation of decisional tasks requiring coordination modalities[456] integrated into environmental conservation plans, locally formalized in view of protecting populations living nearby potential pollution sites: e.g. Taiwan industrial waste facilities in Yakan and Fusin villages.[457] Nonetheless, the actual systematization of deliberative organizational measures emerging according to different cultural landscapes and local communities' knowledge-based perspectives,[458] has practically led to critical undertakings about the significance of local nuclear risk perceptions and radioactive waste hazards still present in today's world.

Social environmental justice issues which have come into evidence for the recognition of public common trust, local risks hazards and safety perceptions, and environmental adaptation and cooperation actions, have been reviewed through regional strategic studies looking at transnational regulatory policies promoted in connection to PPP nuclear industrial processes, and for the local inclusion of social participatory groups.[459] At

[455] Ministry of the Environment, Japan, 2012. " Recent development of environmental policies in Japan." 1. The Recovery from the Great East Japan Earthquake. MOE Report. Page 3. Available at website: https://www.env.go.jp/en/focus/docs/files/20120925-20.pdf Accessed 08/2023.

[456] Christian Bréthaut, Laura Turley, 2020. "Exploring the politics of institutional fragmentation in transboundary river basins." Oxford Research Encyclopedias, Environmental Science. https://doi.org/10.1093/acrefore/9780199389414.013.647

[457] Mei-Fang Fan, 2010. "Justice, community knowledge, and waste facility siting in Taiwan." Public Understanding of Science, Volume 21, No. 4, pp. 418-431.

[458] Note: For analytical purposes about distributed health programs "the emphasis is on having different groups come together to share their perspectives from different knowledge systems. [...] and creating an environment that can support this participatory work in co-creating new knowledge." Center for Health Care Strategies, "Leveraging community knowledge through community-based participatory research." Audrey Nuamah, Anna Spencer, Center for Health Care Strategies, October 17, 2019.

[459] Joanna Burger, James Clarke, Michael Gochfeld, 2011. "Information needs for siting new, and evaluating current, nuclear facilities: ecology, fate and transport, and human health." Environmental Monitoring Assessment, Volume 172, No. 1- 4, pp. 121-134.

municipal level, the housing decontamination activity taking place in Fukushima city has been followed up by city supervisors meeting local inhabitants for direct feed-backs.[460] At the same time, environmental policy studies and governmental national reports have been comparatively issued according to the elaboration of specific regulation approaches incorporating public evaluation criteria, as well as, public appraisal methodologies that in selected countries, as the United Kingdom, have been applied both in theory and practice, e.g. through data analytics and regulatory compliance assessments, also in relation to science and technology development transfers;[461] this possible integration is also due the need of producing institutional decisional interventions while maintaining independent administrative deliberations.[462]

Following up on institutional development studies analyzed mainly through comparative international and national economic reviews, the transnational research activities have basically delivered some strategic reflections about the practical changing issues related to common environmental learning plans, STS regional knowledge-based transfer processes, public environmental networks, and PPP nuclear industry arrangements, which have been highlighted in order to facilitate common socioeconomic transitions on nuclear risk assessment standards. To mention that environmental conservation practices and educational tasks led in Japan, in both public and private spheres, do testify the importance

[460] Ministry of the Environment, Japan, 2015. "FY2014 Decontamination Report. A compilation of experiences to date on decontamination for the living environment conducted by the Ministry of the Environment." MOE Report, 2015. Available at website: http://josen.env.go.jp/en/policy_document/pdf/decontamination_report1503_full.pdf Accessed 08/2023.

[461] UK Environment Agency, 2021. "Regulating for people, the environment and growth, 2020." Applies to England. Research and Analysis Report, 29 December 2021. Available at website: https://www.gov.uk/government/publications/regulating-for-people-the-environment-and-growth-2020/regulating-for-people-the-environment-and-growth-2020 Accessed 08/2023.

[462] See: 1. Simon Dietz, Alec Morton, 2011. "Strategic appraisal of environmental risks: A contrast between the United Kingdom's Stern Review on the economics of climate change and its committee on radioactive waste management." Risk Analysis, Volume 31, No.1, pp. 129-142; 2. Alec Morton, Mara Airoldi, Lawrence D. Phillips, 2009. "Nuclear risk management on stage: A decision analysis perspective on the UK's committee on radioactive waste management." Risk Analysis, Volume 29, No. 5, pp. 764-779.

of maintaining community dialogues and local implementing measures.[463] Instead, environmental assessments on radioactive materials respond to prescriptive laws and mandatory regulation standards timely provided by regional institutional authorities e.g. "regulatory standards for radioactive materials contained in liquid and gaseous waste that are discharged into the environment from nuclear power stations, etc. in Japan are set in light of recommendations of the International Commission on Radiological Protection (ICRP) [...]"[464]

Fundamentally, this constant and rapid integration of functional institutional components can be understood according to comparative local dynamics in governmental innovation contexts, which have been differentiated in terms of science and technology innovation programs S&T, as well as, democratic communitarian routes that tend to incorporate as well local participatory deliberations characterizing, for instance, South-East Asia and Canadian provinces. For example, in Canada's case the nuclear waste management organization (NWMO) established in 2002[465] began public consultation processes for the purpose of assessing public risks' perceptions through local collaboration activities and administrative diffusion of adaptive management policies that have been delivered through annual monitoring action plans.[466] Canada's NWMO in 2020 has collaboratively worked for the incorporation of Indigenous

[463] Ministry of the Environment, Japan, 2003. "Law for enhancing motivation on environmental conservation and promoting of environmental education. " MOEJ, Law No. 130, July 25, 2003. Available at website: https://www.env.go.jp/content/900452874.pdf Accessed 08/2023.

[464] Ministry of the Environment, Japan, 2022. " Booklet to provide basic information regarding health effects of radiation." 2nd Edition, Chapter 6 'Situation concerning the Accident,' Section 6.3: 'Efforts and Progress for Decommissioning.' Available at website: https://www.env.go.jp/en/chemi/rhm/basic-info/1st/index.html (or) https://www.env.go.jp/en/chemi/rhm/basic-info/1st/pdf/basic-1st-06.pdf Accessed 08/2023.

[465] NWMO internet web-portal: http://www.nwmo.ca

[466] See: 1. Genevieve Fuji Johnson, 2007. "The discourse of democracy in Canadian nuclear waste management policy." Policy Sciences, Volume 40, pp. 79-99; 2. Lisa Westerhoff, E. Carina H. Keskitalo, Heather McKay, Johanna Wolf, David Ellison, Iosif Botetzagias, and Bertrand Reysset, 2010. "Planned Adaptation Measures in Industrialised Countries: A comparison of select countries within and outside the EU." Chapter 7, pp. 271-338. In book edition: E.C.H. Keskitalo (ed.) *Developing Adaptation Policy and Practice in Europe: Multi-level Governance of Climate Change*, Springer Science+Business Media B.V. 2010.

Knowledge and Reconciliation Policy in participatory monitoring exercises.[467]

6.1 Qualitative Planning with Post-Recovery Community Measures

Comparative environmental assessment strategies have been reviewed through concurrent planning methodologies undertaken, for instance, among European Union member states, in order to address national adaptation activities associated with sectoral organizational adjustments and industrial innovation development implemented for common trading regions.[468] EU regulators have basically pointed at future green investments to be made on nuclear energy plants if pursued in agreement with EU member states.[469] In addition, comprehensive multiple domains at institutional policy level, have supported knowledge innovation transfers agreements (KT) which have provided a structural basis for industrial regulatory adaptation processes PPP that have been transferred to multilateral sectoral entities, territorial administrative divisions, decentralized managerial units, environment NGO groups, and regional mutual integrated bodies.[470] To specify that e.g. the NEA nuclear energy agency invited 'parties to the protocol on strategic environmental assessment to the Espoo Convention (Kiev Protocol) for a multilateral agreement entering into force on 11 July 2010.[471]

[467] NWMO, Nuclear Waste Management Organization, 2021. "The NWMO 2020 annual report celebrates progress and resilience." NWMO News and Activities, March 23, 2021 Toronto, Ont. Available at website: https://www.nwmo.ca/en/More-information/News-and-Activities/2021/03/23/17/02/The-NWMO-2020-annual-report-celebrates-progress-and-resilience Accessed 08/2023.

[468] Lisa Westerhoff et al., 2010.

[469] Mark Hibbs, 2022. "Why Europe is looking to nuclear power to fuel a green future." Carnegie Endowment for International Peace, Commentary, February 18, 2022. Commentary. Available at website: https://carnegieendowment.org/2022/02/18/why-europe-is-looking-to-nuclear-power-to-fuel-green-future-pub-86468 Accessed 08/2023.

[470] David-Huw Owen, Zach Wahl, 2010. "Defining four pillars for successful applied knowledge transfer." In book edition: R.J. Howlett (ed.): *Innovation through Knowledge Transfer*, 2010, SIST 9, pp. 83-93, Springer-Verlag, Berlin, Heidelberg 2011.

[471] NEA/OECD, 2010. "Protocol on strategic environmental assessment to the Espoo Convention (Kiev Protocol)." Nuclear Energy Agency, Topics section, Division of Nuclear Law, 2022. Available at website: https://www.oecd-nea.org/jcms/pl_29149/protocol-on-strategic-environmental-assessment-to-the-espoo-convention-kiev-protocol Accessed 08/2023.

The public management teams and STS territorial information systems have applied continuous sets of organizational tools and learning-based local diffusion plans: e.g. through Earth observation technology.[472] As consequence, the environment indicative configuration of public-private industrial exchanges PPP has been functional to multilevel governance systems. For comparative analysis, the KT aggregation model that has been developed for formal decision-making relations regarding ex. territorial nuclear waste disposal systems, can be considered in view of long-term territorial adaptation objectives. To tackle multilateral adaptation programs, technology transfer processes among two or more partners have entailed strategic dialogues [473] as well as common understanding of environmental innovation priorities and best practices[474] utilized in changing scenarios. In terms of public critical agendas about environmental governance, the local adaptation plans assessed for multilevel strategic governance directives have included periodic public identifications specified for common learning practices. The actual material planning and implementation of the local policy monitoring dimension has corresponded to different types of structural knowledge approaches, also reviewed through concepts of so-defined "cross-learning processes" Favoring environmental nuclear safety experiences that have evolved according to single countries' public-private monitoring advocacy initiatives, determined in relation to organizational control mechanisms (e.g.) targeting land-sea connectivity at community level.[475]

[472] Ministry of the Environment, Japan, 1993. "The national action plan for agenda 21." The Council of Ministers for Global Environmental Conservation decided the National Action Plan for Agenda 21 on 24 December 1993. Chapter 35 'Science and sustainable development.' Available at website: https://www.env.go.jp/en/earth/iec/agenda/agenda35.html Accessed 08/2023.

[473] Ministry of the Environment, Japan, 2016. "Bilateral cooperation on the dissemination of low carbon technologies towards transformation to decarbonized societies." Joint Statement, the Federal Ministry for the Environment, Nature Conservation, Building and Nuclear Safety of the Federal Republic of Germany, and MOE Japan. 18th May, 2016. Available at website: https://www.env.go.jp/content/900506547.pdf Accessed 08/2023.

[474] Ministry of the Environment, Japan, 2016. "Bilateral cooperation on the dissemination of low carbon technologies towards transformation to decarbonized societies."

[475] Ministry of the Environment, Japan, 2015. "Case Studies: From Ridge to Reef." ICRI International Coral Reef Initiative, Secretariat, c/o Biodiversity Policy Division, MOE, Japan. Available at website: https://www.env.go.jp/nature/biodic/coralreefs/pamph/C-community_EN.pdf Accessed 08/2023.

6.2 National Changing Emergency Protocols

While considering the multilateral organization process of nuclear energy power facilities combined with electric companies managerial provisions validated according to the establishment of technological interdependent decisional strategies, there has been the critical disaster situation of Fukushima Daiichi nuclear power plant case, which has remained a radical disaster experience in the history of Japan's international development. About decentralized national rescue provisions on environment contamination in NPPs, it is clearly remarked that "[...] until the time the accident actually occurred no practical framework had been sufficiently formulated that covered specific methods and the division of duties for responding to contamination caused by the release of radioactive materials into the general environment."[476]

This nuclear industrial crisis started in Japan on March 2011 because of a combination of multiple natural disaster hazards that were assessed on an international, national, and local scale. Scientific regional experts of (IAEA) or the (ICRP)[477] who have acquired nuclear engineering expertise and rational inner-knowledge production at field level have highlighted major local emergency aspects - e.g. on the decontamination municipal projects [478] - related to Fukushima Daiichi nuclear accident, by specifically pointing at the difficulties of technical programming and standardized management dimensions of NPPs in Japan's industrial collapse case. [479] The progressive formation of institutional relations

476 Ministry of the Environment, Japan, 2018. "Decontamination projects for radioactive contamination discharged by Tokyo Electric Power Company Fukushima Daiichi nuclear power station accident." Editorial Committee for the Paper on Decontamination Projects, MOE Japan Report. Page 11. Available at website: http://josen.env.go.jp/en/policy_document/pdf/decontamination_report1807_01.pdf Accessed 08/2023.

477 Ministry of the Environment, Japan, 2018. "Decontamination projects for radioactive contamination discharged by Tokyo Electric Power Company Fukushima Daiichi nuclear power station accident." More information: ICRP International Commission on Radiological Protection. ICRP and Fukushima. Available at website: https://www.icrp.org/page.asp?id=188 Accessed 08/2023.

478 Ministry of the Environment, Japan, 2018. "Decontamination projects for radioactive contamination discharged by Tokyo Electric Power Company Fukushima Daiichi nuclear power station accident."

479 See: Butler D., "Radioactivity spreads in Japan." Nature 2011; Volume 471, pp. 555-556. 29 March 2011.

which were established between the Japanese population and the nuclear energy industry TEPCO, in reference to Fukushima nuclear disaster accident, have necessarily been based on continuous local mediation activities and organizational adaptive changes, involving critical practical elements which have determined an increase of common distrust and fear.[480] Basically, in the aftermath of Japan's earthquakes and tsunami crises in 2011, the diffusion of official national information detailing the Fukushima nuclear power plant's emergency status including comparative specific technical defaults was perceived as partially unreliable and not transparent.[481] At institutional level, programmatic actions to secure required interventions did engage the MOE "[...] to carefully explaining the necessity of Temporary Storage Sites, MOE sought local understanding to secure Temporary Storage Sites, in cooperation with administrative district managers, community group chairpersons and others. Efforts were made to find realistic solutions with the local communities, and candidate sites were selected by administrative district unit."[482] Concomitantly, it has been put into direct cause the private electricity industry TEPCO (Tokyo Electric Power Company) that run the nuclear power plant.[483] During months following the Fukushima nuclear accident, it has also been brought into light the safety defaults mechanisms

[480] Tetsuya Tanimoto, Naoyuki Uchida, Yuko Kodama, Takanori Teshima, Shuichi Taniguchi, 2011. "Safety of workers at the Fukushima Daiichi nuclear power plant." The Lancet, Volume 377, No. 9776, pp. 1489-1490, April 15, 2011. www.thelancet.com.

[481] Tetsuya Tanimoto, Naoyuki Uchida, Yuko Kodama, Takanori Teshima, Shuichi Taniguchi, 2011.

[482] Ministry of the Environment, Japan, 2018. "Decontamination projects for radioactive contamination discharged by Tokyo Electric Power Company Fukushima Daiichi nuclear power station accident."Chapter 4, "Implementation of Decontamination Projects."Page 218. Available at website: http://josen.env.go.jp/en/policy_document/pdf/decontamination_projects_1902_04.pdf Accessed 11/2023.

[483] Note: CBS News report, June 21, 2016: "Tokyo Electric Power Co. President Naomi Hirose's apology followed the revelation [...] that an investigation had found Hirose's predecessor instructed officials during the 2011 disaster to avoid using the word 'meltdown'[...] TEPCO instead described the reactors' condition as less serious 'core damage' for two months after the earthquake and tsunami on March 11, 2011, wrecked plant, even though utility officials knew and computer simulations suggested meltdowns had occurred." CBS News 2016. "Fukushima meltdown apology: 'It was a cover-up.'" Available at website: https://www.cbsnews.com/news/fukushima-tepco-power-japan-nuclear-meltdown-apologizes-cover-up/ Accessed 08/2023.

of NPPs, as well as, the local technical maintenance issues [484] on decontamination projects, which had to be combined with disaster risk planning codes addressed at the local communities, for newly managed municipal risk-reduction preventive plans.[485]

In essence, the potential delivery of disaster risk reduction programs and local implementation safety mechanisms involving people affected by nuclear disaster accidents has been linked with the functional organization of common emergency services and local evacuation systems supporting local targeted areas. As result, Japanese authorities declared a State of Atomic Emergency in 2011 – through the conjugation of national emergency policies supporting international/national medical teams operations. As a matter of fact, national investigations launched in the aftermath of 2011 earthquakes' impacts associated with NPP Fukushima Daiichi accident put to a test the rapid evacuation procedures drafted within national planning measures which required local organizational interactions[486]

[484] Note: It was reported by the MOE, Japan, about Temporary Storage Sites that "[...] personnel from the Fukushima Office for Environmental Restoration explained each matter carefully. Initially, as there were no Temporary Storage Sites, it was difficult to imagine what they would be like. Therefore, we created a model of the Temporary Storage Site, and used it to make clear explanations to landowners and others. In addition, about concerns about the spread of radioactive materials, we used pamphlets to explain that there was no risk of radioactive materials leaking out, and explained that we would conduct monitoring which helped people understand. Furthermore, in coordination with landowners, we were greatly helped by the cooperation of municipal officials and administrative district managers. Through these efforts we made progress in having people understand securing Temporary Storage Sites." Ministry of the Environment, Japan, 2018. "Decontamination projects for radioactive contamination discharged by Tokyo Electric Power Company Fukushima Daiichi nuclear power station accident." Chapter 4, "Implementation of Decontamination Projects." page 220.

[485] Tetsuya Tanimoto, Naoyuki Uchida, Yuko Kodama, Takanori Teshima, Shuichi Taniguchi, 2011.

[486] Note: As example: "Treatment of Domestic Waste in the Areas under Evacuation Orders, water supply and sewerage systems, and waste disposal facilities, etc., had stopped functioning due to damage and evacuation caused by the earthquake disaster, so processing [...] was initially left to the responsibility of the decontamination contractors, but eventually the national government exchanged information with processing facilities in other municipalities, etc., confirmed the decontamination work plans and the extra processing capacity in the area, and took measures to avoid negative impacts." Ministry of the Environment, Japan, 2018. "Decontamination projects for radioactive contamination discharged by Tokyo Electric Power Company Fukushima Daiichi nuclear power station accident." Chapter 4, "Implementation of Decontamination Projects."page 248.

and collective emergency awareness.[487]

Comparing international archival documentation for this research referred to the period from 2011 to 2016 through national newspapers, international science reports and non-profit organizations reviews, the comparative analyses centred on Japan's state of emergency crisis involving national and local evacuation management plans or medical protection schemes, have indirectly put into cause the national post-disaster preparedness measures, followed by environment evaluation procedures, and managerial adaptation conditions.[488] In 2018, disaster waste management is specified through national guidelines that Ministry of the Environment in Japan supports for the Asia-Pacific region, as it is conditional to a number of comparable factors such as: risk reduction policies and risk preparation programs[489] intertwined with post-recovery budgetary plans and local conservation measures. However, consistent interacting spheres of public risk safety commissions on national post-disaster rescue operations promoted in cases of national emergency requirements in NPPs location areas, have progressively led to a formal divide that has grown particularly between nuclear energy operator TEPCO in Japan and national governmental representatives. In fact, it is emphasized that "[...] the Basic Principles of the Act on Special Measures make the nuclear company concerned [...] TEPCO unambiguously responsible, the principles also recognize the social responsibility of the national government for having promoted nuclear policy. Thus, the national government was made responsible to develop response measures, and in Areas under Evacuation Orders, to implement decontamination directly as Special Decontamination Areas."[490]

[487] Koichi Tanigawa, Yoshio Hosoi, Nobuyuki Hirohashi, Yasumasa Iwasaki, Kenji Kamiya, 2012. "Loss of life after evacuation: lessons learned from the Fukushima accident." The Lancet, Volume 379, No. 9819, March 10th, 2012. Pp. 889-891. www.thelancet.com.

[488] Koichi Tanigawa, Yoshio Hosoi, Nobuyuki Hirohashi, Yasumasa Iwasaki, Kenji Kamiya, 2012.

[489] Ministry of the Environment, Japan, 2018. "Disaster waste management guideline for Asia and the Pacific." MOE report 2018. Available at website: https://www.env.go.jp /content/900512396.pdf Accessed 09/2023.

[490] Ministry of the Environment, Japan, 2018. "Decontamination projects for radioactive contamination discharged by Tokyo Electric Power Company Fukushima Daiichi nuclear power station accident."Chapter 6, "Lessons Learned and Future Challenges." Page 388.

In the months that immediately followed, with NPP disaster crises activating national disaster rescue plans, TEPCO as private energy company was involved with nuclear restoration projects, [491] which required multilateral local adaptation plans coordinated in conjunction with national and international Nuclear Agencies and Controlling Authorities ([492]) ([493]) ([494]). The preparatory emergency safety measures developed in combination with the changing technical requirements for nuclear energy facilities in Japan, did include common action plans with monitoring and safeguarding programs targeting territorial land contamination, water radioactive contamination, as well as, local communities' displacement, which have been dealt through regulatory safety proceedings and local reform processes ([495]) ([496]) ([497]). Granting safety preparedness schemes in cases of technical crises at NPP has also meant implementing collaborative projects in Japan, for instance, between the Ministerial agencies and local governments that have decided to commonly undertake such nuclear emergency protection cycles for local communities. [498] Moreover, governmental reforming agendas have formed realist power expressions due to civil society's exposures to

Available at website: http://josen.env.go.jp/en/policy_document/pdf/decontamination_projects_1902_06.pdf Accessed 09/2023.

[491] Nuclear Emergency Response Headquarters Government - TEPCO Integrated Response Office, Report Appendix 1-3, "Current Status of 'Roadmap towards Restoration from the Accident at Fukushima Daiichi Nuclear Power Station, TEPCO' (Step 2 completion)." December 16, 2011. Available at website: https://www.tepco.co.jp/en/press/corp-com/release/betu11_e/images/111216e11.pdf Accessed 09/2023.

[492] Brian Wheeler, Sharryn Dotson, 2011. "Japan's nuclear crisis: Timeline of events." Power Engineering, June 2011. www.power-eng.com. (or) https://www.power-eng.com/nuclear/japans-nuclear-crisis-timeline-of-events/ Accessed 09/2023.

[493] S. Rangarajan, 2011. "Why is 'Radioactivity' such a scary word?" Chemical Business, April 2011. Colour Publications Pvt. Ltd. https://colourpublications.in/pages/books/ Accessed 11/2023. As of 11/2023 direct article cannot be retrieved. The web-link refers to the publishing outlet.

[494] Forbes Asia, 2011. *Thoughts on the crisis in Japan*. Forbes, April 11, 2011.

[495] Brian Wheeler, Sharryn Dotson, 2011.

[496] S. Rangarajan, 2011.

[497] Forbes Asia. *Thoughts on the crisis in Japan*. Forbes, April 11, 2011.

[498] Yoshio Mochizuki, 2014. "Message from Minister of the Environment, Japan." Japan Environment Quarterly (JEQ), Vol. 8, December 2014. Available at website: https://www.env.go.jp/en/focus/jeq/issue/vol08/feature.html Accessed 09/2023.

complex environment hazards that can drive institutional tasks toward field preparation attitudes and local resilient responses.

As testified across provinces, soon after the acute phase of the disaster crisis occurring at Fukushima Daiichi power plant, the governmental representatives were confronted with post-crisis rescue and recovery actions while similarly supporting local disaster victims who lost private family shelters and experienced dramatic disruptions of local community services. To this assessment, the progressive delivery of formal action-plans included, especially, the contribution provided by local safety workers which were engaged in the emergency rescuing operations at Fukushima NPP, among other locations; substantially, the resulting devastating traits of local earthquakes combined with tsunami waves overpowering NPP sea walls,[499] occurring in geographical areas located in the north of Japan led at the time to important socioeconomic structural losses ([500]) ([501]) ([502]). Concurrently, state regulations enforced "[...] Radiation Hazards [exposures through national ordinance measures that set] 'exceptional emergency dose limit to 250 mSv,"[503] adding that the post-crisis regulated environment included health and food distribution measures based on local contamination risks and standardization protocols.[504]

Still at initial stages, the national and international media diffusion provided different disaster information accounts about local NPP recurrent material leakages and water distribution systems' conditions; the TEPCO's emergency management response to the accident has been

[499] Motoko Rich and Hisako Ueno, 2019. "Fukushima, Beaten Down by Nuclear Disaster, Takes Big Typhoon Hit." The New York Times newspaper, Asia Pacific, October 15, 2019. Available at website: https://www.nytimes.com/2019/10/15/world/asia/typhoon-hagibis-fukushima-japan.html 11/2023.

[500] Brian Wheeler, Sharryn Dotson, 2011.

[501] S. Rangarajan, 2011.

[502] Forbes Asia. *Thoughts on the crisis in Japan.* Forbes, April 11, 2011.

[503] Ministry of the Environment, Japan, 2013. "Comparison between ICRP recommendations and domestic laws and regulations." Booklet 'To Provide Basic Information Regarding Health Effects of Radiation.' Chapter 4.2 'Dose Limits.' Available at website: https://www.env.go.jp/en/chemi/rhm/basic-info/2018/pdf/basic-1st-04-02.pdf Accessed 11/2023.

[504] Ministry of the Environment, Japan, 2013. "Comparison between ICRP recommendations and domestic laws and regulations."

investigated by the National Diet of Japan, 2012,[505] on the basis of substantial discrepancies that started to emerge during the emergency recovery processes, as discussed: "Explanations by the government and Tokyo Electric Power Co. are very vague. They only raise the anxiety among us evacuees."[506] For such reasons, public and private specialized development agencies operating in the country but also outside the country's regional boundaries, however interrelated with nuclear energy commissions, such as: IAEA, NRC, EURATOM, as well as Japan Atomic Agency among others, comparatively converged on official technical confrontations which involved updated review analyses about electricity safety distribution networks associated with managerial maintenance systems and constant upgrade of local emergency operations conducted at

[505] The National Diet of Japan, 2012. National Report "The Fukushima Nuclear Accident Independent Investigation Commission." The National Diet of Japan, publication available at website: https://warp.da.ndl.go.jp/info:ndljp/pid/3856371/naiic.go.jp/en/. Accessed 09/2023. Note: Excerpt: "At the time of the accident, neither the Chairman nor the President of TEPCO were present or accessible, an inconceivable situation for an operator of nuclear power plants. The Chairman and the President also had different understandings of the emergency response structure, a fact that very likely contributed to the delay in TEPCO's response to the accident. TEPCO's manual for emergency response to a severe accident was completely ineffective, and the measures it specified did not function. The manual assumed that reactor readings could be monitored, but failed to account for a prolonged station blackout like the one that occurred at Fukushima, which prevented any monitoring [...]. The actual on-site situation of the vent in Unit 1 was not communicated to NISA or the Prime Minister's office, which helped create an atmosphere of distrust between TEPCO's on-site management, the regulatory agencies and the Prime Minister's office [...].The main organizations of the government's accident response system were the Prime Minister's Nuclear Emergency Response Headquarters, the Secretariat of the Nuclear Emergency Response Headquarters of NISA and the Regional Nuclear Emergency Response team. Overall, none of these organizations functioned as planned." *The National Diet of Japan report*, Executive Summary, 2012, (page 33). https://warp.da.ndl.go.jp/info:ndljp/pid/3856371/naiic.go.jp/wp-content/uploads/2012/09/NAIIC_report_lo_res10.pdf Reviewed 11/2023.

[506] Forbes Asia. "Thoughts on the crisis in Japan." Forbes, April 11, 2011.

NPP reactor's buildings ([507], [508], [509],[510]). The distribution of education manuals and data collection gathered in the form of questionnaires for the Fukushima residents has been arranged systematically for knowledge provision measures and educational objectives set in Japan's prefectures.[511]

Furthermore, following on national disaster responses and local emergency reconstruction plans, it became apparent the need to operate through upgraded environmental information addressed to local established communities,[512] national local citizens, and international aid supporting groups, for the purpose of implementing while monitoring cross-regional post-crisis recovery action-plans, and practical health[513]

[507] Ted Lazo, 2013. "Current issues in radiological protection." Nuclear Plant Journal, May-June 2013.

[508] Mark Lynas, 2011. "If we abandon nuclear power, prepare for catastrophic global warming." New Statesman, 21 March 2011. www.newstatesman.com As of 11/2023 direct article cannot be retrieved.

[509] Laura Walter, 2012. "Report: United States not prepared for Fukushima-like emergency." EHS Today, March, 2012. Website:www.ehstoday.com. (or) https://www.ehstoday.com/emergency-management/article/21915198/report-united-states-not-prepared-for-fukushimalike-emergency Accessed 09/2023.

[510] World Nuclear Association, 2018. Current NPP Status: "The priority is removal of used fuel from the remaining three storage pools at the top of the reactor buildings after successful removal of the fuel unit 4. In about ten years, Japanese technicians expect to be ready to begin removal of the melted core material from inside units 1-3. The four reactors will be decommissioned in 30-40 years, which is typical for any nuclear facility, although the process at Fukushima will be quite different to that at other nuclear facilities." WNA Report updated available at website: https://www.world-nuclear.org/focus/fukushima/the-situation-at-fukushima.aspx Accessed 09/2023.

[511] Hirofumi Fujii, 2019. "Development of educational materials for risk communication using the infographics." Ministry of the Environment, Japan, Report, pp. 16, 2019. Available at website: https://www.env.go.jp/content/900406510.pdf Accessed 09/2023.

[512] See: 1) Yujiro Kuroda, Yohei Koyama, Noriko Sato, Ryoko Ando, 2019. "Re-building trust with local communities after the Nuclear accident: Making of 'Information booklet for Returnees' from native's point of view." The Consultancy Meeting on STS Education Support on Return in the Context of Low-dose Radiation, 2019. Available at website: https://www.env.go.jp/content/900406510.pdf Accessed 11/2023. 2) Yujiro Kuroda, 2018. "Rehabilitation of living conditions after NPP accident: the practical experience and lessons learned from working with Iitate people." RICOMET Conference, 2018.06.13 Antwerp. https://kaken.nii.ac.jp/en/grant/KAKENHI-PROJECT-18K11779/ Accessed 11/2023.

[513] Tsutomu Shimura, Naoki Kunugita, *et al.*, 2015. "Radiation occupational health interventions offered to radiation workers in response to the complex catastrophic disaster at the Fukushima Daiichi Nuclear Power Plant." Journal of Radiation Research, Volume 56, No. 3, pp. 413-421.

interventions ([514], [515], [516]). We note that according to a number of national information reports for the same period 2011-2016 reviewed in these papers, characteristic management aspects about functional public recovery initiatives have still remained at a critical stage.[517] Especially when local communities and national or regional anti-nuclear groups have commonly kept raising safety concerns about local environmental risk protection issues, intertwined with common mistrust elements concerning concurrent governmental information provisions, including primary information sources produced by national energy company TEPCO.[518] In post-crisis assessment terms, the scientific nuclear commissions and non-nuclear experts involved have commonly gathered for international and national level workshops while forming technical operating teams, which have been confronted with the specific nature of national nuclear emergency problems that have remained unsolved in relation to complementary management effects of local emergency organizational conditions ([519], [520], [521]). For local decontamination and remediation projects, the EPA international guidelines continue to retain EPA lessons learnt by inviting the public advisory boards to technical agencies because national local representatives and societal groups can provide specific

[514] Ted Lazo, 2013.

[515] Mark Lynas, 2011.

[516] Laura Walter, 2012.

[517] Note: As of 2022, despite the lifting of evacuation oders in Futaba, former residents have decided not to return to Futaba, Fukushima Prefecture, through the lifting of permanent restriction orders, with few exceptions. The Asahi Shimbun, August 30, 2022. "Partial lifting of evacuation order fails to bring life back to Futaba." August 30, 2022. Available at website: https://www.asahi.com/ajw/articles/14706619 Accessed 09/2023.

[518] The National Diet of Japan, 2012. National Report "The Fukushima Nuclear Accident Independent Investigation Commission." The National Diet of Japan, publication NAIIC, available at website: https://warp.da.ndl.go.jp/info:ndljp/pid/3856371/naiic.go.jp/en/. Accessed 09/2023. Findings Excerpt: "After being notified by TEPCO that the situation met the conditions of Article 15 of the Act on Special Measures Concerning Nuclear Emergency Preparedness, it took two hours to issue the Declaration of a Nuclear Emergency Situation, a necessary step in launching the emergency response. In fact, Prime Minister Kan was not fully aware that issuing the "Declaration of an Emergency Situation" was a necessary first step in response to the accident, and those around him failed to advise him correctly." *The National Diet of Japan report*, Executive Summary, 2012, page 34.

[519] Ted Lazo, 2013.

[520] Mark Lynas, 2011.

[521] Laura Walter, 2012.

indications that relate to territorial priorities and progressive resettlement issues.[522]

Nonetheless, national disaster emergency preparedness plans and respective groups' management operations have also shown concrete weak programmatic aspects in terms of post-recovery community processes eventually adapted for the case of Japan's post-Fukushima impacts linked to NPP local accidents, which were publicly experienced through scattered information[523] and scarcely updated governmental responses.[524] For instance, due to the material lack of a consolidated environmental remediation policy in Japan, the IAEA team on mission in 2017 reported its findings by highlighting: "[...] (in) Date City [...] the municipality faced various challenges to implement the remediation works, including the lack of proper national remediation policy and response framework; the influence of sometimes contradicting information in mass media; and the lack of practical experience in remediation and management of large volumes of the residual radioactive material."[525] In essence, there have been into evidence functional dependency conducts for post-disaster mutual regulatory leads, which have directed the emergency disaster management organizations through national and local governments' material relief provisions. At the time of critical exposures, measuring the levels of radioactivity in food products and potable water

[522] EPA, United States, 2013. "Observations and commentary on remediation of the lands off-site from the Fukushima Daiichi reactors." Report of the United States Embassy Science Fellows Support to the Government of Japan - Ministry of the Environment. SRNL-RP-2013-00303 EPA/600/R-13/135. Available at website: http://josen.env.go.jp/en/documents/pdf/workshop_july_17-18_2013_04.pdf Accessed 09/2023.

[523] The National Diet of Japan, 2012. National Report "The Fukushima Nuclear Accident Independent Investigation Commission." The National Diet of Japan, publication available at website: https://warp.da.ndl.go.jp/info:ndljp/pid/3856371/naiic.go.jp/en/. Accessed 09/2023. Findings Excerpt: "After the accident, TEPCO continued to avoid transparency in disclosing information. It limited disclosure to confirmed facts, and failed to disclose information that it felt was uncertain or inconvenient. Some examples of continuing disclosure issues include the delay in releasing electricity demand projections used as the basis for rolling blackouts, and the lack in up-to-date information on the core conditions at the plant." *The National Diet of Japan report*, Executive Summary, 2012, page 20.

[524] Ted Lazo, 2013.

[525] IAEA, 2017. "The 3rd IAEA-MOE experts meeting on environmental remediation. Tokyo, Minami-Soma City, Date City." Summary Report IAEA, 17-21 April 2017. Page 4. Available at website: http://josen.env.go.jp/en/news/pdf/news_170417_01.pdf Accessed 09/2023.

with comparable investigative methods in a resulting common activity was put in place and nationally implemented in 2012.[526] In this situation, national, regional and international institutional counterparts have been confronted with emerging environmental perspectives for disaster risk management (DRR) and rapid recovery missions operating in local disaster affected areas, as in Japan's NPP case; here the local population has required a continued assistance, especially in the aftermath of local crises prompting direct implementation phases by integrating permanent evacuation plans.[527] For example the special decontamination areas (SDA) were identified as Restricted Area or as Deliberate Evacuation Area while the MOE took charge of the corresponding decontamination plans for the SDA involved.[528]

At the same time, in line with follow-up activities on regional emergency monitoring lessons, the international nuclear organizational agencies have been invited at governmental level to commonly assess the environmental planning measures applied in NPP disaster zones, also interrelated with national evacuation plans and local operational interactions involving cross-national emergency teams. The U.S. Federal authorities apply emergency criteria that refer to emergency planning zones (EPZ) with a 10-mile EPZ, and a 50-mile EPZ; the NRC/FEMA retain major decisional functions in the case of NPP accident in the U.S.[529] This type of public facilitation process has been reviewed in connection with the NPPs changing requirements of large-scale energy projects,

[526] Ministry of the Environment, Japan, 2014. "Expert meeting regarding the status of health management of residents following the accident at the Tokyo Electric Power Company's Fukushima Daiichi Nuclear Power Station." MOE Interim Report, December 2014. Available at website: https://www.env.go.jp/content/900411794.pdf Accessed 09/2023.

[527] Laura Walter, 2012.

[528] Ministry of the Environment, Japan, 2018. "Framework and Methods of Decontamination Projects." MOE Report, "Decontamination projects for radioactive contamination discharged by Tokyo Electric Company Fukushima Daiichi Nuclear Power Station Accident." Chapter 3. Page 63. Available at webpage: http://josen.env.go.jp/en/policy_document/pdf/decontamination_projects_1902_03.pdf Accessed 09/2023.

[529] UCS, 2011. "Emergency planning and preparedness for nuclear disasters." The Union of Concerned Scientists (UCS), Offsite Emergency Planning Report, December 2011. Available at website: https://www.ucsusa.org/sites/default/files/2019-09/fact-sheet-emergency-planning.pdf accessed 09/2023.

which have required local performing strategies and common transparency mechanisms for the technical examination of NPP facilities' licenses and concurrent national managerial cycles.[530] Regulatory requirements in Malaysia's case have seen on the control line the Malaysian Atomic Energy Licensing Board (AELB)[531] as well as the IAEA maintaining safety principles and local practical assessments on NPP sites by facilitating objective regulatory criteria and security prospects.[532]

Moreover, in terms of multi risk-hazard perceptions and civilian mistrust issues concerning nuclear energy technologies, the preparation of national policy briefings addressing, at institutional level, respective health and safety concerns about Fukushima disaster case,[533] has specifically led to formal progressive interactions regarding nuclear energy safeguards of industrial safety protection components combined with environmental regulatory standards, which have become a national priority for environmental emergency crises scrutinized in association with local controlling and monitoring events ([534]) ([535]) ([536]) ([537]). Strategic environmental priorities identified in terms of systematic sustainability aspects have pointed at the: 1. facilitation of early warning systems; 2. integration of environmental findings in decision-making consultations; 3. consideration of potential development options; 4. incorporation of EIAs and SEAs in nuclear waste processing plans; 5. clarification of public

[530] Laura Walter, 2012.

[531] N.A. Basri, S. Hashim, A.T. Ramli, D.A. Bradley, K. Hamzah, 2016. "Regulatory requirements for nuclear power plant site selection in Malaysia - a review." Journal of Radiological Protection, Volume 36, No. 4, R96-R111.

[532] N.A. Basri, S. Hashim, A.T. Ramli, D.A. Bradley, K. Hamzah, 2016.

[533] The National Diet of Japan report, Executive Summary, 2012, page 22.

[534] Emily Hammond, 2015. "Nuclear power, risk, and retroactivity." Vanderbilt Journal of Transnational Law, Vol. 48, No. 4, pp. 1059-1082.

[535] Kazutoshi Hasegawa, 2016. "On the accident at Fukushima Daiichi nuclear power plant from the inherent safety points of view." Chemical Engineering Transactions, Volume 48, pp. 511-516.

[536] Alba L. Pineda-Solano, Victor H. Carreto-Vazquez, M. Sam Mannan, 2013. "The Fukushima Daiichi accident and its impact on risk perception and risk communication." Chemical Engineering Transactions, Volume 31, pp. 517-522.

[537] Ranjay Gulati, Charles Casto, Charlotte Krontiris, 2014. "How the other Fukushima plant survived." The Globe, Harvard Business Review, Crisis Management, July-August 2014. Available at website: https://hbr.org/2014/07/how-the-other-fukushima-plant-survived Accessed 09/2023.

management directives and local distributive conditions.[538] In Japan's case, nuclear emergency assistance plans have been managed through the private energy distributor TEPCO[539] among other operating partners, supporting technology operational changes as well as the inclusion of local adaptation guidelines addressing the safety and health issues of NPP technical workers operating at the reactors;[540] but at the same time, the emergence of diffused radiation leakages has entailed different stages of local environmental clean-ups, which have been scarcely clarified at population level ([541]) ([542]) ([543]) ([544]). the MOE in 2011 formally provided "Decontamination Guidelines [...] part 1. ...For the methods for investigation and measurement of the status of environment pollution in the Intensive Contamination Survey Areas [...] part 2. ...Pertaining to decontamination and other measures [...] part 3. ...Pertaining to the collection and transfer of removed soil [...] part 4. ...Pertaining to the storage of removed soil."[545]

538 Ministry of the Environment, Japan, 2003. "Effective SEA System and case studies." MOE and Mitsubishi Research Institute, Inc., Japan, Report, June 2003. Available at website: http://assess.env.go.jp/files/0_db/seika/0184_02/en_all.pdf Accessed 09/2023.

539 Note: About 2012 TEPCO Monitoring operators advisory guidelines: "TEPCO must undergo fundamental corporate changes, including strengthening its governance, working towards building an organizational culture which prioritizes safety, changing its stance on information disclosure, and establishing a system which prioritizes the site...Operators must construct a cross-monitoring system to maintain safety standards at the highest global levels. TEPCO must undergo dramatic corporate reform, including governance and risk management and information disclosure - with safety as the sole priority." The National Diet of Japan report, Executive Summary, 2012, pages 22-23.

540 About NPP Fukushima Daiichi Workers: The Ministry of Health, Labour and Welfare publishes radiation information reports including: "TEPCO Fukushima Daiichi NPP. [And] The status on the exposure dose, health care management and radiation protection of the workers at Fukushima Daiichi Nuclear Power Plant are shown." Available on the official website: https://www.mhlw.go.jp/english/topics/2011eq/workers/tepco/index.html Accessed 09/2023.

541 Emily Hammond, 2015.

542 Kazutoshi Hasegawa, 2017.

543 Alba L. Pineda-Solano, Victor H. Carreto-Vazquez, Mahboobul S. Mannan, 2015.

544 Ranjay Gulati, Charles Casto, Charlotte Krontiris, 2014.

545 Ministry of the Environment, Japan, 2015. "Overview of decontamination methods." FY2014 Decontamination Report, "A compilation of experiences to date on decontamination for the living environment conducted by the Ministry of the Environment - (MOEJ)." Chapter 2, Page 81. Available at website: http://josen.env.go.jp/en/cooperation/pdf/decontamination_report1503_02.pdf Accessed 11/2023.

Moving beyond critical large scale measurement indications, objectively, public understanding forming about regional emergency risk management and national regulatory shifts regarding the NPP monitoring systems, has reflected a state of common uncertainty due to local organizational conditions emerging within a multi-dimensional, sometimes overlapping, negotiation frameworks, when ex. it is stated that "The Daini plant experienced one disruption after another: the earthquake, the tsunami, the flooding, the power loss, threats to the contaminated vessels' integrity, changing in priorities for restoring power…."[546] In sum, multi-agency communication systems reporting about local safety management changes including the Fukushima emergency risk impacts monitored by technical energy operators,[547] have essentially provided an asymmetric information causing detrimental effects for post-recovery assessment conditions and consequent upgrading of activities for local evacuation plans ([548]) ([549]) ([550]) ([551]). It is clarified, however that "According to the Act on Special Measures, [implemented in 2012/01], the consent of a large number of concerned parties was required before starting the decontamination. It took a very long time to identify the land owners and stakeholders, to pay attention to residents' feelings, and to provide [...] detailed explanations to obtain consent of all involved."[552]

To these thematic issues, the aggregation of regulative monitoring policies and local community debates - including corresponding levels of public trust criteria that emerged in association with post-crisis governmental declarations, significantly associated with local cleanup

546 Ranjay Gulati, Charles Casto, Charlotte Krontiris, 2014.

547 Note: At national level "...the failure of the Secretariat of the Nuclear Emergency Response Headquarters to gather and share information concerning the development of the accident and the response was a significant factor." The National Diet of Japan report, Executive Summary, 2012, page 34.

548 Emily Hammond, 2015.

549 Kazutoshi Hasegawa, 2017.

550 Alba L. Pineda-Solano, Victor H. Carreto-Vazquez, Mahboobul S. Mannan, 2015.

551 Ranjay Gulati, Charles Casto, Charlotte Krontiris, 2014.

552 Ministry of the Environment, Japan, 2015. "Basic features of the environmental decontamination in Japan" FY2014 Decontamination Report, "A compilation of experiences to date on decontamination for the living environment conducted by the Ministry of the Environment - (MOEJ)" Chapter 1. Page 16. Available at website: http://josen.env.go.jp/en/policy_document/pdf/decontamination_report1503_01.pdf Accessed 09/2023.

stages of the NPPs affected - had led to mounting questions, which reflected the unclear status of national safety protocols and local recovery models, also due to the case of additional accidents that still occurred at local NPP facility site.[553] Governmental progressive efforts made to decontaminate Special Areas, among other priorities, have been monitored, and in 2015 the MOE released a progress report[554] signaling: each municipality status, the transferring of national financial commitments, and the introduction of specific targeted measures to ensure long-term environmental recovery plans combined with technical reconstruction projects. Additionally, continuous severe accidents managed at the nuclear power plants have determined simultaneous safety measures failures, which overall have raised local communities' alert pressures that have escalated due to the material lack of national preventive plans and territorial provisional shifts ([555], [556]). On the occasion of the 'Great East Japan Earthquake' in 2011, "[...] the TEPCO Fukushima Daiichi NPS accidents in Fukushima Prefecture forced people to seek shelter without any belongings, and they were forced to leave a number of animals in the alert zone."[557] In this occurrence, technological risk perception and technological risk awareness have been undervalued factors for the case of large-scale industrial hybrid projects as the NPPs, which have required functional intervention plans monitored through continuous institutional interactions involving local community's stakeholders.[558] Similarly, the international communities need to directly face changing ecosystems due

[553] Kazutoshi Hasegawa, 2017.

[554] Ministry of the Environment, Japan, 2015. "Progress on Off-site cleanup efforts in Japan." MOE Policy Report, January 2015. Available at website: http://josen.env.go.jp /en/documents/pdf/progress_on_off_site_cleanup_efforts_in_japan_1501.pdf Accessed 09/2023.

[555] Kazutoshi Hasegawa, 2017.

[556] Alba L. Pineda-Solano, Victor H. Carreto-Vazquez, Mahboobul S. Mannan, 2015.

[557] Ministry of the Environment, Japan, 2011. "Response to the Great East Japan Earthquake and Nuclear Power Station Accidents." FY 2011 Annual Report of the Environment, Chapter 2. Page 47. Available at website: https://www.env.go.jp/content/ 900457370.pdf Accessed 09/2023.

[558] Alba L. Pineda-Solano, Victor H. Carreto-Vazquez, Mahboobul S. Mannan, 2015.

to NPP land planning schemes that can require "environmental remediation works in post-accident situations."[559]

For such reasons, after the Fukushima nuclear accident, the managerial evaluation performances and local monitoring processes referring to nuclear environmental impacts have been expanded through qualitative and quantitative territorial measurements that have included local risk and recovery areas with socio-technical interactions. In fact, institutional recovery measures tackling the rebuilding of communities by improving local infrastructures and therefore enhancing responsive environments have shown a propensity to consolidate open information sources and viable communication accesses for respective community members, among other sectors involved.[560] Moreover, when specifically looking at systematic disaster risk protection schemes, it has been advanced a constructive focus on the adoption of technical emergency disaster measures and on the preparation of concurrent field assessments, which have been associated with containment methodologies producing national policy guidelines, also based on local protection needs that remain essential for present generations located in Japan and elsewhere.[561] Under these terms, Japan regulation bodies have proposed to introduce local adaptation measures for the purpose of granting accessibility to open data systems monitoring climatic events, in particular, and re-evaluate on an annual basis effective results and methods applied within and beyond national borders.[562]

[559] Ministry of the Environment, Japan, 2016. "Summary of IAEA-MOE Experts' meeting on environmental remediation of Off-site Areas after the Fukushima Daiichi Nuclear Power Station Accident." MOE, Tokyo, Japan, Meeting Report 4-5- February 2016. Page 4. Available at website: https://www.env.go.jp/content/900506116.pdf Accessed 09/2023.
[560] IAEA, 2013. "The follow-up IAEA international mission on remediation of large contaminated areas off-site the Fukushima Daiichi Nuclear Power Plant." Tokyo and Fukushima Prefecture, Japan 14-21 October 2013. International Atomic Energy Agency, Final Report, NE/NEFW/2013. Available at website: https://www.env.go.jp/content /900483741.pdf Accessed 09/2023.
[561] Alba L. Pineda-Solano, Victor H. Carreto-Vazquez, Mahboobul S. Mannan, 2015.
[562] United Nations, FCCC/IDR.7/JPN, 2019. "Report on the technical review of the seventh national communication of Japan." Page 35. U.N. Framework Convention on Climate Change, 24 January 2019. FCCC/IDR.7/JPN. Available at website: https://www.env.go.jp/content/900446251.pdf Accessed 09/2023.

Comparative environmental topics about the Fukushima Daiichi site accidents have also converged on the safety monitoring aspect of repetitive NPP contamination accidents that have led to a number of local emergencies, which have been under scrutinized despite the diffusion of national safety statements provided by TEPCO's workers,[563] in reference to unsolved management risks and local prevention activities ([564]) ([565]). To note that "[...] under an emergency situation immediately after the accident at Tokyo Electric Power Company (TEPCO)'s Fukushima Daiichi NPS [...] the MHLW [Ministry of Health, Labour and Welfare] set the provisional regulation values for radioactive materials in foods mainly based on the guideline values given by the Nuclear Safety Commission. Then, the FSCJ [Food Safety Commission of Japan] held a total of five meetings, compiled the 'Urgent Report on Radioactive Materials,' and sent it to the MHLW on March 29, 2011. Based on this Urgent Report, the ministry decided to maintain the provisional regulations values as an interim measure. [...] The new regulation was adopted on April 1, 2012."[566] To these complex factors, there are several convergent local environment impacts related to territorial risk management factors, including human regional displacement, health assessment provisions, technical comparative analyses, and local information monitoring reports, which have essentially emerged according to different comparative findings based at regional and national levels. For instance, terrestrial

563 Mari Yamaguchi, The Associated Press, 2017. "Court Holds TEPCO, govt liable for Fukushima safety failures." Article Quote: "The court said the disaster was preventable and that TEPCO ignored safety steps despite knowing of the tsunami risk, while the government failed to oversee the utility. Even though TEPCO deserved severe blame because of its negligence, that does not lighten the government's responsibility, the court said, adding that they should split the cost of the damages." The Seattle Times - Business - Nation & World - March, 17, 2017.

564 Loss Prevention Bulletin, 2015. *Two die in separate Fukushima incidents.* Loss Prevention Bulletin 241. February 2015.

565 Abel J. Gonzalez, 2012. "The recommendations of the ICRP vis-à-vis the Fukushima Dai-ichi NPP accident aftermath." Journal of Radiological Protection, Volume 32, No. 1. DOI 10.1088/0952-4746/32/1/N1.

566 Radiation Health Management Division, Ministry of the Environment, Japan, 2022. "Accident at TEPCO's Fukushima Daiichi NPS and Thereafter (Initiatives by Ministries and Agencies)." Booklet to Provide Information Regarding Health Effects of Radiation. Volume 2. Page 51. National Institutes for Quantum Science and Technology. Available at website: https://www.env.go.jp/en/chemi/rhm/basic-info/1st/pdf/basic-1st-vol2.pdf Accessed 09/2023.

weather impacts have been evaluated for the identification of adaptive risk management options interrelated to technology advancements and socioeconomic shifts analyzed internationally.[567]

Due to regional changing scenarios, the special emergency reports following up on the immediate effects caused by tsunami and earthquake impacts in Japan, have been categorized in a systematic manner because of the rapidity of organizational transition cycles; while the NPP responsive operational programs have instead relied on long-term comparative management procedures and monitoring & evaluation analyses, potentially involving other nuclear states' commissions based ex. in the United States or China ([568]) ([569]). Basically, in the case of progressive technical identifications, the international governmental commissions such as the (ICRP) Commission on Radiological Protection[570] have been in a position to report about major technical recommendations linked to local risk protection factors that have been identified for multidimensional disaster cases, as Japan's earthquakes and tsunami with concurrent follow-up events ([571]). Still, ([572]) ([573]) ([574]) ([575]) ([576]) even if the combination of international and national environmental undertakings defining the verification and validation stages of nuclear

[567] Ministry of the Environment, Japan, 2015. "Environment research and technology development fund FY 2015." MOE Policy Report, September 2015. Available at website: https://www.env.go.jp/policy/kenkyu/suishin/english/gaiyou/pdf/2015_pamphlet_eng.pdf Accessed 09/2023.

[568] Anonymous writer, 2015. "Two die in separate Fukushima incidents." Loss Prevention Bulletin 241. February 2015.

[569] Abel J. Gonzalez, 2012.

[570] See ICRP Website at: https://www.icrp.org/

[571] Abel J. Gonzalez, 2012.

[572] Beattie Jeff, 2011. "U.S. Utilities pledge fresh review of nuke plant readiness." The Energy Daily, Englewood, Issue 53, March 2011. United States.

[573] The Economist, Asia, 2011. *Living with radiation; Coping with Japan's nuclear disaster.* The Economist Intelligence Unit N.A., Incorporated, Volume 399, Issue 8728, London, UK.

[574] Shirouzu Norihiko, Dawson Chester, 2011. "In depth: Design flaw fueled nuclear disaster." The Wall Street Journal Asia; Hong Kong, July 4th, 2011. Dow Jones & Company Inc.

[575] The Economist, Business, 2011. *The troubles of TEPCO; Power in Japan.* The Economist; London, Volume 400, Issue. 8740. July, 2011.

[576] The Economist, Briefing, 2011. *The risks exposed; Japan's nuclear industry.* The Economist; London, Vol. 398, Issue. 8725. March 2011.

energy plants' ecosystem has been processed by major nuclear consulting agencies such as the U.S. Nuclear Regulatory Commission NRC, the International Atomic Energy Agency IAEA, and the national energy company TEPCO in Japan - the local emergency dimension has been intertwined with the effective collapse of a multifunctional energy complex system, which has relied on different safety protection services and local response mechanisms ([577]) ([578]) ([579]) ([580]) ([581]). In terms of local ecosystem protection policies run in Japan, the MOE agencies emphasize critical anti-risk prevention measures related to land and forest conservation services that entail disaster prevention activities and functional mitigation strategies.[582]

National reporting agencies[583] reviewing the Fukushima-Daiichi accident have retraced it as a major collapse while referring to it as a dynamic modifying environment that has increased common environmental awareness about nuclear energy technology provisions and local risk assessment protocols, maintained by regional energy providers. In addition to this, it was stated in 2011 that: "NRC officials have said little about how the Japanese experience might change regulation of the U.S. nuclear industry, saying they want first to understand exactly what occurred at Fukushima-Daiichi."[584] In fact, there is also to consider that there have been some basic disagreements among international nuclear consulting experts about NPP management protection plans and safety preparedness programs, which have stimulated international critical

577 Beattie Jeff, 2011.

578 The Economist, Asia, 2011. *Living with radiation; Coping with Japan's nuclear disaster.*

579 Shirouzu Norihiko, Dawson Chester, 2011.

580 The Economist, Business, 2011. *The troubles of TEPCO; Power in Japan.*

581 The Economist, Briefing, 2011. *The risks exposed; Japan's nuclear industry.*

582 Ministry of the Environment, Japan. 2016. "Ecosystem-based disaster risk reduction in Japan. A handbook for practitioners." Nature Conservation Bureau, MOE, Report, March 2016. Available at website: https://www.env.go.jp/content/900489554.pdf Accessed 09/2023.

583 The Fukushima Report, Available at: http://thefukushimareport.com/ (or) https://www.whoi.edu/know-your-ocean/ocean-topics/ocean-human-lives/pollution/radiation/fukushima-radiation/fukushima-and-the-ocean/ Linked to Woods Hole Oceanographic Institution, 2013. "Fukushima and the Ocean."Presented on May, 9, 2013. Volume 50. No. 1, Spring 2013.

584 Beattie Jeff, 2011. pages 1-2.

debates tackling, in particular, reliability of public information sources and the common state of updated confirmation analyses ([585]) ([586]). In order to draw a distinction line on the Fukushima NPP accidents, the NRC's commissioner confirmed substantive lessons learned declaring, in particular, "[...] the NRC was faced with the need to quickly and effectively understand the implications events on the other side of the globe might have for current and future nuclear power plants in the United States. This challenge is magnified by the reality that plant operation, government regulation, and industry practices associated with the Japanese nuclear power program are different from that of the United States. It would be unwise and incorrect to assume that every change made in response to Fukushima that might need to occur in Japan - or other countries, for that matter - should be applied in this country. [...] The changes that we should consider arise largely as a result of methodically challenging our systems and approaches to assure that they are adequately protective of public health and safety."[587] The current modifications and regulatory management status of the NPP Fukushima-Daiichi and Daini have been summarised for information in table 4 indicating local reactors' capacity and shut down process dating back since 2011 (IAEA data).

[585] The Economist, Asia, 2011. *Living with radiation; Coping with Japan's nuclear disaster.*

[586] Beattie Jeff, 2011.

[587] United States Nuclear Regulatory Commission, 2011."Commissioner Magwood's Comments on SECY-11-0137, 'Prioritization of Recommended Actions to be Taken in Response to Fukushima Lessons Learned.'" Page 13. Decision ITEM: SECY-11-0137. Report available at website: https://www.nrc.gov/reading-rm/doc-collections/commission/cvr/2011/2011-0137vtr.pdf Accessed 09/2023.

Table 4

Japan NPP Status of Fukushima-Daiichi and Daini Reactors Activity

Reactors "Name"	**"Type"**	**"Status"**	**"Location"**	**"Reference Unit Power [MW]"**	**"Gross Electrical Capacity [MW]"**	**"First Grid Connection"**
FUKUSHIMA-DAIICHI-1	BWR	Permanent Shutdown *19-05-2011*	OHKUMA-MACHI	439	460	1970-11-17
FUKUSHIMA-DAIICHI-2	BWR	Permanent Shutdown *19-05-2011*	OHKUMA-MACHI	760	784	1973-12-24
FUKUSHIMA-DAIICHI-3	BWR	Permanent Shutdown *19-05-2011*	OHKUMA-MACHI	760	784	1974-10-26
FUKUSHIMA-DAIICHI-4	BWR	Permanent Shutdown *19-05-2011*	OHKUMA-MACHI	760	784	1978-02-24
FUKUSHIMA-DAIICHI-5	BWR	Permanent Shutdown *17-12-2013*	OHKUMA-MACHI	760	784	1977-09-22
FUKUSHIMA-DAIICHI-6	BWR	Permanent Shutdown *17-12-2013*	OHKUMA-MACHI	1067	1100	1979-05-04
FUKUSHIMA-DAINI-1	BWR	Permanent Shutdown *30-09-2019*	NARAHA-MACHI	1067	1100	1981-07-31
FUKUSHIMA-DAINI-2	BWR	Permanent Shutdown *30-09-2019*	NARAHA-MACHI	1067	1100	1983-06-23
FUKUSHIMA-DAINI-3	BWR	Permanent Shutdown *30-09-2019*	NARAHA-MACHI	1067	1100	1984-12-14
FUKUSHIMA-DAINI-4	BWR	Permanent Shutdown *30-09-2019*	NARAHA-MACHI	1067	1100	1986-12-17

Source: IAEA/PRIS Power Reactor Information System, "Japan." Compiled Model Data, Available at website: https://pris.iaea.org/PRIS/CountryStatistics/CountryDetails.aspx?current=JP (PRIS database last updated 2022-11-10).

The Japanese communities which have been affected by radiation and pollution issues linked to the NPP facilities have testified the need to increase local safety regulation standards and risk communication networks [588] promoting corresponding public local interactions. [589] Sequential policies administered in view of improving local knowledge capacities and make progress in decision-making on decontamination issues, brought the country's councils to recognize that the sharing of public risk communication entails a number of systemic inclusive steps (e.g.) deepening communication practices based on mutuality criteria, and activating institutional inputs through the inclusion of communities, technical experts, scientists, students, etc.,[590] in order to lead rebuilding efforts in a responsive manner. As a matter of clarity, Japan's local prefectures that have experienced serious socioeconomic damages in 2011 have commonly reviewed the organization of NPP technical plans provided by private energy company TEPCO. At review stage, public authorities have clarified the fact that Fukushima plant's technical collapse did cause dramatic territorial shifts, eventually determining the formation of critical risk environment approaches, which have been taken into consideration in view of adopting governmental transition schemes - addressing the NPP operational maintenance, and managerial evaluation plans, critically based on local protection needs - in order to reduce major further causes of NPP technical industrial accidents.[591] For this reason, in 2018 the official studying groups stated that "despite some delays in initial responses and current progress due to a lack of technical knowledge and practical experience, a lack of education about radiation, and the time required to build trust in the community, etc., some progress has been

[588] Pablo Figueroa, 2015. "Governance and risk communication in Fukushima: Notes from Miyakoji." Our World, United Nations University, 14 January 2014. Available at website: https://ourworld.unu.edu/en/governance-and-risk-communication-in-fukushima-notes-from-miyakoji Accessed 09/2023.

[589] The Economist, Asia, 2011. *Living with radiation; Coping with Japan's nuclear disaster.*

[590] Ministry of the Environment, Japan, 2018. "Decontamination projects for radioactive contamination discharged by Tokyo Electric Power Company Fukushima Daiichi Nuclear Power Station accident." MOE, Policy Document, Chapter 5, 'Effects, Verification, and Risk Communication of Decontamination.' Available at website: http://josen.env.go.jp/en/policy_document/pdf/decontamination_projects_1902_05.pdf Accessed 09/2023.

[591] The Economist, Business, 2011. *The troubles of TEPCO; Power in Japan.*

made thanks to the accumulation of knowledge and know-how in the national and local governments, which are the implementation bodies."[592]

As result, national regulatory safety reforms[593] implemented in multilevel public-private organizations incorporating energy distributive changing areas have also led to the affirmation of local environmental protection measures that can be progressively integrated with alternative managerial mandates, particularly concerning the comparative uses of renewable energy resources, such as the gas energy sectors. Development sustainable strategies have in fact comprised long-term risk management approaches fostering local knowledge interactions and integrated operational mechanisms that try to establish mitigation functions in view of environmental risk impacts for selective areas.[594] In more recent years, in Japan have emerged environmental development mandates[595] due to the country's regulatory guidelines promoting transnational and local implementation of energy safety programs designed after Fukushima-Daiichi nuclear disaster crisis. In the specific case of "Decommissioning Scenarios will be considered and established through gathering worldwide information on how to ensure safety of decommissioning in consideration of end of state facilities."[596] Research conducted about the exposition to

[592] Ministry of the Environment, Japan, 2018. "Decontamination projects for radioactive contamination discharged by Tokyo Electric Power Company Fukushima Daiichi Nuclear Power Station accident. Chapter 5. Page 302.

[593] Nicole Jawerth, 2016. "Five years after Fukushima: Making nuclear power safer." IAEA International Atomic Energy Agency, available at webpage: https://www.iaea.org/newscenter/news/five-years-after-fukushima-making-nuclear-power-safer Accessed 09/2023.

[594] Ministry of the Environment, Japan, 2016. "Environment research and technology development fund FY2016." MOE, Environmental Policy Bureau, Office of Environmental Research and Technology, Research Report. Available at webpage: https://www.env.go.jp/policy/kenkyu/suishin/english/gaiyou/pdf/2016_pamphlet_eng.pdf Accessed 09/2023.

[595] Ministry of the Environment, Government of Japan, 2020. "Joint declaration between United Nations Industrial Development Organization and the Ministry of the Environment of Japan." Press & Public Relations Release, available at webpage: http://www.env.go.jp/en/headline/2481.html Accessed 09/2023.

[596] Tatsuya Shinkawa, 2013. "Revised mid-and-long-term Roadmap towards the Decommissioning of TEPCO's Fukushima Daiichi NPP Units 1-4." Agency for Natural Resources and Energy, METI, July 2013, METI report. Page 16. Available at webpage: https://www.env.go.jp/press/files/jp/22699.pdf Accessed 09/2023.

radiation[597] with associated environmental impacts intertwined with this type of industrial disaster crisis has been transmitted both in separate territorial jurisdictions, as well as, according to international regulatory dimensions. Consequently, local communities involved which have remained under environmental monitoring & observation projects on a daily basis, have also been engaged in local sustainability efforts that have reflected common action-based recovery practices through information sharing and educational experimental methodologies, [598] adopted in Japan's multi-hazards case scenarios.

This radical case has indirectly conducted toward an adaptive learning dimension that has resurfaced beyond the scopes of environmental distribution policies, which have still been promoted in terms of common anti-risk perception programs, associated with NPPs organizational reviews, tacitly consolidating local adaptation plans. Further considerations about post-Fukushima PPPs coordination and collaborative aspects are introduced in the next section ([599]) ([600]).

6.3 Multilateral Coordination of Operational Emergency Facilities of Japan

In view of establishing either centralized or decentralized security and monitoring risk assessments that have involved quantitative prediction analyses and environmental prevention plans - focused on environmental risk conditions and local safety domains - the material formulation of country-based approaches has essentially relied on disaster risk impacts that have remained difficult to serialize systematically. [601] Scientific indicators testing country-level knowledge innovation approaches

[597] Ministry of the Environment, Japan, 2021. "Effects of Radioactive Fallout due to Atmospheric Nuclear Testing." Volume 1, Chapter 2.1, 'Exposure Routes' study. Available at webpage: https://www.env.go.jp/en/chemi/rhm/basic-info/1st/pdf/basic-1st-02.pdf Accessed 09/2023.

[598] Omori Naoki, 2021. "Post-Fukushima educational practices." Citizen's Nuclear Information Center, Information Report, February 11, 2021. Available at webpage: https://cnic.jp/english/?p=5314 Accessed 09/2023.

[599] The Economist, Briefing, 2011. *The risks exposed; Japan's nuclear industry.*

[600] The Economist, Business, 2011. *The troubles of TEPCO; Power in Japan.*

[601] Jonas Hagmann, 2012. "Fukushima: probing the analytical and epistemological limits of risk analysis." Journal of Risk Research, Volume 15, No. 7, pp. 801-815.

regarding energy distribution standards,[602] chemical substances dispersion, or global production impacts, have been cooperatively monitored in order to determine environmental regulatory conditions that can reduce the significance of industrial pollution implications transferred to complex societies and local human habitats.[603] Some other emerging indications provided about risk management assessments and local environmental impacts analyzed in EIAs have signaled a persistent status of uncertainty that has characterized normative and socioeconomic formulations on multi-year industrial restructuring programs; sustainable development plans have also referred to the use of national probabilistic analyses exploring localized multi-hazard environment risk areas monitored through systematic regional control models.[604] Updated environment international strategies lined up in comprehensive normative protection requirements have become explicit within national cooperation plans prioritizing environment economic provisions for ecosystems' preservation and community participation.[605]

Concerning national disaster periodical events, as in Japan's case, with multiple earthquake prone zones and local natural hazards, the regulatory implementation of environmental safety procedures[606] concerning

602 Note: To point out that regarding the control of industrial emissions: "on December 16, 2011, the Environmental Protection Agency (EPA) finalized the first national standards to reduce mercury and other toxic air pollution from coal-and-oil-fired power plants. More than 20 years after the 1990 Clean Air Act Amendments, some power plants still do not control emissions of toxic pollutants, even though pollution control technology is widely available." EPA-U.S., 2022. "Cleaner power plants." EPA report, web-page updated on July 26, 2022. Available at website: https://www.epa.gov/mats/cleaner-power-plants Accessed 09/2023.

603 Ministry of the Environment, Japan, 2003. "Environmental performance indicators guideline for organizations." MOE, Fiscal Year 2002, April 2003 Report. Available at webpage: https://www.env.go.jp/policy/j-hiroba/PRG/pdfs/e_p_guide.pdf Accessed 09/2023.

604 Jonas Hagmann, 2011.

605 Ministry of the Environment, Japan, 2006. "Study report on comprehensive support strategies for environment and development in the early 21st century. Republic of Kazakhstan." Overseas Environmental Cooperation Center, Japan. Report available at webpage: https://www.env.go.jp/earth/coop/coop/document/c_report/kazakhstan_h17/english/pdf/000.pdf Accessed 09/2023.

606 H. Kanagawa, Y. Nakayama, 2020. ICLG Study "Japan: Environment & Climate Laws and Regulations 2020." Quote: "After the Fukushima nuclear power plant accident in March 2011 ('2011 Fukushima Accident'), all nuclear power plants in Japan temporarily stopped operations. Many injunction cases (including preliminary injunctions) have been

technology construction areas has been associated with precautionary measures[607] and safeguards mechanisms, which have been established in recent decades.[608] For instance, the maintenance and coordination overview processes run in high-level technology facilities - including the Fukushima Daiichi nuclear plant operations managed by TEPCO company - specifically after major earthquake and tsunami events, have to support unforeseen local risk emergency activities (e.g. health risk assessments),[609] which have also corresponded to the activation of rapid action-plans that can follow up according to internal engineering dynamics and computer adaptive testing models requiring continuous local implementation ([610]) ([611]). It is also important to highlight that "in the recovery period after a nuclear hazard, current exposure doses and possible future health effects are to be assessed based on assumptions as close as possible to the reality, using all information and measurement data available at that point in time."[612]

Additionally, disaster management factors about the Fukushima-Daiichi NPP 2011 events have included technical managerial defaults and

filed to prevent the plants from restarting. However, the judgments of the courts have differed." ICLG Japan, Published: 12-02-2020. Available at webpage: https://iclg.com/practice-areas/environment-and-climate-change-laws-and-regulations/japan Accessed 09/2023.

607 For example: In cases of heavy rain and typhoons, in 2020 the MOE in Japan has had to produce precautionary measures related to flood hazards in Fukushima prefecture while determining cooperative actions with municipalities involved. MOE, Japan, 2020. "The inspection results of large container bags for removed soil in Temporary Storage Sites (TSS) after heavy rain by typhoon Hagibis." Waste & Recycling news, March 17, 2020. Available at webpage: https://www.env.go.jp/en/headline/2440.html Accessed 09/2023.

608 Mohiuddin Ali Khan, 2013. "Earthquake-Resistant Structures. Design, Build, and Retrofit." ISBN: 978-85617-501-2. "Tsunamis, Earthquakes, and Nuclear Power." Chapter 6. Pp. 141-168. Elsevier Oxford.

609 Ministry of the Environment, Japan, 2018. "WHO Reports and UNSCEAR 2013 Report (1/3)." MOE, Japan, Chapter 5.1. booklet. Available at webpage: https://www.env.go.jp/en/chemi/rhm/basic-info/1st/pdf/basic-1st-05.pdf Accessed 09/2023.

610 Kenji Tateiwa, 2015. "Fukushima Daiichi Update." Nuclear Plant Journal, Volume 33, No. 3, May-June, pp. 32-35. https://digitaleditions.nuclearplantjournal.com/MJ15/files/assets/basic-html/index.html#32 Accessed 11/2023. Related info webpage: https://www.nrc.gov/docs/ML1604/ML16041A314.pdf Accessed 11/2023.

611 *Earthquake-Resistant Structures* 2013. ISBN: 978-85617-501-2.

612 Ministry of the Environment, Japan, 2018. "WHO Reports and UNSCEAR 2013 Report." MOE, Japan, Chapter 5.1. booklet. Page 191. *As of 11/2023*, quoted contents moved to page 189, with contextual rephrasing.

territorial emergency conditions that have compromised the knowledge coordination activity streamed at nuclear power reactors' sites.[613] As previously described, TEPCO's company operators[614] have disclosed a series of official statements specifying comparative technical lessons that have been learnt about local emergency maintenance operations of NPP's power reactors in the Fukushima prefecture, while also highlighting the critical importance of maintaining open communication channels made available to the public in the long-term.[615] Public awareness and nuclear energy technologies have been aligned within international cooperation agendas that have subscribed, over the last decades, environmental conservation programs, scaled down to regional governing frameworks responsive to action-led environmental protection measures.[616] However, there is to consider that the promotion of advanced risk management plans and implementation of environmental conservation measures have been reaffirmed in association with national technical investigations concerning the status of social health programs and safety risk awareness campaigning run across local municipalities ([617], [618]). In fact, the direct involvement of national health clusters as well as nuclear authorities in Japan, promoted by governmental prefectures and ministerial agencies, together with other civilian local parties such as social institutes or technical universities, has

613 *Earthquake-Resistant Structures* 2013. ISBN: 978-85617-501-2.

614 Note: TEPCO Company Overview of Kashiwazaki-Kariwa NPS Safety Measures: slide n. 4 "Compliance with Regulatory Standards from Terrorism to Natural Disasters. In compliance with new regulatory standards made by the Japanese Nuclear Regulatory Committed in July 2013, measures have been made against terrorism attacks and serious natural disasters such as earthquakes and tsunami." Available on website: https://www.tepco.co.jp/en/hd/ourbusiness/nuclear/kashiwazaki-kariwa/index-e.html Accessed 09/2023.

615 Kenji Tateiwa, 2015.

616 Ministry of the Environment, Japan, 1994. "Japan's action report on climate change." Environment Agency of Japan, First National Communication Report. Available at webpage: https://www.env.go.jp/content/900446355.pdf Accessed 09/2023.

617 Mike Hayes, 2016. "Cost of Fukushima nuclear disaster rises to $188 billion." International Construction, 14 December 2016. Website: https://www.international-construction.com/ (or) https://www.khl.com/news/cost-of-fukushima-nuclear-disaster-rises-to-188-bn/1123699.article Accessed 09/2023.

618 Justin McCurry, 2012. "World Report. Japan's Tohoku earthquake: 1 year on." The Lancet, World Report, Volume 379, No. 9819, 10th March, pp. 880-881. Available at website: https://www.thelancet.com/journals/lancet/article/PIIS0140-6736(12)60378-X/fulltext Accessed 11/2023.

signaled the need to foster social adaptation merged in post-crisis recovery dynamic scenarios involving comprehensive risk management assessments. At the same time, the local environmental reconstruction efforts have required continuous community interactions in order to better clarify local information exchanges regarding, for instance, radiological risks exposures levels and geological risk factors which might come into main evidence for programmatic actions ([619], [620]).

Similarly, financial future projections about international and national financial costs expected to surface in connection with the risk reduction implementation plans at NPPs, have retained concomitant financial internal /external schemes which include the nuclear decommissioning activities, as well as, the local environmental recovery costs and technical maintenance processes progressively operated in view of achieving specific technology and environmental targets (that have also pointed at an increasing amount of budget approximating from JPY 11 trillion ($95.7 billion) to 21,5 trillion yen ($188 billion).[621] In fact more updated figures produced from the Ministry of Economy, Trade and Industry (METI) have referred to JPY 21.5 trillion ($188 billion)[622] necessary to cover the costs of NPP environmental restoration programs, including the

[619] Justin McCurry, 2012.

[620] Mike Hayes, 2016. "Cost of Fukushima nuclear disaster rises to $188 billion."

[621] Stephen Stapczynski, and Ichiro Suzuki, 2016. "Japan Fukushima cost seen almost doubling to $188 Billion." Bloomberg-Quint news article, published 09/12/2016. Available at webpage: https://www.bloombergquint.com/business/japan-fukushima-cost-seen-nearly-doubling-to-21-5-trillion-yen Accessed 09/2023.

[622] Note: Updated news report 2022: "Around 12.1 trillion yen ($82 billion) has already been spent to deal with the 2011 disaster at the Fukushima No. 1 nuclear power plant, according to sources at the Board of Audit of Japan. That means more than half of the government's total estimated cost of 21.5 trillion yen, including compensation payments and reactor decommissioning expenses, has been used in the 11 years since the meltdowns occurred." Takaoki Yamamoto, 2022. "12.1 trillion yen spent so far on Fukushima nuclear disaster." the Asahi Shimbun, 7 November, 2022.

decommissioning and local compensation plans[623] set for the post-Fukushima Daiichi changing situation.[624]

International governance briefings have in particular highlighted the effects caused by direct environment risk impacts with constant human exposure to disaster risk factors, evidencing unforeseen conditions: e.g "a tremendously powerful offshore earthquake (9.0 on the Richter scale) triggered the tidal wave that reached more than 30 feet high in places on the country's east coast, flattening buildings, sweeping over Sendai's airport and causing a disastrous failure at the Fukushima Daiichi nuclear power plant. Ultimately more than 15,800 people were killed, 10,000 of them in Miyagi prefecture where Sendai is located…"[625] Similar national dramatic experiences that connect to leading causes of major nuclear disaster accidents such as the Chernobyl's tragic case, have essentially advanced a common state of public uncertainty despite the production of international risk hazard estimation studies related to transnational technological disaster crisis ([626], [627], [628]). To add to these issues, that experimental methodologies as probabilistic risk assessments (PRA)[629]

623 Reuters Agency Staff: Yuka Obayashi, Kentaro Hamada, 2016. "Japan doubles Fukushima disaster-related cost to $188bln." Quotation: "The new estimate calls for 7.9 trillion yen for compensation, 4 trillion yen for decontamination, 8 trillion yen for decommissioning, and 1.6 trillion yen for the interim storage facility, the ministry said in a statement." Reuters-Utilities-Electric, published 9/12/2016. Available at webpage: https://www.reuters.com/article/tepco-fukushima-costs-idUST9N1DC00J Accessed 09/2023.

624 Mike Hayes, 2016. "Cost of Fukushima nuclear disaster rises to $188 billion."

625 Rob Verger, 2014. "Three years after." Big Shots, March, pp. 1-2. Copyright of Newsweek Global property of Newsweek L.L.C.

626 Najmedin Meshkati, 2011. "Nuclear Lessons." Notebooks, Technology Review, June 21, Issue: July-August, pp. 8-9. Copyright of Technology Review is the property of Massachusetts Institute of Technology (MIT).

627 Andrew Thatcher, Ana C. Vasconcelos, David Ellis, 2015. "An investigation into the impact of information behavior on information failure: The Fukushima Daiichi nuclear power disaster." International Journal of Information Management, Volume 35, No. 1, pp. 57-63.

628 Scott Peterson, 2012. "The right response." Electric Perspectives, May-June, pp. 76-89. Copyright of Electric Perspectives is the property of Edison Electric Institute Inc. Available at website: https://lsc-pagepro.mydigitalpublication.com/publication/?m=6643&i=113534&p=78&ver=html5 Accessed 11/2023.

629 University of Maryland, 2020. "Assessing natural hazard risks to nuclear facilities." Division of Research, University of Maryland, Headlines article. Available at webpage: https://spac.umd.edu/news/story/assessing-natural-hazard-risks-to-nuclear-facilities Accessed 09/2023.

and resulting multilevel decisional approaches can still expand performance knowledge schemes, prioritizing inclusive strategies that meet concurrent environment investigative requirements.[630]

In Japan's case, the rapid emergency coordination and control management becoming functional in connection to complex energy automated systems of NPPs, have been independently monitored by nuclear energy companies that have been put in charge of local maintenance and supporting operations at the NPPs. [631] For decontamination projects both mechanization and automation procedures have entailed systematic financial measures planned in the short-term period. [632] The resulting coordination mechanisms for the post-crisis recovery phases have progressively converged into trials and errors controlling operations that public-private energy companies and local governmental agencies[633] have decided to implement in order to assess responsive planning activities completed at the local NPPs, ([634], [635]). For the 'Common Specifications' addressing decontamination issues, MOE's workers "[...] continued to improve the specifications step-by-step according to actual conditions of the decontamination sites through a trial and error process,"[636] obtaining responsive feedbacks at the same time.

630 University of Maryland, 2020. "Assessing natural hazard risks to nuclear facilities."
631 Najmedin Meshkati, 2011.
632 Ministry of the Environment, Japan, 2015. "FY2014 Decontamination Report." A compilation of experiences to date on decontamination for the living environment conducted by the MOE. Full report available at webpage: http://josen.env.go.jp/en/policy_document/pdf/decontamination_report1503_full.pdf Accessed 09/2023.
633 Note: Agency for Natural Resources and Energy, Ministry of Economy, Trade and industry, 2019. "Important Stories on Decommissioning 2019." Quotation "Fukushima Prefecture has formulated a Region-wide Evacuation Plan covering 13 municipalities around the nuclear power station, which details the methods of communicating information and the evacuation sites and routes to be used by each municipality. Also, each municipality has established a district-specific evacuation plan. In addition, Fukushima Prefecture and the 13 municipalities have concluded an agreement with TEPCO, so that they will be notified immediately in the event of any anomalies at the power station." Report on Fukushima Daiichi Nuclear Power Station, now and in the future, page 10. Available at webpage: https://www.meti.go.jp/earthquake/nuclear/hairo_osensui/images/reactorpamph2019en.pdf Accessed 09/2023.
634 Najmedin Meshkati, 2011.
635 Scott Peterson, 2012.
636 Ministry of the Environment, Japan, 2015. "FY2014 Decontamination Report." Page 75.

In addition, there is to consider that the situation experienced at Daiichi nuclear power plant during months which followed major tsunami-related disaster events, tended to improve despite a comparable lack of reliable basic information e.g. about public health effects of radiation[637] affecting the local and national populations ([638], [639]). In more recent reports have instead emerged comparative reviews about local risk safety management,[640] common environmental recovery plans,[641] and local safeguards measures diffusion,[642] which have been aggregated in connection with civic environmental adaptation norms. While the presence of uncertain factors in common regional coordination plans has been traced in either direct or indirect local sustainable interactions for qualified knowledge and information exchanging activities, undertaken through shared ICTs network services ([643], [644]). As such, the possible integration of enhanced information through environmental impact assessment (EIA) system[645] becomes functional to the promotion of public education trainings and networked energy conservation policies for sustainable environments.

637 Ministry of the Environment, Japan, 2013."BOOKLET to provide basic information regarding health effects of radiation." MOE, 2nd Edition, Chapter 5, 'Assessments by International Organizations' UNSCEAR 2013 Report (9/9) Comparison with Direct Measurements. Available at webpage: https://www.env.go.jp/en/chemi/rhm/basic-info/1st/05-03-09.html Accessed 09/2023.
638 Andrew Thatcher, Ana C. Vasconcelos, David Ellis, 2015.
639 Scott Peterson, 2012.
640 Jonathan M. Samet, Dayana Chanson, 2015. "Fukushima Daiichi Power Plant Disaster: How many people were affected? 2015 Report." Green Cross, Reliefweb, published 11/03/2015. Available at webpage: https://reliefweb.int/sites/reliefweb.int/files/resources/2015_fukushima_report.pdf Accessed 09/2023.
641 Thisanka Siripala, 2020. "Japan's 3/11 recovery stalled by Fukushima decommissioning delays." The Diplomat, Tokyo Report, Environment, East Asia. Published 13/03/2020. Available at website: https://thediplomat.com/2020/03/japans-3-11-recovery-stalled-by-fukushima-decommissioning-delays/ Accessed 09/2023.
642 IAEA International Atomic Energy Agency, 2020. "Information, June 2012, 2020. Fukushima Daiichi Nuclear Power Station until March. Status Updates." Available at webpage: https://www.iaea.org/sites/default/files/20/06/fukushima_update_12june2020.pdf Accessed 09/2023.
643 Andrew Thatcher, Ana C. Vasconcelos, David Ellis, 2015.
644 Scott Peterson, 2012.
645 Ministry of the Environment, Japan, 2012. "Recent development of environmental policies in Japan." MOE Report, '1. The Recovery from The Great East Japan Earthquake.' Available at webpage: https://www.env.go.jp/en/focus/docs/files/20120925-20.pdf Accessed 09/2023.

In other words, the institutional coordination agreements undertaken by public-private nuclear industry operators based in Japan have been structured in view of promoting diversified programmatic information procedures within municipal bureaus, through technological infrastructure developed in modified stages, which have essentially required rapid and consistent local assessments, as well as, local safety procedures involving contingency measures adopted by local authorities and NGOs coordination groups,[646] accordingly put in charge of providing advisory information to citizens involved ([647], [648]). For these reasons, environmental preservation programs related to the Fukushima prefecture [649] have promoted systematic collaboration, including national governmental entities and regional research groups.

There is to say, on the other hand, that national logistic operations associated with local technical provisions planned in case of environmental disaster crises, have remained interlinked with collaborative exchanging modes of multilevel information systems. For the case of disaster waste management, [650] local adaptive measures correspond to action-led initiatives that still rely on national guidelines and international cooperation with partner institutions involved in disaster waste post-planning progress and regional preparedness schemes.[651]

Through a broader understanding, systematic monitoring information networks and NGO coordination initiatives have had to integrate

[646] Japan Platform, 2020. "Japan: Earthquake & Tsunami. Situation Report 8 April 2011." Report produced by the JP in cooperation with Japan NGO Center for International Cooperation (JANIC). Available at webpage: https://www.japanplatform.org/E/jpf_janic/jpf_janic_20110408.pdf (or) https://www.japanplatform.org/ Accessed 09/2023.

[647] Scott Peterson, 2012.

[648] Najmedin Meshkati, 2011.

[649] Ministry of the Environment, Japan, 2017. "FY2016 JCM feasibility study for low-carbon city in Ayeyarwady Region Study of a low-carbon waste treatment system in Pathein Industrial City." Report, Appendix, Mitsubishi Research Institute, Inc. & Fujita Corporation. Available at webpage: https://www.env.go.jp/earth/coop/lowcarbon-asia/english/project/data/EN_MMR_2016_04-2.pdf Accessed 09/2023.

[650] Ministry of the Environment, Japan, 2022. "Partnerships & information-sharing with international institutions." Archive of Technical References related to Disaster Waste Management Guideline for Asia and the Pacific, March 11, 2022. Available at webpage: http://kouikishori.env.go.jp/en/international_organizations_cooperation/ Accessed 09/2023.

[651] Ministry of the Environment, Japan, 2022. "Partnerships & information-sharing with international institutions."

constructively the work undertaken by local technical regulators, national or international nuclear energy experts, management industrial partners, and district-level population bureaus, which have maintained comprehensive knowledge sharing transfers while fostering applicable transparency approaches, which in the long-term can influence as well local environmental safety outcomes for larger communities ([652]).

Specifically about the private nuclear energy operators in Japan, national information agencies have also been involved with the preparation of updated scientific reports that have provided contradictory signals in terms of common risk preparedness plans,[653] public direct accesses to ICT information platforms,[654] or local risk assessment problems, when related to common risk and safety coordination plans and regulatory adaptation processes in NPP sites ([655], [656], [657]). To clarify impending organization barriers, it is explicated that "the much vilified operator of the tsunami-hit nuclear power plant at Fukushima [...] asserts that government interference in the disaster response created confusion and delays [...] new details of the disaster have emerged that build a picture of an organization that ignored or concealed that its reactors might be vulnerable to quakes and tsunamis, used its close links with regulators and nuclear experts to hijack nuclear policy [...] has worked vigilantly to shut out close scrutiny of the ravaged plant's condition [...]."[658] In order to

652 Andrew Thatcher, Ana C. Vasconcelos, David Ellis, 2015.

653 Kohta Juraku, 2016. "Deficits of Japanese nuclear risk governance remaining after the Fukushima accident: Case of contaminated water management." In Earthquakes, Tsunamis and Nuclear Risks, pp.157-169. Quote: "It was found that many deficits of nuclear risk governance in Japan before and after the Fukushima accident. Not only were they created and embedded before the Fukushima disaster, but it has been remained or even worsened even after many accident reports were published and pointed out many problems and suggested ideas to remedy them." Earthquakes, Tsunamis and Nuclear Risks, abstract text.

654 William H. Saito, 2017. "What Fukushima disaster taught me about risk management in cybersecurity." Forbes, published 20/04/2017. Available at webpage: https://www.forbes.com/sites/williamsaito/2017/04/20/what-fukushima-disaster-taught-me-about-risk-management-in-cybersecurity/?sh=5e7cc3fd681e Accessed 09/2023.

655 Najmedin Meshkati, 2011

656 Scott Peterson, 2012.

657 Andrew Thatcher, Ana C. Vasconcelos, David Ellis, 2015.

658 Hiroko Tabuchi, 2012. "Nuclear operator in Japan exonerates itself in report." New York Times edition, Today's Paper, page 6, June 21, 2012. Available at webpage: https://www.nytimes.com/2012/06/21/world/asia/tepco-operator-of-fukushima-exonerates-itself-in-report.html Accessed 09/2023.

restore institutional confidence with the public, regarding the municipal risk radiation exposure dimension, progressive post-Fukushima periodic monitoring information shared about nuclear management industry promoting systematic recovery action plans, in order to contain the Daiichi NPP technical management problems - such as water leakages, or structural electric errors - has been focused on major comprehensive disaster causes as well as on local environmental impacts;[659] the nuclear risk governance areas have essentially required technical cooperation, as well as, prioritization of consistent interactions involving local community's feedbacks. About the restart process of NPP Tsuruga in Fukui Prefecture, unreliable nuclear safety assessments have emerged as "[...] in February 2020, the nuclear regulator said Japan Atomic Power had been found to have rewritten data analyzing a drilling survey conducted on an area below the Tsuruga complex premises without approval. [...] In seeking approval to reboot the reactor under stricter regulations imposed following the 2011 Fukushima nuclear accident, Japan Atomic Power has been trying to disprove geological expert opinion, published in March 2015, that the fault is active."[660] Since then, in 2022 the NRA Japan Nuclear Regulatory Authority has reopened Tsuruga NPP safety conditional assessments for the activation of NPP reactor n. 2 located in the Fukui Prefecture.[661]

In changing terms, common performance criteria regarding nuclear energy automation systems retracing previous comprehensive adaptation programs for the enhancement of cooperation and collaboration - in particular about NPPs safeguards systems - have remained a constant especially regarding local risk management intertwined with uncertain factors related to control evaluation, and monitoring responsive actions.

[659] Ministry of the Environment, Japan, 2018 "Comprehensive radiation monitoring plan and information disclosure." MOE, 2018 report, Chapter 7, 'Spatiotemporal distribution of ambient dose rates.' Available at webpage: https://www.env.go.jp/en/chemi/rhm/basic-info/1st/pdf/basic-1st-07-01-01.pdf Accessed 09/2023.

[660] Nikkei Asia, 2021. "Japan watchdog halts Tsuruga nuclear safety assessments." Nikkei Asia, August 18, 2021. Available at webpage: https://asia.nikkei.com/Business/Energy/Japan-watchdog-halts-Tsuruga-nuclear-safety-assessment (or) https://www.japantimes.co.jp/news/2023/04/05/national/tsuruga-reactor-safety-assessment-halt/ Accessed 09/2023.

[661] Huaxia, 2022. "Japan's NRA to resume Tsuruga nuclear safety assessment." Xinhua News, October 27, 2022. Available at webpage: https://english.news.cn/20221027/550f1dec6fce40d58c13844e4b0e0353/c.html Accessed 09/2023.

([662],[663]). In addition, it has remained relevant the verification of common information networks and local ICT media platforms that should be able to address multilateral requests formulated from centralized and decentralized stakeholders due to Japan's multiple disaster risk cases; governmental disaster risk plans have also corresponded to dynamic undertakings that have been based on a national safety culture symbolizing stratified social values that reappear at critical times ([664]). Concerning safety recognition patterns, the NRA Japan highlights "national culture can be a factor affecting the performance of the organization both positively and negatively. Sacrifice seen in the Fukushima accident is one of the key diagnostic signal about an organization's resilience."[665]

Under consequential circumstances, the post-Fukushima hard testing ground has remained intertwined with the formation of national safety characteristics, including knowledge legitimization,[666] while mediating public environmental and health protection concerns and territorial safeguarded interests, particularly emerging in view of local reconstruction efforts ([667], [668], [669]). On the one hand, there has been the

662 Peter Behr, 2012. "Interview: Yoichi Funabashi. Lessons from Fukushima." Nieman Reports, Fall 2012, pp. 21-23. Copyright of Neiman Reports is property of Nieman Reports. Available at website: https://niemanreports.org/articles/lessons-from-fukushima/ Accessed 11/2023.

663 Robert Henry, 2013. "Exploring Fukushima to the nth degree." Nuclear Plant Journal, January-February, Volume 31, No. 1, pp. 28-30. Available at website: https://digitaleditions.nuclearplantjournal.com/JF13/files/assets/basic-html/index.html#page28 Accessed 11/2023.

664 Peter Behr, 2012. "Interview: Yoichi Funabashi. Lessons from Fukushima."

665 Hiroko Koike, 2014. "Survey on Japanese culture related to safety culture." Nuclear Regulation Authority (NRA) Japan. Workshop on Global Safety Culture - National Factors Relevant to Safety Culture, Presentation Paper, 8-11 April, 2014. Page 22. Available at webpage: https://gnssn.iaea.org/NSNI/SC/WS_GSC/Presentations/04%20Koike_Hiroko_Survey%20of%20Japanese%20Culture%20Related%20to%20Safety%20Culture.pdf Accessed 09/2023.

666 See: Johan Berglund, 2020. "After Fukushima: Safety culture and fostering critical thinking." Safety Science, Volume 124, April 2020, 104613.

667 Stephane Thibierge, 2012. "Fukushima, la vie après." Art-Press, Volume 423, pp. 72-75. Copyright of Art-Press is the property of Art-Press (International).

668 Takao Suami, 2015. "Legal support to Fukushima municipalities: Law school, lawyers, and nuclear disaster victims." Asian-Pacific Law & Policy Journal, Volume 16, No. 2, pp. 158-185. Available at webpage: http://manoa.hawaii.edu/aplpj/wp-content/uploads/sites/120/2016/01/APLPJ_16.2_Suami.pdf Accessed 11/2023.

669 Winifred Bird, 2016. "Living in limbo." Earth Island Journal, Spring, pp. 31-36. Copyright of Earth Island Journal is property of Earth Island Institute. Available at

need to better understand a collective state of individual exposures to local emergency mobilization dynamics and to a sudden transition combined with common resettlement and reconstruction action-plans, which have been questioned number of times because of the consequences of multiple risk-based energy management projects influencing, for instance, nuclear workers' health safety conditions. Important to remember that "[...] it would be estimated that approximately 24,000 people, whose original living areas have been designated as Areas where Returning is Difficult, still remain evacuated; and a proportion of the evacuees has already resettled in other places and has shown no intention to return to their original houses."[670] Therefore for such reasons, a critical safety awareness has emerged in comparative regional ecosystems that point at disaster risk protection policies recommended for long-term governmental compliance schemes.

Similarly, on the other hand, the nuclear industry remediation plans in Japan have been revisited under enhanced national attention, especially in view of emergent legal community coalitions that have demanded legal compensation claims and re-discussed about residential displacement controversies,[671] which have appeared in more recent years.[672] As for responsive environments, in order to support local reconstruction efforts, Japanese decentralized bureaus have emphasized among other main priorities: 1. to adopt an equal access approach while engaging central authorities at the local level; 2. to act in constructive ways through collaborative projects that lead to a complete rebuilding of local affected areas; 3. to act independently through self-help groups while supporting village level resettlement issues.[673] In fact, at the prefecture level, leading

webpage: https://www.earthisland.org/journal/index.php/magazine/entry/living_in_limbo Accessed 11/2023.

[670] IAEA, 2017. "Summary Report. The 3rd IAEA-MOE experts meeting on environmental remediation." Tokyo, Minami-Soma City, Date City, 17-21 April 2017. Page 1. Available at webpage: http://josen.env.go.jp/en/news/pdf/news_170417_01.pdf Accessed 09/2023.

[671] Paul Jobin, 2020. "The Fukushima nuclear disaster and civil actions as a social movement." The Asia-Pacific Journal, Japan Focus, Volume 18, Issue 9, Number 1. Available at webpage: https://apjjf.org/2020/9/Jobin.html Accessed 09/2023.

[672] Stephane Thibierge, 2012.

[673] Ministry of the Environment, Japan, 2018. "Decontamination projects for radioactive contamination discharged by Tokyo Electric Company Fukushima Daiichi Nuclear Power

regulatory bodies have promoted technical community practice guidelines established by concerned local authorities. Substantially, the public and private attention turned on national local reconstruction plans and civic legal orientations, has determined both popular and unpopular reactions concerning the nuclear power industry in Japan, while assisting on the association of newly formed civic protest movements. [674] During decontamination projects, each different municipality did experience progressive reconstruction measures however according to alternated circumstances that have directly impacted on municipal groups' rebuilding stages, due to the changing situation found at the time. [675] In essence, the affirmation of democratic practices and collective indications aligned in order to provide support on anti-nuclear environmental positions, has emerged in national as well as in local institutional environments, including decentralized public coordination entities. [676] Basically the continued presence of additional risks related to national consumption modes that include food distribution practices, health risk assessments, and disaster risk exposures, [677] has guided toward the formulation of provisional regulative measures able to implement risk assessment plans that rely on multi-level institutional cooperation and participation of field organizations, involving multi-party stakeholders. [678]

Station Accident." MOE Report, Editorial Committee for the Paper on Decontamination Projects, March 2018, Page 9-10. Available at webpage: http://josen.env.go.jp/en/policy_document/pdf/decontamination_report1807_01.pdf Accessed 09/2023.

[674] Paul Jobin, 2013. "The Roadmap for Fukushima Daiichi and the sacrifice of Japan's clean-up workers." The Asia-Pacific Journal, Japan Focus. Volume 11, Issue 28, Number 2. Available at webpage: https://apjjf.org/2013/11/28/Paul-Jobin/3967/article.html Accessed 09/2023.

[675] Ministry of the Environment, Japan, 2018. "Decontamination projects for radioactive contamination discharged by Tokyo Electric Company Fukushima Daiichi Nuclear Power Station Accident."

[676] Winifred Bird, 2016.

[677] Ministry of the Environment, Japan, 2020. "Setting of standard limits for radioactive materials in foods and distribution/consumption restrictions." Booklet to Provide Basic Information Regarding Health Effects of Radiation, 2nd edition, Chapter 8: Radioactive Materials in Foods. Report available at webpage: https://www.env.go.jp/en/chemi/rhm/basic-info/1st/08-01-01.html Accessed 09/2023.

[678] Hrabrin Bachev, 2019. "Assessment of preparedness and agri-food impacts of Fukushima nuclear accident: Implications for improvement of disaster risk management." Disaster, Diversity and Emergency Preparation L.I. Magnussen (Ed.). Open Access by IOS Press.

In sum, public-private regulatory interactions concurrently pursued for the actual preparation of environmental energy proposals[679] and community organizational plans arranged during months following the disaster recovery activities, have essentially pointed to a series of regulatory development issues, concerning technology security adaptation and local information processes, also involving the prioritization of environmental supporting agreements[680] applied across different municipalities[681] - e.g. through implementation of effective partnerships with national agencies and local regulatory partners assigned to enhance responsive disaster planning at community level.[682] For instance, at prefecture level, technical coordination practices arranged for emergency reconstruction efforts, undertaken in specific disaster zones, have been supported by local educational information centres in order to allow for cooperative mediation activities, also in cases of local environmental disputes.[683]

In retrospective view, social mobilization factors that emerge through co-management practices or the formation of community trained organizations,[684] associated with disaster management zones occurrences have basically stimulated the reassessment of local development plans and corresponding national financial reviews drafted in connection with decentralized costing provisions, which have become available for the distribution of public reconstruction programs, targeting local

[679] Benjamin C. McLellan, Qi Zhang, N. Agya Utama, Hooman Farzaneh, and Keiichi N. Ishihara, 2013. "Analysis of Japan's post-Fukushima energy strategy." Energy Strategy Reviews, Volume 2, No. 2, pages 190-198.

[680] Ministry of the Environment, 2020. "About the conclusion of 'Cooperative Cooperation Agreement on future-oriented environmental measures for reconstruction of Fukushima...that challenges from the environment, and hope for the future." Japanese Government information, published 27/08/2020. Available at website: https://www.gov-base.info/en/2020/08/27/125124 (or) https://www.gov-base.info/ Accessed 09/2023.

[681] Winifred Bird, 2016.

[682] Ministry of the Environment, Japan, 2022. "Disaster waste management information site." Webpage on State of Disaster Waste Treatment & Archives, Cabinet Office Disaster Management Information. Available at website: http://kouikishori.env.go.jp/en/ Accessed 09/2023.

[683] Takao Suami, 2015.

[684] Md. Tariqul Islam, 2013. "People's participation in protected areas of Bangladesh." APC 1st Asia Parks Congress, Japan 2013, Parks Connect., Presentation. Available at webpage: https://www.env.go.jp/en/nature/asia-parks/pdf/wg3/APC_WG4-26_Md.%20 Tariqul%20Islam.pdf Accessed 10/2023.

collectivities differently affected by environmental contamination[685] in local disaster areas.[686] To this type of ecosystem, there have been into consideration legal modifying aspects about safety regulation proposals and intertwined managerial processes concerning local construction buildings, which have to refer to technical protection codes; for instance: national compensation laws have been applied in Japan's case to the responsible TEPCO energy company, managing the nuclear disaster facilities' responsive reconstruction cycles ([687], [688]). As international comparative best practices, it is emphasized about "energy standards for buildings [that] [...] the federal government [U.S.] participates in the code development process, including provision of extensive analysis of proposed provisions; must adopt codes for its own buildings that are at least as stringent as the professional standard; [...] States must either certify that they have reviewed new code versions, or that they have adopted them."[689]

About environmental cohesive initiatives for best practices, it can be added that civilian engagements undertaken by local emergency action groups have stimulated democratic symposiums[690] about the formation of practical emergency guidelines, underlining an essential primary attention

685 Ministry of the Environment, 2020. Quote: "The Ministry of the Environment has been working on the environmental restoration of Fukushima since 2012, such as decontamination and treatment of special waste." Japanese Government information, published 27/08/2020. Available at webpage: https://www.gov-base.info/en/2020/08/27/125124 (This original web-link dated 2020.08.27 is not available as of 10/2023). MOE Gov Base Archive currently available at this webpage: https://www.gov-base.info/page/15?s=Fukushima Accessed 10/2023.

686 Takao Suami, 2015.

687 Takao Suami, 2015.

688 Winifred Bird, 2016.

689 Ministry of the Environment, Japan, 2000. "Detailed description of best practices. United States of America No. 2." G8 Environmental Futures Forum 2000 on "Domestic Best Practices Addressing Climate Change." Full Report available at webpage: https://www.env.go.jp/earth/g8_2000/forum/g8bp/detail/usa/usa02.html Accessed 10/2023.

690 Ministry of the Environment, 2020. Quote: "...Fukushima Prefecture and the Ministry of the Environment cooperate to promote the active participation of a wide range of citizens, companies, municipalities, etc. by holding symposiums and recommending good practices." Japanese Government information, published 27/08/2020. Available at webpage: https://www.gov-base.info/en/2020/08/27/125124 (This original web-link dated 2020.08.27 is not available as of 10/2023). MOE Gov Base Archive currently available at this webpage: https://www.gov-base.info/page/15?s=Fukushima Accessed 10/2023.

to be given to national safety and security awareness promoted across local prefectures, as well as, environmental administrative bureaus, facilitating the diffusion of national reconstruction plans, when based on credible environmental evaluative and monitoring assessments ([691],[692]).

Besides, the initiation of collective anti-risks protection initiatives promoted by civil society groups, national educators, industry development officers, and local prefectures as in Japan's case, has served to acknowledge respective public barriers or political boundaries, while enhancing independent networking interactions, particularly in view of facilitating environmental reconstruction efforts, as well as, environmental awareness campaigns centred on renewable energy programs, particularly validated in connection with technology adaptation plans and local anti-disaster measures.[693] Regionally-based ministerial meetings have also solicited the implementation of disaster environment policies based on cooperative networking platforms allowing countries to engage in multilevel IT assistance coordination efforts for reduction of environmental degradation, as well as for the use of preventive monitoring technologies introduced in cases of decentralized environmental interventions.[694] Science-based research institutions have effectively referred to eventual progressive limitations observed within local contingency planning schemes, in case of a nuclear power station NPS disaster crisis, despite the development of safety precautionary measures[695] that for example, TEPCO company has continuously

[691] Takao Suami, 2015.
[692] Winifred Bird, 2016.
[693] Winifred Bird, 2016.
[694] Yuichiro Takahashi, 2016. "Results of the 18th tripartite environment ministers meeting among Korea, China and Japan (TEMM18)." Japan Environment Quarterly (JEQ), Volume 14, August 2016. Available at webpage: https://www.env.go.jp/en/focus/jeq/issue/vol14/topics2.html#c1 Accessed 10/2023.
[695] C. Pistner, M. Englert, 2017. "Nuclear power and nuclear safety post Fukushima." Institute for Applied Ecology, Oko-Institut e.V. DPG-AKE-AGA: Nuclear Energy and Security, Munster, 29/03/2017. Available at webpage: https://www.oeko.de/fileadmin/oekodoc/DPG_Nuclear_Safety.pdf

explored through different probabilistic methodologies and quantitative modulation analyses ([696],[697]) for NPS.[698]

As point of reference, at country-level, Japan has already been exposed to technological nuclear hazards and complex industrial related accidents, which have been contained through public-private collaborative agencies' working efforts deepened with pressing operating tasks managed nationally and internationally by nuclear safety agencies such as: the U.S. based NRC, and Japan Atomic Energy Agency JAEA, with respective governmental officials.[699] Despite the existence of previous contingency plans and local safety assessments, the 2011 nuclear industrial meltdowns at NPS prompted both international scientists and regional public organizations to demand for accountable reporting indications and mutual information transparency of national communication systems detailing in parallel with nuclear industry representatives, and TEPCO operating agencies.[700] Further decisional supporting processes directed at the enhancement of technical disaster management areas - including local safety and protection plans set in connection to nuclear technology industries - have led to the improvement of common knowledge environments, related with technical regulatory services and concurrent normative applications, specifically focused on local management routes and environmental risk assessment guidelines ([701],[702]).

In addition, it has been argued that a systematic national transition to comprehensive regulatory energy approaches can primarily lead toward

696 Akira Nakamura, Masao Kikuchi, 2011. "What we know, and what we have not yet learned: Triple disasters and the Fukushima nuclear fiasco in Japan." Public Administration Review, Volume 71, No. 6, (November-December 2011), pp. 893-899.

697 John Downer, 2014. "Disowning Fukushima: Managing the credibility of nuclear reliability assessment in the wake of disaster." Regulation & Governance, Volume 8, No. 3, pp. 287-309.

698 TEPCO, 2022. "Safety measures of nuclear power station." Tokyo Electric Power Company, Power Supply Facilities, 'Creating disaster-resistant nuclear power station.' Full news report available at website: https://www.tepco.co.jp/en/challenge/csr/nuclear/stations-e.html Accessed 10/2023.

699 Akira Nakamura, Masao Kikuchi, 2011.

700 Akira Nakamura, Masao Kikuchi, 2011.

701 Akira Nakamura, Masao Kikuchi, 2011.

702 John Downer, 2014.

more accurate quantitative and qualitative local predictions, which have increased the public attention in terms of nuclear risk factors of NPP industrial accidents and local operational uses of multiple engineering systems; this route has also shown a potential fragmentation in both managerial and administrative conducts, regarding either centralized or decentralized renewable energy acquisitions ([703], [704]). For instance, at international ministerial meetings focused on climate energy sustainability[705] in an inductive way, they do refer to 'ecosystem-based approaches'[706] that can link urban-rural living environments through the implementation of renewable energy infrastructures dependent on public-private partnerships, as well as, on diversity of local services provision which entail increasing efficiency standards and local system adaptive performances.

Essentially, some foundational aspects about the integration of technological management coordination through territorial participatory assessments, related to national disaster crisis transitions, have been debated in connection to the existence of historical lessons to be learnt from previous severe emergency crises such as: the Hiroshima and Nagasaki II World War nuclear emergency cases; therefore for basic reasons, progressive anti-disaster sustainable adaptation plans managed in association with local risk awareness environments, while supported through national information platforms[707] and networked communication

[703] Takashi Kuroda, 2016. "10 Lessons from Fukushima. Reducing risks and protecting communities from nuclear disasters." Fukushima Booklet Committee. pp. 1-72. Available at website: http://fukushimalessons.jp Accessed 11/2023.

[704] John Downer, 2014.

[705] Ministry of the Environment, Japan, 2021. "Annex I. Recommendations for ocean energy and offshore renewables accelerated development and deployment." ANNEXES Joint G20 Energy-Climate Ministerial Communiqué, July 23, 2021. "Energy Transition and Climate Sustainability Working Groups." Annexes available at webpage: https://www.env.go.jp/press/files/jp/116565.pdf (or) https://www.meti.go.jp/press/2021/07/20210726010/20210726010-1.pdf Accessed 10/2023.

[706] Ministry of t he Environment, Japan, 2021. "Annex I. Recommendations for ocean energy and offshore renewables accelerated development and deployment."

[707] Note: The METI report recalls that "[...] the Cabinet of Japan approved the 'National Plan for Adaptation to the Impacts of Climate Change' in November 2015. Since then, concerted efforts have been taken by the entire government for promotion of adaptation measures in the country." METI, 2017. "Climate change adaptation good practices by Japanese private sector." page 2. Booklet compiled by METI of Japan's "Fiscal Year 2017 Climate Change Adaptation Effect Visualization Project [...]" by Mitsubishi UFJ Morgan

systems, have entailed systematic policy reviews granting potential access for the establishment of local organizational opportunities ([708],[709],[710]). In order to accomodate formal requests[711] for the organization of evaluative and monitoring systems to avoid regional environmental hazards and loss of human life, technology channeled trials for anti-disaster risk scenarios have been planned at the local level in order to analyse risk exposure conditions e.g. floods, loss of energy power, etc., in cases of local reconstruction and protection of local infrastructures, tackled among preventive security priorities.[712]

Under similar conditions, state development with advanced standardization procedures for multi-layered automation cycles of energy performing systems, has been analytically reconsidered due to functional modified criteria that are identified in relation with environmental awareness assessments ([713], [714]). Institutional performance reviews conducted by national, as well as, by international governance experts about remaining open challenges of automated energy systems[715] such as: low-carbonization standards; energy demand increases; renewable energy

Stanley Securities Co., the project consultant. Available at webpage: https://www.sc.mufg.jp/english/company/news/000014701.pdf Accessed 10/2023.

708 John Downer, 2014.

709 Takashi Kuroda, 2016.

710 Akira Nakamura, Masao Kikuchi, 2011.

711 METI, 2017. "Climate change adaptation good practices by Japanese private sector." Ministry of Economy, Trade and Industry, METI, Japan. Report, November 2017. Available at webpage: http://copjapan.env.go.jp/cop23/event_en/nov15/pdf/Climate_Change_Adaptation_Good_Practices_by_Japanese_Private_Sector_en.pdf Accessed 10/2023.

712 METI, 2017. "Climate change adaptation good practices by Japanese private sector."

713 Kara Schmitt, 2012. "Automations influence on nuclear power plants: A look at three accidents and how automation played a role." Work, Volume 41, pp. 4545-4551. IOS Press.

714 David Skeen, 2013. "Fukushima, a game changer." Nuclear Plant Journal, Volume 31, No. 3, May-June 2013, pp. 22-24. Available at webpage: https://nuclearplantjournal.com/uploads/digital/MJ13.pdf Accessed 11/2023.

715 The JT Editorial Board, 2020. "Following the crowd, Suga makes a bold climate pledge." Quote: "The energy grid must be transformed. New modalities of power generation, delivery and storage are required. In addition to reducing the use of coal, the government is looking at solar, wind and hydrogen technologies. While cognizant of the public relations problems surrounding nuclear energy, the government is reluctant to reduce its commitment to that technology." The Japan Times, published on 29/10/2020. Available at webpage: https://www.japantimes.co.jp/opinion/2020/10/29/editorials/following-crowd-suga-makes-bold-climate-pledge/ Accessed 10/2023.

generation facilities efficiency;[716] have pointed at the constitution of local technical procedures that have been monitored in parallel with ex. nuclear facilities' isolation and optimization conditions. Essentially technical energy field operators have had necessarily to conform to subsequent organizational transitions ([717], [718]). In connection to such development aspects, industrial energy performances and regional automation contexts have called public attention on the direct application of functional methodologies, through which the centralized roles and responsibilities of principal operators managing, for instance, local NPPs assessment projects, have been reconfigured in view of promoting innovation changing designs of complex automated systems, that have still to depend on local collaborative outcomes, and productive interactions supporting overall decision-making responsive environments.[719] But at the same time, the facilitation of low carbon economies has also meant a potential shift toward functional management systems rearranging post-disaster crisis partnerships in energy investment markets opening regionally and nationally.[720]

About the post-Fukushima industrial emergency - e.g. water pollution abnormalities[721] - at the nuclear power facilities, technical assessment reviews produced by international nuclear agencies and specialized nuclear experts have identified explicable safety weaknesses related to key technical requirements of different risk control areas,[722] which have been

[716] Ministry of the Environment, Japan, 2021. "Practical guide for Scenario Analysis in line with the TCFD recommendations 3rd edition." MOE, Climate Change Policy Division. Report available at: https://www.env.go.jp/content/900498777.pdf Accessed 10/2023.

[717] Kara Schmitt, 2012.

[718] David Skeen, 2013. "Fukushima, a game changer." Nuclear Plant Journal.

[719] Kara Schmitt, 2012.

[720] Ministry of the Environment, Japan, 2021. "Practical guide for scenario analysis in line with the TCFD recommendations 3rd edition."

[721] Takatoshi Wako, 2012. "Industrial wastewater management in Japan." Environment Management Bureau, Ministry of the Environment, Japan. Technical Report available at webpage: https://www.env.go.jp/en/focus/docs/files/20120801-51.pdf Accessed 10/2023.

[722] Zheng Lixin, 2013. "Post-Fukushima safety improvement measures for NPPs in China." China Nuclear and Radiation Safety Center, Conference presentation, August 26-29, 2013, Vienna. Available at webpage: https://nucleus.iaea.org/sites/gsan/act/tmonaftermath fukushima/Shared%20Documents/25%20Post-Fukushima%20Safety%20Improvement %20Measures%20for%20NPPs%20in%20China.pdf (or) https://inis.iaea.org/ collection/NCLCollectionStore/_Public/52/017/52017999.pdf?r=1 Accessed 10/2023.

discussed in terms of national safety planning and local performance impacts.[723] In relation to the multi-stage 'reconstruction and recovery'[724] plans, the designated local areas put under evacuation orders have been re-integrated to the development of municipalities in recent years. It can be additionally considered that public risk awareness procedures and communication knowledge platforms have involved local safety preparedness initiatives, as well as, responsive procedural modifications, when connected to local risk prevention of nuclear NPP accidents: e.g. "effectiveness of decontamination procedures and associated waste generation."[725]; national preparedness plans have been assessed in terms of functional aggregated elements, which have included public trust, public negotiation conditions, local availability of independent sources of communication, and collaborative governmental exercises mediating a common technical understanding ([726],[727]).

At the same time, the increasing presence of multilateral specialized energy operators at local NPPs has played an influential role in the standardization process of operational proceedings associated with local precautionary measures, and local control assessments that must be able to prepare and prevent changing conditions of controlling automation processes, in cases of severe natural hazards or man-made environmental disasters.[728] In order to confirm the national security standards of NPP in

723 David Skeen, 2013.

724 Ministry of the Environment, Japan, 2018. "Efforts toward recovery from the accident. Activities in areas under evacuation orders." Booklet to Provide Basic Information Regarding Health Effects of Radiation, Chapter 9/9.4. Available at webpage: https://www.env.go.jp/en/chemi/rhm/basic-info/2018/09-04-03.html Accessed 10/2023.

725 Ministry of the Environment, Japan, 2016. "Summary of IAEA-MOE experts' meeting on environmental remediation of off-site areas after the Fukushima Daiichi Nuclear Power Station accident." IAEA-MOE Experts' Meeting, Tokyo, Japan, 4-5 February 2016. Page 3. Available at webpage: https://www.env.go.jp/content/900506116.pdf Accessed 10/2023.

726 Steven Hanna, Tetsuji Yamada, Hiroaki Kondo, Akira Watanabe, and Ryohji Ohba, 2016. "International workshop at Fukushima, Japan, on dispersion and deposition modeling for nuclear accident releases: Transfer of science from academic to operational models." (Meeting Summaries). Bulletin of the American Meteorological Society, Volume 97, February, pp. ES31-ES36.

727 Kara Schmitt, 2012.

728 Michael J. Walker, Elise M. Henry, 2012. "Response to the changing perspectives of U.S. and Japanese nuclear energy policies in the aftermath of the Fukushima Daiichi

Japan, "the government will leave judgment [...] to the specialist of the Nuclear Regulatory Authority. When the Nuclear Regulation Authority [NRA] admits the compliance to regulatory standards, the government will respect the judgment and will proceed with the restart of the nuclear plant [NPP]."[729] For this reason, comparative international analyses produced about "Fukushima Daiichi Risk-Disaster Response"[730] have been critical about national safety preparedness in action-plans and the local regulatory evolution, particularly in case of complex NPP structural designs, which have required permanent assessments for safety coordination standards, health implementation mechanisms, as well as, regulatory integration of responsive public organizations involved at prefecture level in Japan's case.[731] The country in 2020 has fixed a common roadmap on environmental safety objectives which do better specify reassessed standard targets on local pollution of industrial production systems (EPZs); in the case of nuclear safety protection it is specified as ex.: "To supplement, finalize and apply technical standards and requirements on chemical, radiation and nuclear safety while checking, inspecting and punishing violations in line with legal stipulations."[732]

Similarly, it can also be considered that comprehensive control requirements of NPPs which have been designed to enhance decision-making accountability and technical responsive approaches, seen in reference with progressive environment regulatory adaptations, have also incremented transnational comparative technical debates: e.g. regional forums on disaster risk management experiences,[733] regarding the

disaster (by Daniel A. Dorfman)." Pace Environmental Law Review, Volume 30, No. 1, Fall, pp. 291-298.

729 Ministry of the Environment, Japan, 2014. "Japan's climate change policies." MOE Report, 18th March, 2014. Page 45. Presentation available at webpage: https://www.env.go.jp/en/focus/docs/files/20140318-83.pdf Accessed 10/2023.

730 Michael J. Walker, Elise M. Henry, 2012.

731 Michael J. Walker, Elise M. Henry, 2012.

732 Ministry of the Environment, Japan, 2012. "The National strategy on environment protection to 2020 with visions to 2030." The National Strategy on Environment Protection to 2020, with Visions to 2030 was approved by the Prime Minister in his Decision 1216/QD-TTg on September 05, 2012. Page 3. Full Document Available at webpage: https://www.env.go.jp/air/tech/ine/asia/vietnam/files/law/QD1216-English.pdf Accessed 10/2023.

733 World Bank, 2017. "Sharing Japanese expertise in emergency preparedness and response (EP&R) systems at national and local levels." WB, IBRD, IDA, Featured Story,

effective causes connected to NPP electric power interruptions during earthquake and tsunami disaster events ([734], [735]). About Japan's environment energy reform, there is to consider that environmental legal disputes associated with the private energy company TEPCO have led to independent investigations that have deepened multiple changing facets of public-private hierarchical organizational functions, which have been exercised through local management plans, and public knowledge transfers, specified in terms of asymmetric information, including some regulatory weaknesses featuring progressive difficulties in different institutional environments.[736] In order to favour incremental objectives of national adaptation plans, the 2020 environment strategy roadmap mentions "To further strengthen and consolidate State management agencies in charge of environment protection from central to local levels, placing focus on provincial, district and communal levels in order to improve their capability of enforcing environment protection laws."[737]

To this, the environment safety promotion and protection cultures manifested in reference to the nuclear development industry have been advanced through theoretical and practical approaches for reformed energy distribution models, which have been reviewed in terms of common applicable modifications for regulatory targets - e.g. "METI [Ministry of Economy, Trade and Industry] is monitoring the overall impact on nuclear power profitability as electricity industry reforms move into the final stage"[738] thus including environmental co-adaptation and cooperation processes. In retrospective view, it has been highlighted that after Fukushima Daiichi's disaster case "it [has remained] unclear how

October 13, 2017. Available at webpage: https://www.worldbank.org/en/news/feature/2017/10/12/sharing-japanese-expertise-in-emergency-preparedness-and-response-systems-at-national-and-local-levels Accessed 10/2023.

734 Michael J. Walker, Elise M. Henry, 2012.

735 Atsuyuki Suzuki, 2014. "Managing the Fukushima Challenge." Risk Analysis, Volume 34, No. 7, pp. 1240-1256.

736 Atsuyuki Suzuki, 2014.

737 Ministry of the Environment, Japan, 2012. "National strategy on environment protection to 2020 with visions to 2030." Page 11.

738 NECG, 2019. "#26 - Japan - Nuclear power and electricity reform." Nuclear Economics Consulting Group, 26 February, 2019. Report available at webpage: https://nuclear-economics.com/wp-content/uploads/2019/02/26-Japan-nuclear-power-and-electricity-reform-update.pdf Accessed 10/2023.

much radioactive waste resulted from the earthquake and tsunami: the government puts the estimate at 25 million tons; experts at the Japan Research Institute put the figure at 80 million tons; Japanese national broadcasters have put it at 100 million tons."[739] Therefore, the parallel constitution of international and national technical NPP industrial communication reports, referring to quantitative risk assessment measurements, has been classified according to comparative managerial regulatory requirements, which have been verified through multiple information distributed activities, and multilevel networked information practices that can deliver public information with available accessing tools through e.g.: nuclear industry debriefings; [740] waste management platforms; 3D contamination maps-decontamination methods; [741] eventually validated within national and local agencies.

Furthermore, at the time of crisis, there have been in place governmental supervisory activities in order to re-evaluate technical local conditions for the national reconstruction efforts led, but not only, at Fukushima's prefecture. Local invested efforts done in order to promote territorial administrative identifications have been analysed in relationship with nuclear radiation crises and contamination impacts.[742] However, it has come into consideration the fact that centralized and decentralized power systems have directly struggled to monitor local territorial accesses related to local environmental impacts, and human housing settlements with permanent relocation effects, which have been experienced during

[739] Jade Media, 2011. "Japan struggles to find spot for waste released after March quake, tsunami." Nuclear Waste News, October, page 6. Copyright of Nuclear Waste News is property of Jade Media Partners.

[740] World Nuclear Association, 2020. "Nuclear Power in Japan." World Nuclear Association, Country Profiles report, updated September 2020. Available at webpage: https://world-nuclear.org/information-library/country-profiles/countries-g-n/japan-nuclear-power.aspx Accessed 10/2023.

[741] Ministry of the Environment, Japan, 2016. "Summary of the 2nd IAEA-MOE experts' meeting on environmental remediation of off-site areas after the Fukushima Daiichi Nuclear Power Station accident." Tokyo and Fukushima, Japan, 14-18 November, 2016. Available at webpage: http://josen.env.go.jp/en/news/pdf/news_161118_01.pdf Accessed 10/2023.

[742] Steve Featherstone, 2016. "Fukushima five years later." Popular Science, March-April, pp. 72-77. Copyright of Popular Science is property of Bonnier Corporation. POPSCI.COM. Available at webpage: https://www.popsci.com/fukushima-five-years-later/ Accessed 11/2023.

rapid emergency operations, actualized across Japanese prefectures, moreover, as stated "[there were] bags filled with contaminated soil and debris stack up on a site in Naraha… [and] workers buil[t] a new seawall along the Fukushima's coast."[743] Responsive legislation designed to regulate water treatment disposals and soil contamination include the 'Soil Contamination Countermeasures Law.' Through this national legislation, the ministerial bureaus have conducted surveys in reference to ex. agricultural land contamination by "[...] checking the implementation of the law, [...] collect[ing] and organiz[ing] information on cases of soil contamination by designated hazardous substances [...] collected by prefectural governments and the municipal governments which are designated by ordinances based on Article 64 of the Act."[744] At a collective level, the planned risk reduction and resettlement measures have tackled the classification system of restricted areas that were evacuated in 2011;[745] those involved areas have therefore been reclassified together with local safety levels set against local risk radiation exposures.[746] In the case of decontamination plans for the housing sector, table 5 reports about the status of municipalities outside Fukushima area as of 2015.[747]

743 Steve Featherstone, 2016. Page 75.

744 Ministry of the Environment, Japan, 2020. "Review results on SAICM national implementation plan of Japan." MOE Report, March 2020. Page 48. Available at webpage: https://www.env.go.jp/content/900414530.pdf Accessed 10/2023.

745 Ministry of the Environment, Japan, 2015. "FY2014 Decontamination Report." A compilation of experiences to date on decontamination for the living environment conducted by the Ministry of the Environment, March 2015. Available at webpage: http://josen.env.go.jp/en/policy_document/pdf/decontamination_report1503_full.pdf Accessed 10/2023.

746 Ministry of the Environment, Japan, 2015. "FY2014 Decontamination Report."

747 Ministry of the Environment, Japan, 2015. "FY2014 Decontamination Report."

Table 5

"Progress of implementation of decontamination and other measures based on decontamination implementation plan outside Fukushima Prefecture (Housing) "

"(as of end of December, 2014) (Number of houses/buildings)"

	(a) "Planned number"	(b) "Outsourced number"	(c) "Completed number"	"Number of unnecessary decontamination works in (a),(b) and (c) [the number that decontamination works were determined to be unnecessary by prior monitoring results]"
"Iwate Prefecture	18,621	15,321	15,321	(15,207)
Miyagi Prefecture	10,228	8,503	7,350	(2,972)
Ibaraki Prefecture	47,276	47,276	47,266	(45,143)
Tochigi Prefecture	38,054	37,718	34,065	(13,712)
Gunma Prefecture	6,192	6,192	6,165	(4,760)
Saitama Prefecture	0	0	0	0
Chiba Prefecture	19,159	19,159	19,159	(10,919)
Total number"	139,530	134,169	129,326	(92,713)

Source: Ministry of the Environment, Japan, 2015. "FY2014 Decontamination Report." A compilation of experiences to date on decontamination for the living environment conducted by the Ministry of the Environment, March 2015. Full table: page 64. Available at webpage: http://josen.env.go.jp/en/policy_document/pdf/decontamination_report1503_full.pdf Accessed 11/2023.

From the operational side, nuclear clean-ups and decommissioning activities managed by the energy company TEPCO have been analyzed for being quite problematic particularly on meeting the basic essential needs put forward by the local civic groups involved in the stabilization of critical environmental situations, concerning monitoring and evaluative assessments about: local water pollution, human displacement, generational living standards, and territorial adaptation based on local distributive policies. This combination of multiple factors overall has not only affected the local communities, but also charged them with additional regulatory conditions, affecting decentralized reconstruction aims and future planning projects ([748],[749]).

It is reported by the MOE on decontamination planning that "[...] the decontamination implementation plan allowed much involvement of citizens by stipulating enhanced support for citizens and volunteers in the decontamination implementation. [...] some municipalities were not able to establish temporary storage sites. Some took a long time to decide the scope of decontamination and the formulation of the decontamination implementation plan because they were not able to reach agreement with residents."[750] To such critical points, the national contingency and safety assessments as well as risk prevention analyses conducted for recurrent disaster management crises at NPPs have been carefully reviewed by nuclear international agencies operating in Europe, the United States[751] or in partner countries, in order to identify the common lessons learnt in Japan and compare them with local environmental assessing processes set under DRR strategies.[752] Management risk plans have essentially focused on functional factors such as: 1. Industrial regulatory monitoring changes; 2. Public-private environmental inquiring interactions at NPPs management facilities; 3. Public confrontation exercises, with

[748] Steve Featherstone, 2011. "The future of Fukushima prefecture." Bloomberg Businessweek, March-April, pp. 1-4. Copyright of Bloomberg Businessweek is property of Bloomberg L.P.

[749] RoSPA 2011. "News: Government outlines next moves in nuclear review." The RoSPA Occupational Safety & Health Journal, August, pp. 1-2. Copyright of RoSPA Occupational Safety & Health Journal is property of Royal Society for the Prevention of Accidents.

[750] Ministry of the Environment, Japan, 2015. "FY2014 Decontamination Report." Page 17.

[751] NRC, 2020. "Plant-specific Japan lessons-learned activities." U.S. Nuclear Regulatory Commission, Japan Lessons Learned information page. Webpage has been reviewed under a new title in 2021: "Plant-Specific Safety Enhancements after Fukushima." Available at webpage: https://www.nrc.gov/reactors/operating/ops-experience/japan-dashboard/japan-plants.html Accessed 10/2023.

[752] Dudley, N., Buyck, C., Furuta, N., Pedrot, C., Renaud, F., and K. Sudmeier-Rieux (2015). *Protected Areas Tools for Disaster Risk Reduction. A handbook for practitioners*. Tokyo and Gland, Switzerland: MOEJ and IUCN, 44pp. Available at webpage: https://www.env.go.jp/en/nature/asia-parks/world_6th/EcoDRRhandbook_En.pdf Accessed 10/2023.

comparative technical discussions, drawing together transregional, national, and local civilian counterparts.[753]

Putting more attention on larger ecosystem protection policies has therefore led to the conceptual adoption of "Shared governance: including collaborative management, with different stakeholders having varying degrees of influence, or joint management with a pluralist management board and sharing decisions. Transboundary protected areas, which stretch across national or federal borders, and thus imply cooperation between different countries or regions, are one important form of shared governance."[754]

Similarly, public review analyses conducted by international nuclear experts,[755] DRR planners and Protected Area organizers[756] have underlined the fact that socioeconomic contingencies combined with local reconstruction efforts and managerial maintenance targets for NPPs, favouring environmental local safety related to nuclear waste treatment programs have led to common territorial identifications promoting continuous adaptive learning and incremental networking advocacy capacities. In due course, yearly based institutional monitoring evaluative plans have indirectly determined common local trusting behaviours[757] interrelated to societal perceptions on nuclear risk exposure levels.[758] Through comparative demographic cognitive patterns, recent public policy studies have additionally suggested different windows of

[753] RoSPA 2011. "News: Government outlines next moves in nuclear review."

[754] Dudley, N., Buyck, C., Furuta, N., Pedrot, C., Renaud, F., and K. Sudmeier-Rieux (2015). P. 6.

[755] Jacob Bukoski, 2015. "Post-Fukushima: The impacts on Japanese public opinion of nuclear power." Yale Environment Review (YER), article published 23/03/2015. Available at webpage: https://environment-review.yale.edu/post-fukushima-impacts-japanese-public-opinion-nuclear-power-0 Accessed 10/2023.

[756] Dudley, N., Buyck, C., Furuta, N., Pedrot, C., Renaud, F., and K. Sudmeier-Rieux (2015).

[757] Honda A., Wiwattanapantuwong J., Abe T., 2014. "Japanese university students' attitudes toward the Fukushima nuclear disaster." Journal of Environmental Psychology, Volume 40, pp. 147-156. In: Jacob Bukoski, 2015. Yale Environment Review, article published 23/03/2015. Available at: https://environment-review.yale.edu/post-fukushima-impacts-japanese-public-opinion-nuclear-power-0 (or) https://www.sciencedirect.com/science/article/abs/pii/S0272494414000528?via%3Dihub Both Accessed 10/2023.

[758] Fenella Saunders, 2017. "First person: M.V. Ramana." American Scientist, Research Triangle Park, Volume 105, January-February 2017, pp. 8-9.

interpretation about the changing status of local public risk perceptions after the Fukushima NPP disaster crisis.[759] For objective reporting, in table 6 (a,b,c,d sections) we have selected recent articles showing short abstracts, which have been directly quoted on table 6 due to comparative essential findings, creating a discussion ground about the Fukushima NPP accident reviewed within recent international studies cited in this research.

[759] Fenella Saunders, 2017. "First person: M.V. Ramana."

Table 6
Study Abstracts on Post Fukushima Disaster Crisis of Japan

A."Public support for nuclear power generation has decreased in Japan since the Fukushima Daiichi nuclear accident in March 2011. This study examines how the factors influencing public acceptance of nuclear power changed after this event. The influence factors examined are perceived benefit, perceived risk, trust in the managing bodies, and pro-environmental orientation (i.e. new ecological paradigm)." [760] (p. 98).	**B.** "We conducted a longitudinal study (*N*=790) in Switzerland: one survey was done five months before and one directly after the accident in Fukushima. We assessed acceptance, perceived risks, perceived benefits, and trust related to nuclear power stations. In our model, we assumed that both benefit and risk perceptions determine acceptance of nuclear power. We further hypothesized that trust influences benefit and risk perceptions and that trust before a disaster relates to trust after a disaster. Results showed that the acceptance and perceptions of nuclear power as well as its trust were more negative after the accident. In our model, perceived benefits and risks determined the acceptance of nuclear power stations both before and after Fukushima. Trust had strong effects on perceived benefits and risks, at both times." [761] (p.333).

[760] Norifumi Tsujikawa, Shoji Tsuchida, and Takamasa Shiotani, 2015. "Changes in the factors influencing public acceptance of nuclear power generation in Japan since the 2011 Fukushima Daiichi nuclear disaster." Risk Analysis, Volume 36, No. 1, pp. 98-113.
[761] Vivianne H.M. Visschers, Michael Siegrist, 2013. "How a nuclear power plant accident influences acceptance of nuclear power: Results of a longitudinal study before and after the Fukushima disaster." Risk Analysis, Volume 33, No. 2, pp. 333-347.

C. "The nuclear accident in Fukushima and the subsequent discussions about nuclear power influenced public acceptance of this technology. The aim of the present study was to examine why after the Fukushima accident some people converted from supporting nuclear power to opposing it or became undecided [...] Results suggest that changes in benefits perception were mainly responsible for people's changes in attitude toward nuclear power. People perceived somewhat more risks related to nuclear power after the accident in Fukushima. This change in risk perception did not explain the attitudinal changes of proponents into opponents of nuclear power, however."[762] (p. 356).

D. "The attitude of local communities near a nuclear power plant (NPP) is a key factor in nuclear policy decision making in Japan. This case study compared local citizens' attitudes in 2010 and 2011 toward the benefits and drawbacks of hosting Kashiwazaki-Kariwa NPP. The Fukushima accident occurred in this period. After the accident, benefit recognition of utility bill refunds clearly declined, while that of public facilities did not, suggesting the influence of a bribery effect. The negative shift of attitudes about hosting the NPP after the accident was more modest in Kariwa Village, which saw a large expansion of social welfare programs, than in the other two areas, which lacked such a budget expansion."[763] (p. 808).

Essentially, the institutional identifications for reprocessing energy technology programs set in association with risk adaptation plans have relied on participatory, as well as, regulatory indications with material technical contributions of international consultation agencies and national and local energy operators. The integration of public-private partnerships PPP through socioeconomic interventions particularly intertwined with industrial energy development programs[764] has relied on comparative vital factors that can reflect intra-regional trading exchanges including: a.

762 Michael Siegrist, Bernadette Sūtterlin, Carmen Keller, 2014. "Why have some people changed their attitudes toward nuclear power after the accident in Fukushima?" Energy Policy, Volume 69, pp. 356-363.

763 Takaaki Kato, Shogo Takahara, Masashi Nishikawa, Toshimitsu Homma, 2013. "A case study of economic incentives and local citizens' attitudes toward hosting a nuclear power plant in Japan: Impacts of the Fukushima accident." Energy Policy, Volume 59, pp. 808-818.

764 Keith Baker, 2004. "Renewable energy technology programs in Australia." Presentation to the 14th Asia Pacific Seminar on Climate Change, Sydney, Australia. Available at webpage: https://www.env.go.jp/en/earth/ap-net/documents/seminar/14th/baker.pdf Accessed 10/2023.

local engaged communities; b. political consensus framed into cooperative diffused measures; and c. connection to technology-driven adaptive knowledge.[765] On the other hand, for the public coordination of rapid emergency programs in cases of NPP disaster events, there have been into consideration different sub-themes summarized in table 7.

Table 7

NPP Coordination Highlights

1. "The nuclear industry in Japan's case has been the result of long-term management evolution formulations and local public acceptances. 2. The configuration of nuclear industries aside the Fukushima NPP energy cluster has raised safety as well as security indications prior to the 2011 disaster crises. 3. The nuclear workers performing at different NPP energy assets have received less attention about safety norms and instructive orientations just supporting the companies' planning exercises of complex automated systems. 4. The Fukushima catastrophe has raised national preoccupations about TEPCO management operations and NPP cleaning-up activities with high financial cost scenarios."[766]

Source: Masatsugu Hayashi, Larry Hughes, 2013.

A comparative public policy analysis on local security coordination has shown a substantial divide that has formed between decision-making acting bodies, public-private power energy industries related to NPP, and environmental stakeholders' associations, which in distinctive manners have supported either nationally, transnationally, or locally, a continued integration of common networked information and the ICT media differentiation within responsive environments. Political effective implications rising from public safety awareness plans promoted nationwide are discussed in the next section of this study.

7.1 From Emergency to Mediation to Mitigation Awareness Debates

National awareness plans in Japan's disaster cases have led to the identification of critical management areas scrutinized in association with governmental economic reviews tackling fundamental organizational

[765] Keith Baker, 2004. "Renewable energy technology programs in Australia."

[766] Masatsugu Hayashi, Larry Hughes, 2013. "The policy responses to the Fukushima nuclear accident and their effect on Japanese energy security." Energy Policy, Volume 59, pp. 86-101.

aspects of the nuclear industry ([767],[768],[769]). For instance, post-disaster recovery assistance activities have been the result of pre-planning strategies that might be able to reduce severe natural/man-made disaster impacts on direct communities involved.[770] For the actual preparation of local risk monitoring studies[771] focused on national citizens' propensity toward nuclear power companies' programs established in Japan, the programming research activity has entailed a material collection about national citizens' collective opinions regarding, in particular, the multilevel distribution process advanced in the case of nuclear energy industrial development.[772] To which, formal or informal environmental policy indications [773] have similarly provided specific coordination tendencies for the possible reduction of local operations managed at nuclear power facilities spread across the country.

About the industrial energy sphere, it can be observed that public-private energy management organizations and concurrent ministerial offices have usually formed national advisory councils e.g. inter-agency

767 Eliza Strickland, 2012. "Can Japan phase out nuclear power? The country wants to go nuclear-free, but many obstacles remain" NA-IEEE SPECTRUM November, pp.13-14. www.SPECTRUM.IEEE.ORG (or) https://spectrum.ieee.org/can-japan-phase-out-nuclear-power Accessed 10/2023.

768 NPJ editorial archive, 2013. "Fukushima Safety Conference. Lessons learned." Nuclear Plant Journal, Volume 31, No. 1, January-February, pp. 35-37. www.NuclearPlantJournal.com (or) https://digitaleditions.nuclearplantjournal.com/JF13/files/assets/basic-html/index.html#page35 Accessed 11/2023.

769 Anthony Wohns, 2014. "Fukushima's lessons for Boston: Debating the future of nuclear energy." Harvard International Reviews, Volume 35, Winter, pp. 4-5.

770 Ministry of the Environment, Japan, 2013. "Protected areas, natural hazards and disaster recovery." 1st Asia Parks Congress (APC), Japan 2013, Draft Message from WG1 on Natural Disasters and Protected Areas. Available at webpage: https://www.env.go.jp/en/nature/asia-parks/pdf/wg1_message.pdf Accessed 10/2023.

771 See: article researching about citizen's technical monitoring in Japan: Carolynne Hultquist, Guido Cervone, 2018. "Citizen monitoring during hazards: validation of Fukushima radiation measurements." GeoJournal, Volume 83, No. 2, pp. 189-206. DOI: 10.1007/s10708-017-9767-x

772 Eliza Strickland, 2012.

773 See: this article is focused on public health assessments: Yingying Sun, Tingting Yan, 2019. "The use of public health indicators to assess individual happiness in post-disaster recovery." International Journal of Environmental Research and Public Health, Volume 16, No. 21: 4101. Available at webpage: https://www.ncbi.nlm.nih.gov/pmc/articles/PMC6862458/ Accessed 10/2023.

technical advisory councils, [774] for the facilitation of international knowledge information exchanges about comparative nuclear regulatory environmental safety conditions, as well as, safety maintenance operations reprogrammed for NPP energy reactors' development, planned in future energy blueprints ([775],[776]). However, there is still to consider that at an international level, multilateral corridors on nuclear energy programs have been redesigned, for instance, in the U.S. Department of Energy's (DOE) research centres - with U.S. Nuclear Waste Technical Review Board (NWTRB)[777] and U.S. Nuclear Regulatory Commission (NRC)[778] - in order to clarify technical regulatory positions maintained by private energy groups and public distribution agencies, formally engaged on the

[774] Ministry of the Environment, Japan, 1990. "An act to control toxic substances and hazardous and nuclear wastes, providing penalties for violations thereof, and for other purposes." Philippines Republic Act, No. 6969: "Toxic Substances and Hazardous and Nuclear Waste Control Act 1990." Document available at webpage: https://www.env.go.jp/en/recycle/asian_net/Country_Information/Law_N_Regulation/Philippines/phillipines1.pdf Accessed 10/2023.

[775] Eliza Strickland, 2012.

[776] Anthony Wohns, 2014.

[777] Note: NWTRB national plan statement:"The mission of the U.S. Nuclear Waste Technical Review Board is to perform unbiased and ongoing technical and scientific peer review of the U.S. Department of Energy's (DOE) nuclear waste management activities. [...] The Board provides objective technical information to Congress, the Administration, DOE, government and non-government organizations, and the public on a wide-range of issues related to spent nuclear fuel and high-level waste management and disposition." U.S. Nuclear Waste Technical Review Board, 2017. Official website, available at webpage: https://www.nwtrb.gov/about-us/mission#:~:text=The%20mission%20of%20the%20U.S.%20Nuclear%20Waste%20Technical,Department%20of%20Energy%E2%80%99s%20%28DOE%29%20nuclear%20waste%20management%20activities. Accessed 10/2023. *As of 11/2023 the website moved.* Access to: Federal Register 2017 provides NWTRB agenda information. Available at webpage: https://www.govinfo.gov/content/pkg/FR-2017-05-10/pdf/2017-09344.pdf Accessed 11/2023.

[778] Note: Fukushima Daiichi: ANS Committee Report, 2012. Excerpt: "There is no aspect of the Fukushima Daiichi accident that a priori indicates that the level of safety of NPPs in the United States is unacceptable. The Committee agrees with the U.S. Nuclear Regulatory Commission (NRC) Near-Term Task Force (NTTF) that the current level of safety provides adequate protection to the health and safety of the U.S. public. However, from a public confidence viewpoint, it is unacceptable to have an accident of the visibility and societal consequences of the Fukushima accident occurring somewhere in the world every 25 to 30 years." American Nuclear Society (ANS), Special Committee on Fukushima, "Full Report: Fukushima Daiichi," March 2012, Revised on June 2012, page 22. Available at webpage: http://fukushima.ans.org/report/Fukushima_report.pdf Accessed 10/2023.

preparation of common lessons learned from the post-Fukushima critical situations ([779],[780]).

Instead, societal networked experiences synthesized through public policy opinion polls, national policy centres and international anti-nuclear groups, have fundamentally grown in favour of a reconsideration about public evaluation procedures which can indirectly target nuclear energy development with long-term NPP construction projects, including local safety monitoring operations of existing industrial nuclear security programs that might converge toward the decommissioning[781] of nuclear energy utilities in the future ([782], [783]). In support of environmental knowledge exchanges, governmental guidelines have suggested to promote business voluntary environments[784] in view of Global Warming Countermeasures that should facilitate public access to environmental information through industry and representative stakeholders' cooperation.[785] In essence, over the last decade, public emerging expectations about changing dimensions of a national nuclear energy policy direction, have been advanced in terms of transnational governmental engagements, e.g. on the use of alternative energy sources for supply substitution, undertaken in view of complex translocal[786]

[779] Anthony Wohns, 2014.

[780] NRC Japan's Lessons Examples from direct available websites:
a. https://www.nrc.gov/reactors/operating/ops-experience/japan-dashboard.html - Accessed 10/2023.
b. https://public-blog.nrc-gateway.gov/tag/fukushima/ - Accessed 10/2023.

[781] Katharina Wecker, 2019. "Germany's atomic phaseout: How to dismantle a nuclear power plant." Deutsche Welle (DW), Environment Article, published 11/03/2019. Available at website: https://www.dw.com/en/germanys-atomic-phaseout-how-to-dismantle-a-nuclear-power-plant/a-47823766 Accessed 10/2023.

[782] Eliza Strickland, 2012.

[783] Anthony Wohns, 2014.

[784] Ministry of the Environment, Japan, 2013. "Japan's sixth national communication under the United Nations Framework Convention on Climate Change." The Government of Japan, December, 2013. Page 102. Full Report available at webpage: https://www.env.go.jp/content/900446396.pdf Accessed 10/2023.

[785] Ministry of the Environment, Japan, 2013. "Japan's sixth national communication under the United Nations Framework Convention on Climate Change."

[786] Note: Translocal Approach (TA) is seen: "[...] as a new form of collective learning for sustainability [...] this approach is inspired by sustainability discourse and the social learning theory." Shogo Kudo, Doreen I. Allasiw, Kanako Omi, Melissa Hansen, 2020. "Translocal learning approach: A new form of collective learning for sustainability." Resources, Environment and Sustainability, Volume 2, December 2020, 100009. Abstract

action-led processes that have been lined up in order to support functional safety recognitions for environmental sustainability. Toward this path, local preparedness measures for multilevel operational plans have been combined with disaster risk emergency contingencies which have required mandatory regulatory improvements.[787]

Similarly, there has been in place the formation of a national and international attention about scientific and nuclear-related procedural modalities conforming to public safety objectives of nuclear power utilities. Public-private nuclear energy utilities have been managed by nuclear contract operators in view of favouring technical optimization changes and common local recognitions of safety protection dynamics, recalling regulatory trust, as well as, environmental anti-risk prevention analyses, which are implemented in response to the needs of local communities involved in this process.[788] In order to achieve public safety regulations and environmental knowledge access conditions, the responsible international entities put in charge of nuclear regulatory measures such as the IAEA, and nuclear regulatory safety commissions, have progressively adapted to changes by targeting local development with multiple action-plans implementation, tackling the nuclear industry operating in nuclear member countries as in Japan's case.[789] About local development, in particular, the issue of remediation of radioactive contamination in the environment[790] has been discussed at international symposiums highlighting current prospects for local decontamination through e.g. reconstruction and restoration projects that entail cooperation with local residents,[791] but at the same time, open communication with international counterparts such as the IAEA, put in charge of practical

quotation. Available at webpage: https://www.sciencedirect.com/science/article/pii/S2666916120300098 Accessed 11/2023.

[787] NPJ editorial archive, 2013. "Fukushima Safety Conference. Lessons learned."

[788] NPJ editorial archive, 2013. "Fukushima Safety Conference. Lessons learned."

[789] NPJ editorial archive, 2013. "Fukushima Safety Conference. Lessons learned."

[790] Ministry of the Environment, Japan, 2019. "International symposium on remediation of radioactive contamination in the environment." MOE Environmental Remediation, News & Topics, July 11, 2019. Information available at webpage: http://josen.env.go.jp/en/news/ Accessed 10/2023.

[791] Ministry of the Environment, Japan, 2019. "International symposium on remediation of radioactive contamination in the environment."

independent reviews for coordination and implementation of consensus-based performing systems.[792]

As a consequence, a regulatory availability of functional territorial dispositions concerning the systemic activities of nuclear power plants has favoured policy interactions facilitating local civilian dialogues with associated public confrontations, particularly opened for the re-establishment of common secure and safety areas involving technical programming directives. The resulting compromises on locally-driven Nuclear Policy (NP) objectives rely - as pointed out - in "[...] the form of the alliance between civil activists and political parties becom[ing] a critical factor in policy change."[793] In connection with specific regional regulatory aspects, institutional international authorities such as the U.S. NRC's Agency and nuclear energy safety commissioners based at NRA Japan, have been confronted with territorial operational performances verified at nuclear power energy sites,[794] while set in conjunction with management testing scenarios, and sustainable exchanging reviews, structured as means to "[...] empower regional and local authorities [that become involved] with various strategic/action planning territorial exercises [...]."[795] These public technical exercises have been conducted in view of granting common safety interactions, as well as, updated action-plans involving institutional inspections and maintenance of local safety

[792] Ministry of the Environment, Japan, 2019. "International symposium on remediation of radioactive contamination in the environment."

[793] Sung Chull Kim, Yousun Chung, 2018. "Dynamics of nuclear power policy in the post-Fukushima era: Interest structure and politicisation in Japan, Taiwan and Korea." Asian Studies Review, Volume 42, No. 1, pp. 107-124. Page 110.

[794] Note: About the Nuclear Regulatory Authority (Japan) to note that in relation to a "Periodic Facility Inspection [and the] Integrated load performance test: the integrated performance test is the last inspection item of the Periodic Facility Inspections for nuclear power reactor facilities to verify whether operation status of each facility is normal and its parameters show appropriate values when operating with an approximately rated output." NRA, Japan, 2022. "The flow of review and inspection for checking conformity to New Regulatory Requirements." Presentation available at: https://www.nra.go.jp/data/000118257.pdf Accessed 10/2023/ NRA's direct Webpage: See: Section 2. Inspections; and subsection: 3) Periodic facility inspections, *link to pdf* Flow Chart: Available at webpage: https://www.nra.go.jp/english/regulatory/20150826.html Accessed 10/2023.

[795] Ministry of the Environment, Japan, 2016. "French experience on long term energy & climate planning." Presentation to the Vision Committee, MOEJ, Tokyo, 29 November 2016. Page 10. Available at webpage: https://www.env.go.jp/content/900530280.pdf Accessed 10/2023.

operations ([796],[797]). In nuclear member states, there have been progressive environmental policy dialogues regarding the nuclear waste disposal activities associated with national storage management requirements,[798] that the nuclear industry has integrated in connection with other major technical developments about national construction models of nuclear hazardous waste sites, managed by nuclear countries like in Finland or in Sweden.[799]

In other words, specific territorial assessments linked to public and private nuclear energy partnerships PPPs, still based on national/regional risk safety proceedings and DRR recovery protection plans, associated with energy industrial development, have essentially increased governmental technical priorities, currently related to the establishment of multilateral alternative renewable energy reforms for hydroelectric, wind, and solar energy sectors, practically envisioned as in Japan's case.[800] At the same time, there have been technical and organizational conditions aggregating locally at national nuclear power plants NPP, which have entailed comparative systematic developments about public safety and protection measures that need to be verified through permanent security reviews operated by national and international nuclear regulation bodies,

[796] Brian Wheeler, 2012. "Understanding the future of nuclear after Fukushima." Power Engineering, September 1, 2012, p. 12. Available at website: www.power-eng.com or https://www.power-eng.com/nuclear/understanding-the-future-of-nuclear-after-fukushima/ Accessed 11/2023.

[797] Ken Koyama, 2013. "Japan's post-Fukushima energy policy challenges." Asian Economic Policy Review, Volume 8, No. 2, pp. 274-293.

[798] Note: In the NRA's 2022 assessment review, about Fukushima NPP, the NRA Commission highlights in particular "[...] overall risks of the Specified Nuclear Facility shall be reduced and optimized through the assessment of each process and stage; and in conducting risk assessment for the overall Specified Nuclear Facility and each equipment, reduction and optimization of risks shall be sufficient to ensure on-site and off-site safety through the assessment including the impact on wide area of off-site environment.[...]" NRA Commission document decided on 22 July 2022. "Review results document on the application for approval to amend the implementation plan pertaining to Specified Nuclear Facility (Installation of ALPS Treated Water Discharge Facility) of Tokyo Electric Power Company Holdings Fukushima Daiichi Nuclear Power Station. page 3. NRA Japan. Doc. Available at webpage: https://www.nra.go.jp/data/000399110.pdf Accessed 10/2023.

[799] News Reports, Jade Media, 2013. "Nuclear waste news." Nuclear Waste News, October 24th, 2013, p. 7. Jade Media Partners LLC. Available at website: https://www.thefreelibrary.com/Japan.-a0350573515 Accessed 10/2023.

[800] Ken Koyama, 2013.

as the NRA Japan, put in charge of local technical inspections and local assessments' diffusion for public environmental guidelines, including the status of residential living areas with local risk preparedness activities and emergency-related protection procedures ([801],[802]) locally required.

7.2 The Role of R&D Commissions and Local Knowledge-Based IT Exchanges

Regarding field research and innovation development processes, the formation of adequate engineering designs matching with complex energy safety components [803] has been the result of long-term regional cooperation initiatives, which have been actively programmed by state officials and multilateral decision-making bodies, operating in association with industrial energy stakeholders involved in renewable energy projects and environmental protection policies ([804],[805],[806]). Overall, technical enhanced monitoring in comparative M&E evaluation settings, advanced in Japan during the post-recovery crises managed after Fukushima's disaster events at NPP, have led to national industrial policy reviews, integrating local costs and economic damages caused at the NPP, as well as, concurrent control analyses related to national safety standards.[807] For decontamination projects, the Ministry of the Environment "MOE has budgeted approx. JPY 2.9 trillion (= USD 27 billion up to FY2017 for

801 Brian Wheeler, 2011.

802 Ken Koyama, 2013.

803 Zeng Ming, Liu Yingxin, Ouyang Shaojie, Shi Hui, Li Chunxue, 2016. "Nuclear energy in the post-Fukushima era: Research on the developments of the Chinese and worldwide nuclear power industries." Renewable and Sustainable Energy Reviews, Volume 58, May 2016, pages 147-156.

804 Professional Engineering News, 2011. "Fight for future of nuclear in wake of Japan accident. Nuclear confidence shaken" Professional Engineering, p. 4. Copyright of Professional Engineering is property of Professional Engineering Publishing.

805 Scott Peterson, 2012. "The right response." Electric Perspectives, (EP), Volume 37, No. 3, pp. 77-82, May/June 2012. Available at webpage: https://lsc-pagepro.mydigital publication.com/publication/?m=6643&i=113534&p=84 Accessed 11/2023.

806 Matthew Cotton, 2015. "Structure, agency and post-Fukushima nuclear policy: an alliance-context-actantiality model of political change." Journal of Risk Research, Volume 18, No.3, pp. 317-332.

807 Professional Engineering News, 2011. "Fight for future of nuclear in wake of Japan accident."

decontamination."[808] As underlined in the text, the centralized authorities and local institutional counterparts such as local municipalities, have released national investigative reports, including joint industry statements highlighting the lack of protection and preparedness in the case of Japan's nuclear disaster case in 2011.[809] Essentially, local post-recovery responses and common health rehabilitation processes - such as: "1. creation of a low-carbon society; [...] 2. restoration from nuclear disaster; [...] 3. revitalization of local areas; [...] 4. restructuring of industrial zones and rice mills; [...] 5. securing disaster-resilient independent distributed power"[810] - have entailed a systematic facilitation of technical responsive mechanisms, supporting as well local IT communication networks[811] and media information platforms able to provide upgraded environmental accounts about the evolving risk conditions at the local NPPs.[812] In terms of risk communication in Japan there is also to consider that "knowledge has not diffused regardless of the massive news reports; [and] disagreements between experts and the laypersons still exist as to: the necessity of precautionary measures; [and] the evaluation of the objectivity in risk assessments."[813]

In this type of context, environmental and managerial impact assessments concerning industrial risk & safety crises have incremented both qualitative and quantitative analyses based on regional, national, and local environmental coordination plans, which have been formalized by

[808] Ministry of the Environment, Japan, 2018. "Environmental remediation in Japan." MOE report, March 2018. Page 16. Available at webpage: http://josen.env.go.jp/en/pdf/progressseet_progress_on_cleanup_efforts.pdf Accessed 10/2023.
[809] Professional Engineering News, 2011. "Fight for future of nuclear in wake of Japan accident."
[810] Ministry of the Environment, Japan, 2018. "FY2017 Study of city-to-city collaboration project for low carbon society." MOE, Japan, project report, March 2018. Page 1-57. Mitsubishi Research Institute Inc., Fujita Corporation. Page 1-3-37. Available at webpage: https://www.env.go.jp/earth/coop/lowcarbon-asia/english/project/data/EN_MMR_2017_02.pdf Accessed 10/2023.
[811] Michio Murakami, Akiko Sato, Shiro Matsui, Aya Goto, Atsushi Kumagai, Masaharu Tsubokura, *et al.*, 2017. "Communicating with residents about risks following the Fukushima nuclear accident." Asia Pacific Journal of Public Health, Volume 29, No. 2_suppl., pp. 74S-89S. https://doi.org/10.1177/1010539516681841
[812] Scott Peterson, 2012. "The right response."
[813] Toshiko Kikkawa, 2014. "The current status of risk communication in Japan." MOE, Japan, Keio University, Page 8. Presentation available at webpage: https://www.env.go.jp/content/900408606.pdf Accessed 10/2023.

central governmental representatives familiar with the organizational control proceedings required at the industrial nuclear energy operating sites.[814] About technical nuclear emergencies, it has been programmed "the Nuclear Disaster Countermeasure Priority Area [which] is basically to be established for each facility considering its inherent risk and the degree of potential impact at the time of the accident. [...] for reprocessing facilities with a large inventory of radioactive materials, it is set up that fire and explosion due to fine metal particles from fuel cladding or organic solvent, criticality accidents, leakage or loss of function due to damage or failure of equipment or piping, or spent fuel handling failure must not cause the risk of excessive radiation exposure to the public."[815] To this framework, there is also to consider the evolution of locally-based reporting agencies' information with a regular confirmation and validation of interrelated territorial environment aspects, concerning safety control measures, implemented through national industry partnerships PPPs, and international commissioners' exchanging reviews,[816] when the case.[817] In relation to "nuclear disaster control measures: [...] the Nuclear Emergency Act stipulates special measures for the obligations, etc. of licensees concerning nuclear disaster prevention, the issuance of declaration of a nuclear emergency situation, establishment of nuclear emergency response headquarters, and the implementation of emergency response measures [...] taking into consideration the particularity of nuclear disasters. [...] Following TEPCO Fukushima Daiichi NPS accident, the Nuclear Emergency Act was amended on September 19, 2012, including the enhancement of measures to prevent nuclear emergency, and the strengthening of the Nuclear Emergency

[814] Scott Peterson, 2012. "The right response."

[815] NRA, Japan, 2020. "National report of Japan. For the Seventh Review Meeting. Joint convention on the safety of spent fuel management and on the safety of radioactive waste management." Nuclear Regulation Authority, Report, October 2020. Page 80 - page 73. Available at webpage: https://www.nra.go.jp/data/000366720.pdf Accessed 10/2023.

[816] See: U.S. Senate Hearing 112-959. 2012 "Lessons from Fukushima one year later: NRC's implementation of recommendations for enhancing nuclear reactor safety in the 21st century." U.S. Subcommittee on clean air and nuclear safety and the Committee on environment and public works U.S. Senate. March 15, 2012. Available at webpage: https://www.govinfo.gov/content/pkg/CHRG-112shrg25036/html/CHRG-112shrg25036.htm Accessed 10/2023.

[817] Scott Peterson, 2012. "The right response."

Response Headquarters and other bodies in a nuclear emergency."[818] Due to a resulting formal attention about risk communication protocols, the regional populations as well as international monitoring expert groups have been associated with comparative territorial information processes maintained in view of technical environmental evaluations, however dependent on selective decentralized organizational policies established at municipal and provincial level - also in order to ensure consistent local communication transfers managed across controlling and implementing municipal authorities ([819], [820]).

As such, structural public-private interactions about conditional governing indications, that have been related with local citizens' risk perceptions and industrial business groups' interventions have been combined with socio-cultural representative dimensions. For example, "in December of FY2020, Chairman [...] and Commissioner [...] visited the Nuclear Disaster Control Center in Kagoshima Prefecture, and exchanged views on regulatory problems pertaining to nuclear facilities with local parties including the Governor of Kagoshima Prefecture and the Mayor of Satsumasendai City." [821] Multilateral public-private relations have essentially reflected a national support for renewable energy policies, incorporating nuclear energy technology research e.g. "technological development [advanced] in response to new markets and climate change." [822] But, at the same time, pragmatic directions that have corresponded to public local acceptances or rejections of NPP structural conditions, have expanded in reference to local development plans, intertwined with automated energy plants' dynamics for processing and

[818] NRA, Japan, 2020. "National report of Japan. For the Seventh Review Meeting. Joint convention on the safety of spent fuel management and on the safety of radioactive waste management." Pages 39-40.

[819] Scott Peterson, 2012. "The right response."

[820] Matthew Cotton, 2015.

[821] NRA, 2020. "FY 2020 Annual Report." Nuclear Regulation Authority, Japan, Report, Page 6. Available at webpage: https://www.nra.go.jp/data/000384155.pdf Accessed 10/2023.

[822] Ministry of the Environment, Japan, 2021. "Practical guide for scenario analysis in line with the TCFD recommendations 3rd edition." MOE Climate Change Policy Division, March 2021. Report Page 3-70. Available at webpage: https://www.env.go.jp/policy/policy/tcfd/TCFDguide_3rd_EN.pdf Accessed 10/2023.

manufacturing,[823] while producing relative stability across time.[824] Comparatively, knowledge innovation and local learning processes aligning to national and international managerial orientations about NPPs development, have emerged in terms of a dual dimension with open confrontation positions, recalling either the diffusion of technology innovation model systems[825] or the containment of nuclear energy designs, entailing a complete reduction in structural future plans.[826] About local environmental aspects, contextual contributions promoting national safety and recovery projects defined in terms of local protection plans, local public awareness campaigns, and local technical safeguards standards (e.g. for radiation exposures) have enhanced common local responses on programmatic disaster risk methodologies, which can still depend on local NPP management having complex processing stages, interlinked with technical changing organizations.[827] For instance, about the environmental sea area monitoring activities, "In cooperation with the IAEA Environmental Laboratories, the NRA has conducted joint collection and comparison of analysis results for marine samples near the Fukushima Daiichi NPS every year since FY2014, and for the sample collection carried out in November 2020, independent experts in environmental radioactivity from Japan, delegated by the IAEA, participated instead of IAEA experts due to COVID-19 pandemic, and they checked the sample collection situation."[828]

Consequentially, as an institutional prerogative the actual diffusion of local administrative cooperation facilitating performance and operational understanding of multilevel material occurrences has been maintained at

823 Ministry of the Environment, Japan, 2021. "Practical guide for scenario analysis in line with the TCFD recommendations 3rd edition." Page 3-195

824 Matthew Cotton, 2015.

825 Note: About regional automation processing "demand for solar, wind, hydro, geothermal, and biomass power generation facilities increases due to FIT policy incentives, atc. As a result, business opportunities for related control equipment expand, impacting P/L." Ministry of the Environment, Japan, 2021. "Practical guide for scenario analysis in line with the TCFD recommendations 3rd edition. Page 3-196

826 Matthew Cotton, 2015.

827 Lars Lofquist, 2013. "After Fukushima: nuclear power and societal choice." Journal of Risk Research, Volume 18, No. 3, pp. 291-303.

828 NRA, 2020. "FY 2020 Annual Report." Nuclear Regulation Authority, Japan, Report, page 84.

the NPP locations, while facing direct implications regarding annual budgetary provisions and technical building requirements,[829] particularly enforced after Fukushima NPP disaster crisis.[830] The revaluation process of the nuclear energy industry designs undertaken at national and international level has been analyzed in connection with existing democratic participatory relations, which have been encouraged in view of achieving a common multi-agency cooperation, associated with public learning activities, also introduced by international nuclear agencies (IAEA/OECD/NRC/NRA),[831] national nuclear committees' members (centralized energy commissions), and political local representatives or party groups becoming engaged according to different territorial dimensions.[832] Through respective professional capacities, the pursuance of long-term management plans about Japan's NPP national performance criteria, has also been challenged because of interdependent transformative conditions, which have reflected the modified uses of different renewable energy technology designs, as well as, of locally-available safety protection plans, which can be subjected to a material fragmentation intertwined with local anti-risk preparedness dynamics.[833] For example, based on the NRA report: technology regulatory standards have entailed that "The technology used for design and construction of spent fuel interim storage facilities is evaluated in the process of the review of Design and Construction Plan. [...] based on the quality management

[829] See: Fukushima Prefectural Government, 2012. "Plan for revitalization in Fukushima Prefecture. (Second Version) [Outline]." Published by: Revitalization & Comprehensive Planning Division, Planning & Coordination Department, Fukushima Prefectural Government, December 2012. Available at webpage: https://www.pref.fukushima.lg.jp/download/1/plan_for_revitalization2_outline.pdf Accessed 10/2023.

[830] Daniel A. Dorfman, 2012. "The changing perspectives of U.S. and Japanese nuclear energy policies in the aftermath of the Fukushima Daiichi disaster." Pace Environmental Law Review, Volume 30, No. 1, Fall, pp. 255-290.

[831] Note: On Nuclear Agencies international collaborative orientations: "the NRA has continued to share findings and lessons learned from the accident at TEPCO's Fukushima Daiichi NPS with the international community, and collaborated with international organizations and nuclear regulatory bodies in other countries through collecting information and exchanging opinions for improving international nuclear safety and related matters." Nuclear Regulatory Authority, Japan, 2019. "Annual Report." Chapter 1 "Ensuring Trust in Nuclear Regulatory Administration." page 2. Available at webpage: https://www.nra.go.jp/data/000347153.pdf Accessed 11/2023.

[832] Daniel A. Dorfman, 2012.

[833] Lars Lofquist, 2013.

policy reviewed upon licensing, licensees are required to develop a design and development plan and to implement investigation, verification and validation. These quality management activities ensure that spent fuel interim storage facility complies with the requirements for performance, the purpose of usage, intended usage method."[834]

In association with the possible identification of municipal distribution programs focused on decontamination from radiation, environmental monitoring procedures have entailed practical limitations in view of distinct environmental assessment plans being related to the management of local NPPs, including the material disposal of nuclear fuel waste and the technological verification of complex automated changes.[835] In addition, a comprehensive approximation of nuclear environmental safety policies conducted at national level has been reconfigured according to the allocation of national economic resources managed for the actual maintenance of multilateral efficient energy production industries permanently assessed across Japan's developed region. At the same time, common environmental efforts converging on regulative adaptation plans for the local remediation operations, activated immediately after the Fukushima emergency crisis, have entailed continuous practical exercises, pursued through local restoration activities in local contaminated areas, which have required nuclear waste disposal measures, as well as, environmental monitoring integrated tasks, particularly proximate to targeted locations identified at municipal and prefecture level. [836] Therefore, local state officials and transnational industry management operators based at the local NPPs have followed up with corresponding feedbacks through public recovery and restoration programs, which have kept evolving especially when associated with both decontamination projects and decommissioning operations, performed at separate local

[834] NRA, 2020. "National Report of Japan. For the seventh review meeting; joint convention on the safety of spent fuel management and on the safety of radioactive waste management." Nuclear Regulation Authority Report, October 2020. Pages 112- 113. Available at webpage: https://www.nra.go.jp/data/000366720.pdf Accessed 10/2023.

[835] Lars Lofquist, 2013.

[836] Lincoln L. Davies, Alexis Jones, 2015. "Fukushima's Shadow." Vanderbilt Journal of Transnational Law, Volume 48, No. 4, pp. 1083-1123. Available at webpage: https://scholarship.law.vanderbilt.edu/cgi/viewcontent.cgi?article=1210&context=vjtl Accessed 11/2023.

NPP sites in the post-Fukushima period.[837] For a brief outlook focused on "Special Decontamination Areas [established under the] 'Act on Special Measures Concerning the Handling of Environmental Pollution by Radioactive Materials discharged by the [NPS] associated with the Tohoku District [..] by the end of March 2018, whole area decontamination work was completed in all 100 municipalities in eight prefectures including Intensive Contamination Survey Areas, except for Restricted Areas."[838] As of 2020, see full MOE's SDAs map on table 8.

Table 8

Japan SDA: Mapped Surveyed Areas

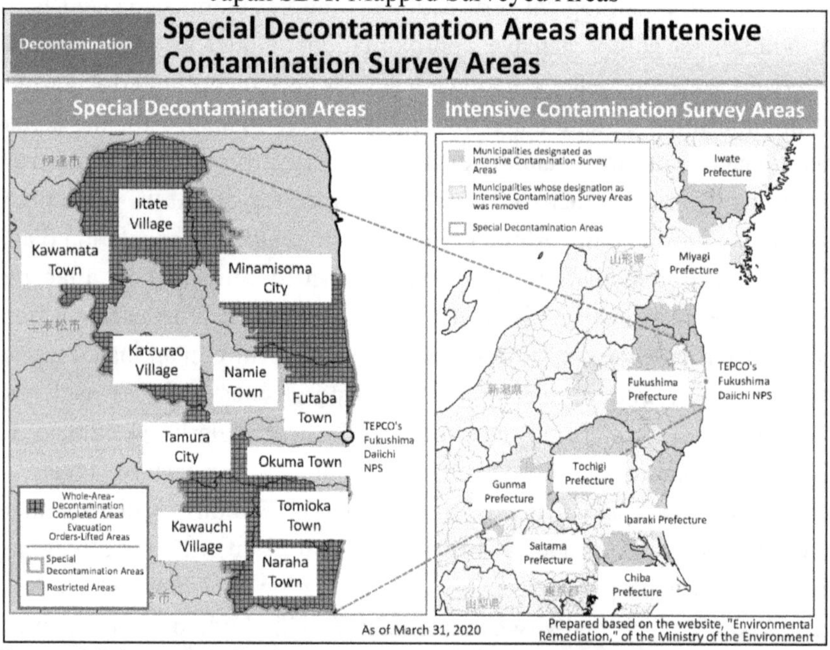

Source: Ministry of the Environment, Japan, 2020. "Special Decontamination Areas and Intensive Contamination Survey Areas." Chapter 9: 'Efforts towards Recovery from the Accident,' 9.1 'Decontamination.' Available at website: https://www.env.go.jp/en/chemi/rhm/basic-info/1st/09-01-04.html Accessed 10/2023.

[837] Lincoln L. Davies, Alexis Jones, 2015.

[838] Ministry of the Environment, Japan, 2020. "Special Decontamination Areas and Intensive Contamination Survey Areas." Chapter 9: 'Efforts towards Recovery from the Accident,' 9.1 'Decontamination.' MOE, Booklet to Provide Basic Information Regarding Health Effects of Radiation (3rd edition). Page 92. Available at webpage: https://www.env.go.jp/en/chemi/rhm/basic-info/1st/09-01-04.html Accessed 10/2023.

8.1 Comparative Public Safety Reviews

Comparatively, despite public policy enforcement of stricter local restoration measures and technical increasing standards, an international and national polarization concerning the nuclear industry development has engaged [839] both civilian anti-nuclear counterparts and pro-nuclear national campaigners on the promotion of transparent information, involving comparative knowledge methodology approaches and common local understanding about nuclear regulatory information spheres validated in different countries such as India, Europe, or the United States.[840] For these reasons, the actual preparation and distribution of environmental safety assessments combined with national resilience awareness plans, which have been led at local community level, have become strategic development priorities, particularly when put in relation to governmental NPP risk assessments, [841] projected in view of sustainable[842] energy objectives set in the long-term.[843] Similarly, when considering the status of national NPP remediation activities[844] for the

[839] Lincoln L. Davies, Alexis Jones, 2015.

[840] Upendra Choudhury, 2012. "The impact of the Fukushima Daiichi nuclear crisis on anti-nuclear movements in India." Social Alternatives, Volume 31, No. 2, pp. 39-44.

[841] Note: In the case of environmental reporting following national EIA procedures in Japan, the 'Impact Mitigation Report' remains mandatory: "[...] the purpose of obligatory Impact Mitigation Reporting is to disclose the progress of the measures taken to the citizens who are interested, and to complement the substance of measures taken by having opinions from the Minister of the Environment etc.[...]" Ministry of the Environment, Japan, 2012. "Environmental Impact Assessment in Japan." MOE, Environmental Impact Assessment Division, Report, May 2012, page 14. Available at webpage: https://www.env.go.jp/en/focus/docs/files/20120501-04.pdf Accessed 10/ 2023.

[842] Note: Japan's dependency on energy imports: "Of total primary energy supply (508,327 kiloton of oil equivalent (ktoe), 85 percent (433,725 ktoe) was imported. The breakdown of primary energy was coal 23 percent, oil 44 percent, gas 17 percent, and other 17 percent. For power generation (in Gigawatt hours (GWh), of a total 1,250,738 GWh, thermal generation accounted for 881,891 GWh (71 percent); hydro for 81,595 GWh (7 percent); nuclear for 251,744 GWh (20 percent): and other 3 percent." Stephen Harner, 2011. "Japan's energy dependence." Forbes, June 17, 2011. Available at webpage: https://www.forbes.com/sites/stephenharner/2011/06/17/japans-energy-dependence/?sh=4972bde412c6 Accessed 10/2023.

[843] Upendra Choudhury, 2012.

[844] IAEA, 2017. "Off-site environmental remediation in Fukushima continuing." IAEA Department of Nuclear Energy, News, March 16, 2017. Available at webpage: https://www.iaea.org/newscenter/news/off-site-environmental-remediation-in-fukushima-continuing Accessed 10/2023.

development of nuclear energy power plants, comparative information - e.g. contained within the Information Archival System of the NRA's website "N-ADRES"[845] - and learning training methods about local security safeguards and environmental protection guidelines have been multiplied, also through diffusion of constructive meetings for involved local stakeholders, pointing at material impacts about NPP efficiency performances and NPP security management operations ([846], [847]). Parallel to this, the Information Management Systems (IMS) in Japan have continuously facilitated ex. "the NRA continued cross-division cooperation relating to Accident Analysis Committee Meetings and response to media in related on-site investigations. [...]."[848]

As result, the possible policy enhancement tackling public safety measures has been substantiated through quantitative and qualitative research analyses, which have put into question national energy regulatory decisions that have been approved particularly in cases of rapid technological changes and comparative reformed stages, indirectly addressing regional industrial liable systems.[849] In Japan's case, under "the Reactor Regulation Act [which] provides for the 'allegation process regarding safety information of nuclear facilities' [...] the NRA investigates allegation cases responding to information provided by employees and any others on potential illegal activities committed by nuclear operators [...] to ensure the impartiality and transparency of investigations by the NRA, the Nuclear Facility Safety Information Allegation Committee consisting of external experts was set up."[850] Furthermore, at international level, single countries' regulatory systems can converge toward the adoption of specific territorial anti-risk measures designed in parallel with energy regulative operations, traced in

[845] NRA, 2020. "FY 2020. Annual Report." Nuclear Regulation Authority, Report. Page 7. Available at webpage: https://www.nra.go.jp/data/000384155.pdf Accessed 10/2023.

[846] Peter M. Schwarz, Joseph A. Cochran, 2012. "Renaissance or requiem: Is nuclear energy cost effective in a post-Fukushima world?" Contemporary Economic Policy, Volume 31, No. 4, pp. 691-707.

[847] Upendra Choudhury, 2012.

[848] NRA, 2020. "FY 2020. Annual Report." Nuclear Regulation Authority, Report. Page 7. Available at webpage: https://www.nra.go.jp/data/000384155.pdf

[849] Peter M. Schwarz, Joseph A. Cochran, 2012.

[850] NRA, 2020. "FY 2020. Annual Report." Nuclear Regulation Authority, Report. Page 7-8. Available at: https://www.nra.go.jp/data/000384155.pdf

connection with supportive multilevel management plans, which have involved nuclear waste disposal activities and public reformed approvals, especially concerning the national licensing operations.[851]

In terms of national constitutional rights about land contamination in territorial living areas, it was stressed out that "the government proposed 'Act on Special Measures for Reconstruction and Rehabilitation of Fukushima' [which] was enacted on March 2012, one year after the Accident."[852] The institutional recognition[853] processed about effective local structural needs for disaster afflicted areas has essentially reflected national policy directives, which have tended to frame local rebuilding efforts put in conjunction with the affirmation of technical transfer mechanisms increasing formal and informal periods of local widespread cooperation, while extending in selective manners the protection living rights of individuals[854] that have been directly exposed to such complex disaster events.[855] For instance, the classified governmental selection for the "community revitalization plans"[856] with adoption of more inclusive methodologies makes direct reference to ecosystems protection efforts associated with local resilient communities based in Asia-Pacific. Fundamentally, in view of reaffirming multilateral reorganization models

[851] Peter M. Schwarz, Joseph A. Cochran, 2012.

[852] Kenji Fukuda, 2015. "Need for a rights-based approach in government support for the victims of Fukushima nuclear accident." Asia-Pacific Law & Policy Journal, Volume 16, No. 2, pp. 186-193. Page 190.

[853] Note: About the DRR and Recovery programs in Asia, it is stated "We recognize that disasters in Asia are a significant and ever-present threat, as exemplified by the Indian Ocean tsunami of 2004, the 2011 Great East Japan Earthquake and tsunami, and typhoon Haiyan/Yolanda in 2013, [...] we also recognize that ecosystem based disaster risk reduction and protected areas enhance local resilience in areas of high risk of disasters. [...]." Ministry of the Environment, Japan, 2013. "Asia Protected Areas Charter." MOE doc. of 17 November, 2017. Page 2. Available at webpage: https://www.env.go.jp/en /nature/asia-parks/pdf/3-1_asia_protected_areas_charter.pdf Accessed 10/2023.

[854] See: Shunichi Yamashita, Noboru Takamura, 2015. "Post-crisis efforts towards recovery and resilience after the Fukushima Daiichi Nuclear Power Plant accident." Japanese Journal of Clinical Oncology, Volume 45, No. 8, August 2015, pages 700-707.

[855] Kenji Fukuda, 2015.

[856] Ministry of the Environment, Japan, 2015. "Result of selection of model areas for the project to formulate community revitalization plans to achieve 'low-carbon, sound material cycle and natural symbiosis' in fiscal year 2015." MOE, Policy Strategy Division, April 9, 2015. Available at webpage: https://www.env.go.jp/en/policy/plan/crp.html Accessed 10/2023.

managed for the implementation of societal practical guidelines, in cases of ex. nuclear-related disaster risk accidents, the environmental mitigation management policies run by prefectures, local municipalities, and national/regional integrated expertise bodies have been focused on comprehensive systematic operational issues, regarding the living sustainability of entire communities, ([857],[858]).

At comparative review stage, progressive energy policy studies considered about the adoption of alternative renewable energy technologies have been particularly scrutinized by the democratic environmental party leaders and governmental technical committees, who have constantly looked into responsive strategic and effectiveness criteria of public-private energy transition models PPPs, requiring structural adaptive reforms but, at the same time, enhanced environmental trading tariffs' measures addressed at national and local populations. [859] Compatible regional coordination processes undertaken for commercial renewable energy strategies have additionally led to the formation of technical review assessments and political national re-orientations, which have reaffirmed the necessary maintenance of nuclear power energy systems, as in Japan's case, however managed in view of enhancing public-private partnerships PPP, for common renewable energy distribution assets, granting a decentralized organizational transition for institutionally-reformed renewable energy systems.[860]

9.1 A Final Collection of Comparable Selective Issues

In this book review, it has been reported some evidence about the Japan's Fukushima Daiichi NPP nuclear accident issues and public-private environmental partnerships PPPs, reflecting political and industrial changing orientations. For methodology purposes this literature analysis combined with a comparative documentation process has also been

[857] Stephen G. Burns, 2012. "Global nuclear energy law and regulation symposium. The Fukushima Daiichi accident: The international community responds." Washington University Global Studies Law Review, Volume 11, No. 4, pp. 739-779.

[858] John S. Duffield, 2016. "Japanese energy policy after Fukushima Daiichi: Nuclear ambivalence." Political Science Quarterly, Volume 131, No.1, pp. 133-162.

[859] John S. Duffield, 2016.

[860] John S. Duffield, 2016.

pursued by using the EBSCO database, selecting the time-period from 2011 to 2015. This comparable review collection has taken place during 2017, when I have directly researched through the EBSCO archive Business Source Complete BSC by using as research keyword: *Fukushima Daiichi accident*.

The complete reference resulting list has included approximately 1,151 articles. In total, EBSCO - BSC articles have been scrutinized starting from the listed number 1 to 600, with direct references extracted from same database EBSCO - BSC. Thus, the comparable categorization of main themes - about the *Fukushima Daiichi accident* - has been prepared through the final selection of articles, which have been grouped into four specific dimensions and catalogued: by article title, year of publication, by author and publisher. In summary, in order to provide a thematic overview, I have found recurrent selective information areas which have therefore been classified in this research into four specific dimensions. These comparative four dimensions have been reported as follows: (a) Japan Fukushima Disaster Crisis Events - (b) Public Agency Events - (c) Environmental Safety Events - (d) Nuclear Cleanup Events; all the a-b-c-d- categories are ordered in final 65 selected news articles. These comparative literature-based findings have essentially confirmed, in a chronological order, the continuous emerging discrepancies, connected with extreme critical unreadiness of national emergency planning dispositions analyzed in relation to the disaster case of Fukushima NPP industrial management failures occurring in Japan. As specified, Table 9 has been arranged into (a), (b), (c), (d) sections for comparative overview purposes.

Table 9: Overview: Fukushima Daiichi Nuclear Disaster Articles-News

(a)

Fukushima – Japan Disaster Crisis Events	News/Articles Publication Date	Reporters/Authors	News Agency/Journal
Nuclear Power in Europe after Fukushima: A Special Report	01 March 2011	-	Stratfor Analysis, page 76
Japanese Nuke Crisis Deepens With Explosion, Spent Fuel Fire, Releases	16 March 2011	Lobsenz George	Energy Daily, Issue 51.
Why Fukushima Won't Kill Nuclear Power	06 April 2011	Lester Richard K.	Wall Street Journal, Eastern edition, New York, N.Y.
U.S. Nuke Industry Sets Fukushima Response Plan	10 June 2011	-	Energy Daily, Issue 111, page 5.
Reactor Core Melted Fully, Japan Says: Fuel Breached Vessel Floor, Operator Says, In Its Gravest Fukushima Status Report	01 December 2011	Obe Mitsuru, Fowler Tom	Wall Street Journal (Online), New York, N.Y.
Broad Array of Offshore Firms Provide Help at Fukushima	19 December 2011	Russel Pam	ENR: Engineering News-Record, Vol. 267 Issue 18, page 14
World News: Bad Data Guided U.S. Call On Fukushima	23 February 2012	Landers Peter	The Wall Street Journal Asia, Hong Kong:6
Fukushima's Fate Inspires Nuclear Safety Rethink	09 March 2012	Peter Aldhous	Daily News
Nuclear Pushes On Despite Fukushima	09 March 2012	Dawson Chester, Spegele Brian, Williams Selina	Wall Street Journal, Eastern edition, New York, N.Y.

World News: An Altered Japan Marks a Year After Quake --- Country Commemorates Anniversary With Prayers for Victims. Reflection on Losses and Protests Against Nuclear Energy	12 March 2012	Hayashi Yuka, Wakabayashi Daisuke, Obe Mitsuru	Wall Street Journal, Eastern edition, New York, N.Y.
Japan's 'Plan B' on Fukushima Cleanup	16 September 2013	Normile Dennis	ENR:Engineering News-Record, Vol. 271, Issue 11, page 10

(b)

Public Agency Events	**News/Articles Publication Date**	**Reporters/Authors**	**News Agency/Journal**
Japanese Government Confirms Meltdown	01 March 2011	-	Stratfor Analysis; page 49
NRC Chair Warns Of 'Lethal' Radiation At Japan Nuke Plant	17 March 2011	Beattie Jeff	Energy Daily, Issue 52
Putting Numbers on Japan's Radioactivity Risk	22 March 2011	Herper Matthew	Forbes.com; page 27
NRC: 'Possible Leakage Paths' For Melting Fuel in Japan Nuke Core	07 April 2011	Lobsenz George	Energy Daily, Issue 67, page 1
Katsunobu Sakurai. The Mayor Who Shamed Japan	02 May 2011	Beech Hannah	Time International (South Pacific Edition) Vol. 177, Issue 17
TEPCO Maps Fukushima Shutdown	02 May 2011	Normile Dennis, Russel Pam Radtke	ENR : Engineering News-Record, 08919526
IAEA Probes Accident In Japan	25 May 2011	Obe Mitsuru	Wall Street Journal, Eastern Edition, New York, N.Y.

Panel Vows to Review Tepco's Activities	17 June 2011	Obe Mitsuru	Wall Street Journal (Online), New York, N.Y.
Tokyo Faulted for Crisis Readiness	20 June 2011	Crawford David; Obe Mitsuru	Wall Street Journal; New York, N.Y.
Panel Won't Seek Blame in Nuclear Accident	23 June 2011	Hayashi Yuka	Wall Street Journal (Online), New York, N.Y.
NRC Members Question Japan Recommendations	20 July 2011	Beattie Jeff	Energy Daily, Issue 137.
Invisible Menace: Murky Science Clouded Japan Nuclear Response	16 August 2011	Hayashi Yuka	Wall Street Journal, Eastern edition, New York, N.Y.
Japan Misstated Radiation	09 September 2011	Obe Mitsuru	Wall Street Journal (Online), New York, N.Y.
Past Haunts Tally of Japan's Nuke Crisis	23 December 2011	Hayashi Yuka	Wall Street Journal, Eastern edition, New York, N.Y.
World News: Panel Finds Serious Errors in Japan	27 December 2011	Dvorak Phred, Obe Mitsuru	Wall Street Journal, Eastern edition, New York, N.Y.
Japan's Nuclear Crisis Plan Still Lags	19 March 2012	Dawson Chester	Wall Street Journal, Eastern edition, New York, N.Y.
World News: Premier Admits Mistakes in Japan's Nuclear-Safety Actions	28 March 2012	Sekiguchi Toko	Wall Street Journal, Eastern edition, New York, N.Y.: A.8.
Tokyo Adds to Citizens Allowed to Go Home	30 March 2012	Obe Mitsuru	Wall Street Journal (Online), New York, N.Y.
Japan Faces Opposition to Reactor-Restart Plan	06 June 2012	Warnock Eleanor	Wall Street Journal (Online), New York, N.Y.

World News: Japan Panel Blames Disaster on Negligence	06 July 2012	Obe Mitsuru, Dvorak Phred	Wall Street Journal, Eastern edition, New York, N.Y.
(NRC) Jaczko Warns On 'Pushback' On Japan Safety Changes	09 July 2012	Beattie Jeff	The Energy Daily, Englewood, no.131.
Tokyo Rally Is Biggest Yet to Oppose Nuclear Plan	16 July 2012	Hiroko Tabuchi	New York Times, July 16, 2012
World News : Japan Weighs End to Nuclear Power	22 August 2012	Iwata Mari, Mochizuki Takashi	Wall Street Journal, Eastern edition, New York, N.Y.
World News: Asia: In Reversal, Japan Utility Says Nuclear Crisis Was Avoidable	15 October 2012	Dvorak Phred, Smith Rebecca	The Wall Street Journal Asia, Hong Kong: 4.
Japan's Nuclear Dilemma	March 2013	-	Stratfor Geopolitical Diary, page 7.
World News: Japan Nuclear Plant Finds New Leaks	08 April 2013	Iwata Mari	Wall Street Journal, Eastern edition, New York, N.Y.:A.15.
World News: Japan Will Help Utility Plug Leaks at Plant	28 August 2013	Iwata Mari	Wall Street Journal, Eastern edition, New York, N.Y.
World News: Japan Seeks To Revive Nuclear Power	25 February 2014	Iwata Mari	Wall Street Journal, Eastern edition, New York, N.Y.

(c)

Environmental Safety Events	News/Articles Publication Date	Reporters/ Authors	News Agency/Journal
Red Alert: Nuclear Meltdown at Quake-Damaged Japanese Plant	01 March 2011,	-	Stratfor Analysis; page 55
Second Explosion at Quake-Damaged Japanese Plant	01 March 2011,	-	Stratfor Analysis; page 59
Dispatch From Tokyo: In Wake of Disaster, Japan Is At War.	14 March 2011	Weinberg Neil	Forbes.com
U.S. Sounds Alarm on Radiation	17 March 2011	Shirouzu Norihiko; Smith Rebecca	Wall Street Journal, Eastern edition, New York, N.Y.
Fear of Japan's Radiation is Overdone	20 March 2011	Herper Matthew	Forbes.com; page 6
Disaster in Japan: U.N. Agency Sees Flaws in Response	22 March 2011	Hansen Flemming Emil	Wall Street Journal, Eastern edition, New York, N.Y.
Disaster in Japan: At Plant, Repair Is Painstaking Task ---Smoke Briefly Shrouds Progress, But Kan Voices Optimism: 'We Are Seeing a Light at the End'	22 March 2011	Landers Peter	Wall Street Journal, Eastern edition, New York, N.Y.
Disaster in Japan: Radioactivity Spreads to New Regions ---More Countries Restrict Food Imports As Traces of Contamination Are Found	26 March 2011	Osawa Juro, Kachi Hiroyuki	Wall Street Journal, Eastern edition, New York, N.Y.
Helplessness and Humility In The Nuclear Age	28 March 2011	-	Maclean's, Vol. 124, Issue 11/ Rogers Media Inc.
World News: Worries Mount Over Residents Still Near Plant	04 April 2011	Koh Yoree, Wakabayashi Daisuke, Inada Miho	Wall Street Journal, Eastern edition, New York, N.Y.
Eerie Hush Descends On Japan's Nuke Zone	18 April 2011	Wakabayashi Daisuke	Wall Street Journal, Eastern

			edition, New York, N.Y.
Safety Gaps Found at Nuclear Plants	16 May 2011	Smith Rebecca	Wall Street Journal (Online), New York, N.Y.
In Depth: Fresh Tales of Chaos Emerge From Early in Nuclear Crisis	19 May 2011	Hayashi Yuka; Dvorak Phred	The Wall Street Journal Asia; Hong Kong
Radiation Threat Rattles Japan's Food Chain	06 August 2011	Dvorak Phred; Osawa Juro	Wall Street Journal, (Online); New York, N.Y.
World News: Japan Struggles With Tainted Reactor Water – The Key to Cooling Damaged Nuclear Plants Now Poses Major Radioactive Worry, Storage Challenge	29 February 2012	Dvorak Phred	Wall Street Journal, Eastern edition; New York, N.Y.
Displaced Japanese Town Tries to Stay Intact: Namie, Population 21,000, Survived Centuries of War, Disasters and Distress, but Struggles in Aftermath of Nuclear Crisis	03 March 2012	Hayashi Yuka	Wall Street Journal (Online); New York, N.Y.
World News: Industry Alters Designs in an Effort to Make Future Plants Safer	09 March 2012	Smith Rebecca	Wall Street Journal, Eastern edition; New York, N.Y.:A.10
World News: New Leak Found at Japan Plant	10 April 2013	Iwata Mari	Wall Street Journal, Eastern edition; New York, N.Y.

(d)

Nuclear Cleanup Events	**News/Articles Publication Date**	**Reporters/Authors**	**News Agency/Journal**
Innovating The Way To a Clean Energy Future	April 2011	Fiscor Steve	Coal Age, Vol. 116, Issue 4, page 4
Japanese Nuclear Cleanup Workers Detail Lax Safety Practices at Plant	14 June 2011	Dvorak Phred	Wall Street Journal, Eastern Edition; New York, N.Y.
Nuclear Agency Urges Japan to Fix Cleanup Plan	15 October 2011	Obe Mitsuru	Wall Street Journal (Online), New York, N.Y.
In Depth: Cleanup of Radiation Leak Confounds Japan, Residents	01 November 2011	Ono Yumiko	The Wall Street Journal Asia; Hong Kong
World News: Japan Cleanup to Take Decades	09 March 2013	Obe Mitsuru	Wall Street Journal, Eastern edition, New York, N.Y.
World News: Nuclear-Plant Cleanup to Test Tokyo – As Government Takes Over Fukushima Daiichi Effort, Its Commitment and Competence Are Questioned	04 September 2013	Dvorak Phred; Iwata Mari	Wall Street Journal, Eastern edition, New York, N.Y.
World News: Tokyo Takes Larger Role in Nuclear Cleanup	08 August 2013	Iwata Mari, Dvorak Phred	Wall Street Journal, Eastern edition, New York, N.Y.
World News: Fukushima's Toughest Cleanup Stage Ahead	08 March 2014	Iwata Mari	Wall Street Journal, Eastern edition, New York, N.Y.

9.2 Research Conclusion

This transition policy process that has been advanced in Japan has basically allowed normative revitalization incorporating dependent organizational elements, which are interconnected with the necessity to meet community safety standards, and local risk protection of living environments. Public policy reforms targeting the nuclear energy sector and implemented for contextual nuclear-based energy industries, aggregating post-Fukushima rehabilitative transition, have suggested to opt for a comparative innovative understanding concerning ministerial centralized relationships and transnational energy companies' technology organization ([861],[862]).

Moreover, it has come into consideration the elaborate preparation of national and local energy training activities connected with organizational and strategic negotiation capacities, which have been functional in order to redefine public negotiations undertaken in view of corresponding multilevel energy reforms, including the management of multiple government energy assets.[863] In fact, environmental reconstruction plans combined with local administrative boundaries have been tackled in view of establishing material propositions that have involved local technical understanding and knowledge learning diffusion operated through multilevel risk disaster scenarios; it can be noted that "…the disaster affected not only the Fukushima NPP but also many ports, steel mills, oil refineries, auto mobile plants, shipyards, and electronic components manufacturers." [864] Therefore, multiple risk hazard exposures of multilevel sector industries have to be taken into account also for the case of NPP environmental programs, especially when local introductory safety measures have been modified in view of country-level operational methodologies and future programmatic expectations.[865]

[861] John S. Duffield, 2016.

[862] Diane Brady, 2011. "Anne Lauvergeon. The CEO of French nuclear giant Areva on the lessons of Fukushima, going long on nuclear, and the costs of spending on safety." Bloomberg Businessweek, April 18-April 24, p. 1.

[863] Diane Brady, 2011.

[864] Elspeth Thomson, 2011. "China's nuclear energy in light of the disaster in Japan." Eurasian Geography and Economics, Volume 52, No. 4, pp. 464-482. Page 473.

[865] Elspeth Thomson, 2011.

Comparatively, progressive national NPP construction plans have received a distinct attention, it has been highlighted that: "In other areas of Asia, Vietnam, Malaysia and Indonesia have indicated that they will continue their own development plans. Likewise India announced it would examine all of its reactors but would not halt its plans to construct new NPPs. Only Thailand declared that all plans for nuclear power would be halted until officials have examined emergency measures [….] Germany, Switzerland, and Italy differ from other European countries by reacting more radically to the disaster at Fukushima."[866] The alteration of national regulatory reforms and local programmed actions, regarding the NPPs civil industry has contributed to the inclusion of comparative multilateral energy scenarios, which can rely on sponsoring consultative processes of national and international energy organizations, such as: the IAEA with its member states supporting the integration of complementary safety standards and local 'action-plans' approved internationally.[867] For instance, it is already provided a list of effective safety protection measures identified by the IAEA agency for the promotion of cooperative action-plans looking at:

- " safety assessments of [NPPs] in light of lessons learned from the Fukushima accident";
- "strengthening peer reviews conducted by the IAEA";
- "strengthening emergency preparedness and response capabilities";
- "strengthening the effectiveness of national regulatory bodies";
- "strengthening the effectiveness of operating organizations with respect to nuclear safety";
- "reviewing and strengthening IAEA Safety Standards and improving their implementation";
- "improving the effectiveness of the international legal framework";
- "facilitating the development of the infrastructure necessary for Member States embarking on a nuclear power program";
- "strengthening and maintaining capacity building (i.e., ensuring available of human resources necessary for safe nuclear power operation).[...]"

Source: Stephen G. Burns, 2012.([868]).

[866] Elspeth Thomson, 2011.p. 474
[867] Stephen G. Burns, 2012.
[868] Stephen G. Burns, 2012. p.752

Therefore, the preparation of regional institutional objectives about international legal frameworks regarding the NPPs development has been formulated in view of science and technology (STS) programs, projecting comparative knowledge-based information dimensions, which have been revisited according to country-level management specifications. After Japan's local hazard risk exposures and concurrent disaster events, the nuclear regulatory commissions such as the NRC in the U.S., have reviewed corresponding licensing and permission operations that have been required for the construction and local maintenance of NPPs' energy reactors.[869]

As such, national environmental implementation programs, including NPPs safety activities have involved technical processing periods of comparative institutional dialogues and local democratic leaderships combined with regional business knowledge decisions, which have been supported in line with decade-long renewable energy development strategies.[870] To this evolution, the NPP environmental hazardous issues have remained controversial due to the projection of a nuclear safety culture that has emerged after the Fukushima catastrophe.

Finally, national environmental monitoring reviews conducted in Japan have pointed at the persistence of local emergency conditions, which have raised concerns, seen also in connection with multilateral information feedbacks emanating directly from competent national authorities, operating under centralized ministerial agencies and transnational energy companies, manifesting a fragmentary evaluative correspondence

[869] Nuclear News, 2011. "Organizing petition NRC to halt permit process in wake of Japan events. " Nuclear Waste News, Volume 31, No. 8, pp. 2-3.

[870] Morgan O'Rourke, 2011. "In the wake of the quake: Rethinking nuclear safety." Risk Management Magazine, Volume 58, No. 4, May, pp. 24-26.

([871],[872],[873],[874]). For this reason, national data information provision has been associated either positively or negatively with regional decision-making processes that should increase a transparent sharing of data documentation and data collection, while supporting the evolution of normative compensatory schemes addressed to the people that were exposed to unforeseen disaster events in 2011.[875] The (STS) paradigm about science technology and societies indicating comparative industrial environmental risks, configured commercial technologies, and sociological analyses, can be adopted in order to better specify the distinctive nature of regional industrial systems operating within societal changing determinants, which can become very controversial in terms of local applicable environmental models and operable development programs.[876]

Tangible complications emerging about the mass disposal systems of NPPs have been interrelated with pragmatic assumptions referring to community mitigation norms associated to national nuclear safety cultures, which instead have been drastically shifted due to Japan's Fukushima NPP multiple disaster accidents.[877] Regional documented propositions concerning the legal and normative observations advanced by state officials and NPP energy operators have been nationally criticized because of a set of local emergent disaster causes, which have also led to serious national implications at socioeconomic level.[878]

Therefore, multiple NPPs industrial energy designs including national and international safety action-plans, involving local monitoring systems,

[871] Kenji E. Kushida, 2014. "The Fukushima nuclear disaster and the democratic party of Japan." The Japanese Political Economy, Volume 40, No. 1, pp. 29-68.
[872] Jing Liu, Michael Faure, 2016. "Compensation for nuclear damage : a comparison among the international regime, Japan and China." International Environmental Agreements: Politics, Law and Economics, Volume 16, pp. 165-187.
[873] William E. Kastenberg, 2015. "Ethics, risk, and safety culture: reflections on Fukushima and beyond." Journal of Risk Research, Volume 18, No. 3, pp. 304-316.
[874] Eiji Yamamura, 2015. "Transparency and views regarding nuclear energy before and after the Fukushima accident: Evidence on micro-data." Pacific Economic Review, Volume 20, No. 5, pp. 761-777.
[875] William E. Kastenberg, 2015.
[876] William E. Kastenberg, 2015.
[877] Eiji Yamamura, 2015.
[878] Kenji E. Kushida, 2014.

have been engineered under the supervision of controlling authorities, which have become accountable about the continuous reporting status of national energy facilities, upgraded in cases of local emergency situations. [879] At the same time, the consequential increase of complementary safety mechanisms has led to the elevation of financial management requirements, as well as, of technical information capacities, which have tended to reflect the regulatory dimension of nuclear power states that have been engaged on a common diffusion of local innovation reforming plans, and the maintenance of legal safety conditions, however completed in a distinctive way.[880]

Comparative international policy studies addressing in particular the multilevel collaborative efforts for NPPs assessment cycles regulated in parallel with local management conducts, have put a major accent on preferential evaluative systems and public risk perceptions, indicating the uncertainty and mediation dimension, which have been related to public-private partnerships PPPs organizational development ([881],[882],[883]). PPP organizational interactions have been based on regional supporting systems incorporating contextual elements tackling: common knowledge diffusion, technology knowledge transfers, and knowledge innovation capacities, characterizing multilateral governance adaptation with local resilience contingency planning, established within and between national technocratic boundaries ([884],[885],[886]). The Cabinet Office of Japan, Disaster Management Unit, introduces annual white papers on DM that have been reported on the final Annex of this study. As nuclear emergency measures

[879] Kenji E. Kushida, 2014

[880] Jing Liu, Michael Faure, 2016.

[881] Manuel Fischer, 2015. "Collaboration patterns, external shocks and uncertainty: Swiss nuclear energy politics before and after Fukushima." Energy Policy, Volume 86, pp. 520-528.

[882] Younghwan Kim, Minki Kim, Wonjoon Kim, 2013. "Effect of the Fukushima nuclear disaster on global public acceptance of nuclear energy." Energy Policy, Volume 61, pp. 822-828.

[883] Shun Deng Fam, Jieru Xiong, Gordon Xiong, Ding Li Yong, Daniel Ng, 2014. "Post-Fukushima Japan: The continuing nuclear controversy." Energy Policy, Volume 68, pp. 199-205.

[884] Manuel Fischer, 2015.

[885] Younghwan Kim, Minki Kim, Wonjoon Kim, 2013.

[886] Shun Deng Fam, Jieru Xiong, Gordon Xiong, Ding Li Yong, Daniel Ng, 2014.

and resilience strategies, we summarize nuclear preparedness issues for the year 2020 reported by the Cabinet Office of Japan for comparative guidance that can be further investigated in a prospective research activity.

Final Annex[887]

Cabinet Office Japan

Disaster Management in Japan

Official Website: https://www.bousai.go.jp/en/

Reports Selected year 2020

"White Paper on Disaster Management 2020"
https://www.bousai.go.jp/en/documentation/white_paper/2020.html

DM Nuclear Policy

"Chapter 2: Progress of Measures for Nuclear Disasters"
https://www.bousai.go.jp/en/documentation/white_paper/2020.html

Selected Sections:

S1 - S3: "Nuclear Emergency Preparedness" Measures

"Section 1. Nuclear Emergency Preparedness Systems"
"1-1 Nuclear Emergency Preparedness System under Non-Emergency Conditions"
https://www.bousai.go.jp/en/documentation/white_paper/pdf/2020/PI2-1.pdf

Main Highlights:
" In the case of a nuclear emergency, the resultant damage would be immense and extensive, so the whole government must work together cohesively to develop

887 Access to Official Website in English Language, only.

and promote nuclear emergency response measures. [...] The Nuclear Emergency Preparedness Council has been established within the Cabinet Office to promote nuclear emergency preparedness measures by the government as a whole under non-emergency conditions. [...]." (WP, 2020, page 103).

1-2 Nuclear Emergency Preparedness System in an Emergency

Main Highlights:
"In the event of a nuclear emergency involving the release of a large quantity of radioactive material, a Nuclear Emergency Response Headquarters will be established. The main role of this headquarters will be to ascertain the actual situation on the field and the extent of the damage and to take overall charge of coordinating related national government organizations and local governments bodies to ensure that emergency response measures suited to the situation are implemented swiftly and accurately.[...]." (WP, 2020, page 103).

"Fig. 1-2-1 - Crisis Management System in Nuclear Emergencies" (WP, 2020, page 104).

Main Highlights:

"National Government":
"Prime Minister's Office Team at the Nuclear Emergency Response Headquarters Secretariat"[...].

"Secretariat of the Nuclear Regulation Authority's ERC":
"ERC Team at the Nuclear Emergency Response Headquarters Secretariat" [...].

"Urgent Area":
"Rapid Response Center at Nuclear Facilities; On-Site Disaster Management Headquarters; Local Government" [...].

"Section 3. Enhancing and Strengthening Local Nuclear Emergency Preparedness Systems"
"3-1 Formulating and Supporting Local Plans for Disaster Risk Reduction/Evacuation Plans"

https://www.bousai.go.jp/en/documentation/white_paper/pdf/2020/PI2-3.pdf

Main Highlights:

" Under the Basic Act on Disaster Management, local governments must prepare Local Plans for DRR with Nuclear Emergency Response Measures [...] that set out the basic response to be adopted by prefectures and municipalities in dealing with a nuclear emergency.[...]." (WP, 2020, page 107).

Main Highlights:
"In March 2015, the Cabinet Office established Local Nuclear Disaster Management Councils [...] to serve as working teams for resolving issues in areas where nuclear power plants are located. Its aim in doing so was to support efforts to flesh out and enhance the content of the Local Plans for DRR and Evacuation Plans formulated by prefectures and municipalities in accordance with 'Future Responses to Enhancing Local Plans for DRR' [...]." (WP, 2020, page 107).

" 3. Enhancing Nuclear Emergency Response Measures."

Main Highlights:
" The Committee of Related Ministries and Agencies on Nuclear Emergency Response Measures was convened in April 2016 [...] to facilitate [...] nuclear emergency response measures [...]. At this meeting, committee members decided to establish subcommittees focused on three themes: **cooperation between front-line response units** [...]; **cooperation between private sector business operators** [...]; and **approaches to the provision of information, including diffusion calculations** [...]." (WP, 2020, page 112).

Graphic Scheme: "Fig. 3-2-2" (WP, 2020, page 113).

See below:

Fig. 3-2-2 Key Points of Study Results at the Subcommittee for Enhancing Nuclear Emergency Response Measure

Key Points of Study Results at the Subcommittee for Enhancing Nuclear Emergency Response Measures

The following recommendations by the National Governors' Association were put together in addition to the Stance on Enhancing Nuclear Emergency Response Measures (decided on March 11, 2016 at the Inter-Ministerial Council for Nuclear Power):

1. Cooperation between front-line response organizations

(1) Activities of these organizations should be **presented with actual examples, and emergency responses clearly indicated by the community**.

(Example activities)
- Police: Guiding vehicles carrying personnel dispatched to affected areas
- Firefighters: Supporting transport of those who require assistance evacuating
- Japan Coast Guard: Supporting the evacuation of residents by patrol boats
- SDF: Supporting evacuation

(2) **Initiatives such as the sharing of information and exchange of views should be promoted** through community liaison conferences[*1] **during normal times**.

(3) **The system of a joint operations coordination center[*2] should be used** according to discussion among stakeholders **in the event of an unforeseen situation in the nuclear disaster**.

(4) **Cooperation should be ensured by the community taking advantage of the features of each organization**.

*1 Community liaison conference
A conference comprising related ministries and agencies (including front-line organizations) and nuclear operators to coordinate collaboration in emergency responses and support of the nuclear site.

*2 Joint operations coordination center
Front-line response units organized each time a disaster takes place share information at this center as required.

1. Cooperation between front-line response organizations

(1) **Provisions to be included in the agreement between the local government** and private business operator **will be collated and presented**.

(Example provisions)

- **Setting of measures to manage exposure doses** and decision on **an exposure dose management method** for conducting tasks.
- Better understanding of **preparation for materials and equipment** such as protective clothing and masks by the **local government** and **dissemination of methods and procedures for distributing these materials and equipment**.
- **The local government will bear and compensate** the cost required for conducting tasks and the loss caused by conducting tasks in principle.
- **Regular training opportunities will be provided** for private business operators who actually engage in the work.

1. Cooperation between front-line response organizations

(1) If the risk of fatalities directly caused by natural disasters (earthquakes, tsunamis, heavy snowfall) is extremely high, **evacuation for natural disasters will be prioritized over that for nuclear disasters.**

(2) **Awareness** of residents and private business operators **will be raised regarding complete adherence to sheltering indoors** and **evacuation information will be provided to residents via various tools,** including a prefectural/municipal disaster management radio communication system.

(3) About the diffusion calculation:

- **Details of support (e.g. execution of calculation and explanation of results) will be made clear as pre-disaster measures** to enhance evacuation plans.
- **The points to note will be collated for local governments to make decisions and take responsibilities during an emergency.**

Source: Japan Cabinet Office. "White Paper on Disaster Management 2020." Available at website: https://www.bousai.go.jp/en/documentation/white_paper/pdf/2020/PI2-3.pdf

Women's Participation Rates at *Local Disaster Management Councils* across Japan, 2019.

"Page A-69"

"Fig. A-44 Female Representation in Local Disaster Management Councils (by Prefecture, 2019)"

	Prefectural Disaster Management Council			**Municipal Disaster Management Council**		
	Total Members	**Of which, Female Members**	**Proportion of Women (%)**	**Total Members**	**Of which, Female Members**	**Proportion of Women (%)**
Hokkaido	68	5	7.4	3,911	128	3.3
Aomori	59	10	16.9	773	40	5.2
Iwate	76	14	18.4	1,144	97	8.5
Miyagi	58	9	15.5	833	61	7.3
Akita	60	4	6.7	719	78	10.8
Yamagata	62	8	12.9	995	60	6.0
Fukushima	54	8	14.8	1,003	53	5.3
Ibaraki	51	6	11.8	1,240	107	8.6
Tochigi	52	10	19.2	586	67	11.4
Gunma	47	6	12.8	989	86	8.7
Saitama	69	12	17.4	2,138	240	11.2
Chiba	52	8	15.4	1,550	171	11.0
Tokyo	73	11	15.1	2,207	243	11.0
Kanagawa	57	13	22.8	1,005	128	12.7
Niigata	72	16	22.2	876	50	5.7
Toyama	67	11	16.4	515	32	6.2
Ishikawa	70	7	10.0	461	28	6.1
Fukui	56	3	5.4	501	49	9.8
Yamanashi	64	6	9.4	578	54	9.3
Nagano	77	15	19.5	1,939	141	7.3
Gifu	61	10	16.4	913	77	8.4
Shizuoka	58	5	8.6	1,053	97	9.2
Aichi	68	5	7.4	1,482	167	11.3
Mie	60	5	8.3	915	91	9.9
Shiga	59	12	20.3	490	48	9.8
Kyoto	66	14	21.2	757	61	8.1
Osaka	58	5	8.6	1,315	139	10.6
Hyogo	56	8	14.3	1,294	128	9.9

Nara	61	7	11.5	853	77	9.0
Wakayama	55	7	12.7	610	49	8.0
Tottori	65	28	43.1	407	57	14.0
Shimane	73	34	46.6	607	52	8.6
Okayama	58	9	15.5	508	83	16.3
Hiroshima	59	4	6.8	822	55	6.7
Yamaguchi	60	7	11.7	615	62	10.1
Tokushima	81	39	48.1	557	37	6.6
Kagawa	60	8	13.3	441	53	12.0
Ehime	61	5	8.2	487	32	6.6
Kochi	58	7	12.1	754	73	9.7
Fukuoka	61	4	6.6	1,199	196	16.3
Saga	70	18	25.7	378	41	10.8
Nagasaki	68	13	19.1	671	45	6.7
Kumamoto	56	6	10.7	1,635	109	6.7
Oita	58	6	10.3	548	48	8.8
Miyazaki	53	4	7.5	709	47	6.6
Kagoshima	63	7	11.1	1,124	65	5.8
Okinawa	54	7	13.0	632	57	9.0
Total	**2,904**	**466**	**16.0**	**45,739**	**3,959**	**8.7**

Source: Cabinet Office of Japan, 2020. "White Paper on Disaster Management 2020. Appendix." Page A69. Available at Website: https://www.bousai.go.jp/en/documentation/white_paper/pdf/2020/App.pdf

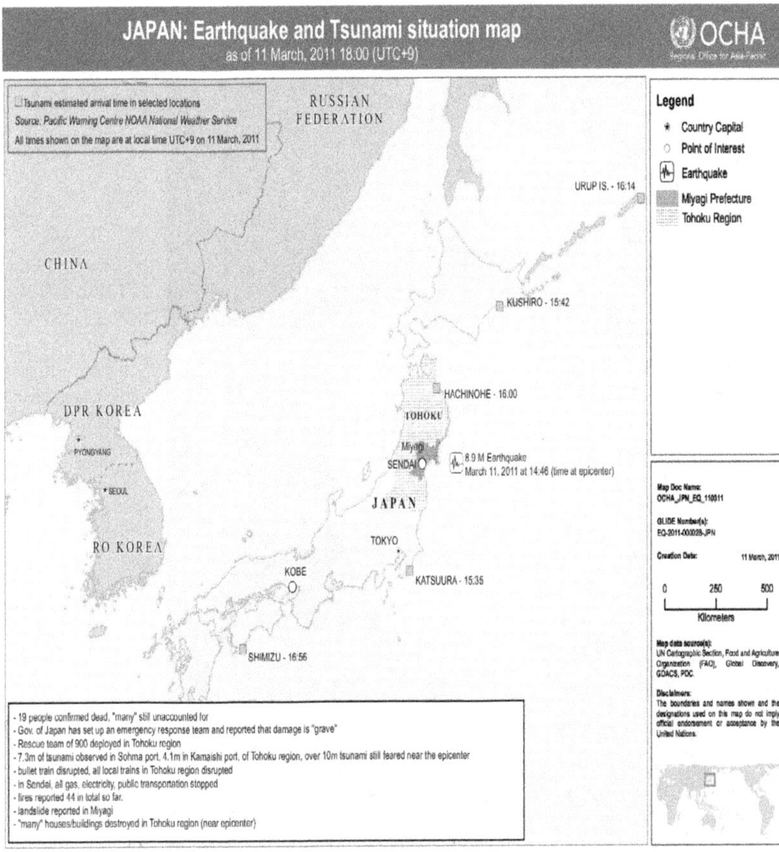

Source: OCHA Services, Reliefweb. "Japan: Earthquake and Tsunami situation map (as of 11 Mar, 2011 18:00 [UTC+9]" Published 11 March 2011. UN Office for the Coordination of Humanitarian Affairs. Map available online at: https://reliefweb.int/map/japan/japan-earthquake-and-tsunami-situation-map-11-mar-2011-1800-utc-9 Accessed 11/2023.

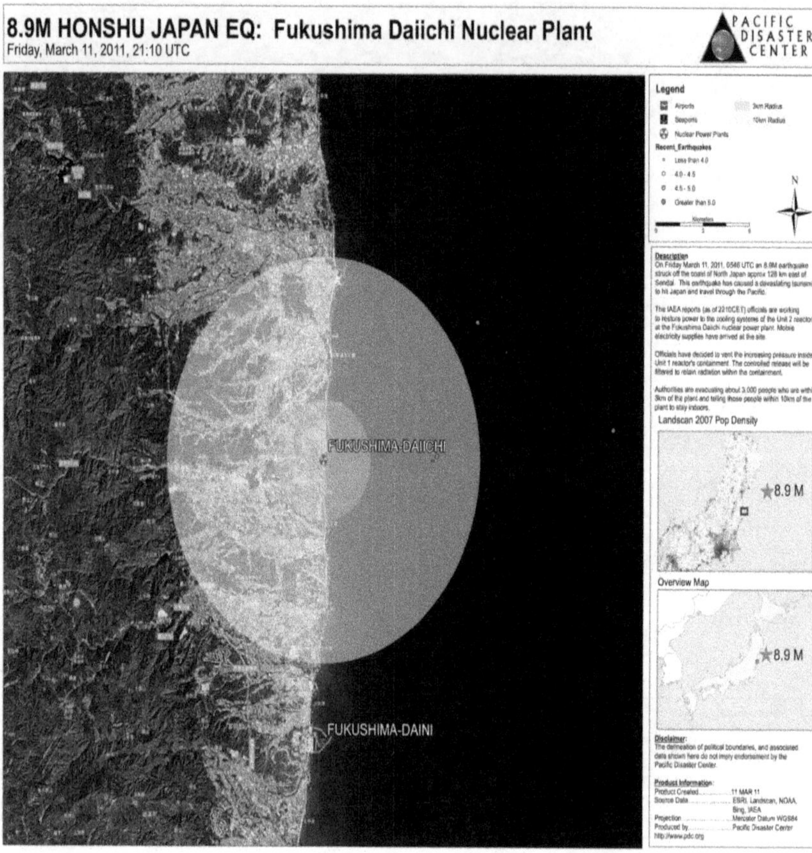

Source: OCHA Services, Reliefweb. "Japan: 8.9M Honshu Earthquake - Fukushima Daiichi Nuclear Plant (11 Mar, 2011)." Published 11 March 2011. UN Office for the Coordination of Humanitarian Affairs. Map available online at: https://reliefweb.int/map/japan/japan-89m-honshu-earthquake-fukushima-daiichi-nuclear-plant-11-mar-2011 Accessed 11/2023.

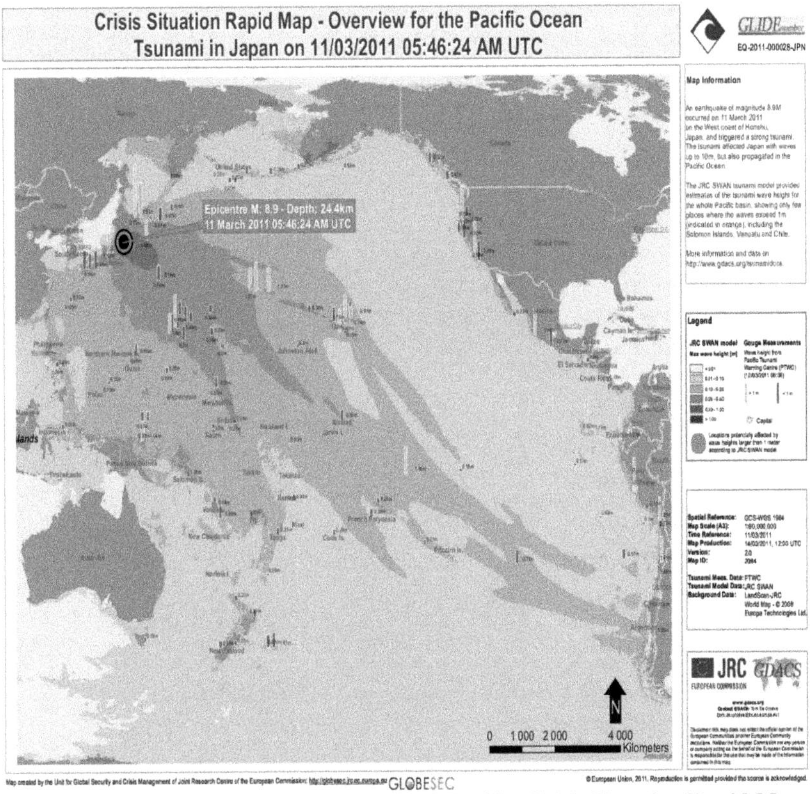

Source: OCHA Services, Reliefweb. "Japan, Pacific: Crisis Situation Rapid Map - Overview for the Pacific Ocean Tsunami in Japan (on 11 Mar, 2011)." Published 11 March 2011. UN Office for the Coordination of Humanitarian Affairs. Map available online at: https://reliefweb.int/map/japan/japan-pacific-crisis-situation-rapid-map-overview-pacific-ocean-tsunami-japan-11-mar-2011 Accessed 11/2023.

Bibliography

- Adelphi, (2018). “Networking communities: How municipalities can learn from each other and increase their capacity for adaptation.” Adelphi independent think tank based in Germany, web-page article. Available at website: https://www.adelphi.de/en/project/networking-communities-how-municipalities-can-learn-each-other-and-increase-their-capacity Last Accessed 08/2023.
- Agboola, J. I. (2011). “The changing socio-ecology of Japan’s Ishikawa coast.” Our World, United Nations University, 26 October, 2011. Available at website: https://ourworld.unu.edu/en/the-changing-socio-ecology-of-japans-ishikawa-coast Last Accessed 08/2023.
- ANU, Japan Institute, (2021). “Local knowledge as the basis of disaster management in Asia.” Australian National University, ANU College of Asia & the Pacific, Public Event, 20 October 2021. Available at website: https://japaninstitute.anu.edu.au/events/local-knowledge-basis-disaster-management-asia Last Accessed 08/2023.
- Aoki, M. and Rothwell, G. (2013). “A comparative institutional analysis of the Fukushima nuclear disaster: Lessons and policy implications.” *Energy Policy*, Volume 53, pp. 240-247.
- APEIS-IEA, (2004). “Technical Summary. IEA, Integrated Environmental Assessment.” Asia-Pacific Environmental Innovation Strategy Project, Report. Available at website: https://www.env.go.jp/en/earth/ecoasia/APEIS/iea/pdf/TS_IEA.pdf Last Accessed 08/2023.
- Ash, J.S. (2011). “Radiation or Riots: Risk perception in nuclear power decision making and deliberative approaches to resolving stakeholder conflict.” *Politics & Policy*, Volume 39, No. 3, pp. 317-344.
- Ashina, S. (2009). “Model analysis for low carbon society (1) Japan’s case.” National Institute for Environmental Studies. The 18th Asia-Pacific Seminar on Climate Change “Building an Architecture of an Effective Future Regime.” 2-3 March 2009, Vietnam. Full Report. Available at website: https://www.env.go.jp/en/earth/ap-net/documents/seminar/18th/0-2_NIES_Mr.ShuichiAshina.pdf Last Accessed 08/2023.
- Bachev, H. (2019). “Assessment of preparedness and agri-food impacts of Fukushima nuclear accident: Implications for improvement of disaster risk management.” Disaster, Diversity and Emergency Preparation L.I. Magnussen (Ed.). Open Access by IOS Press.
- Baker, K. (2004). “Renewable energy technology programs in Australia.”

Presentation to the 14th Asia Pacific Seminar on Climate Change, Sydney, Australia. Available at webpage: https://www.env.go.jp/en/earth/ap-net/documents/seminar/14th/baker.pdf Last Accessed 10/2023.

- Basri, N.A. Hashim, S. Ramli, A.T. Bradley, D.A. and Hamzah, K. (2016). "Regulatory requirements for nuclear power plant site selection in Malaysia - a review." *Journal of Radiological Protection*, Volume 36, No. 4, R96-R111.
- Behr, P. (2012). "Interview: Yoichi Funabashi. Lessons from Fukushima." Nieman Reports, Fall 2012, pp. 21-23. Copyright of Neiman Reports is property of Nieman Reports. Available at website: https://niemanreports.org/articles/lessons-from-fukushima/ Last Accessed 11/2023.
- Bird, W. (2016). "Living in limbo." Earth Island Journal, Spring, pp. 31-36. Copyright of Earth Island Journal is property of Earth Island Institute. Available at webpage: https://www.earthisland.org/journal/index.php/magazine/entry/living_in_limbo Last Accessed 11/2023.
- Brady, D. (2011). "Anne Lauvergeon. The CEO of French nuclear giant Areva on the lessons of Fukushima, going long on nuclear, and the costs of spending on safety." *Bloomberg Businessweek*, April 18-April 24, p. 1.
- Bréthaut, C. and Turley, L. (2020). "Exploring the politics of institutional fragmentation in transboundary river basins." *Oxford Research Encyclopedias*, Environmental Science. https://doi.org/10.1093/acrefore/9780199389414.013.647
- Bukoski, J. (2015). "Post-Fukushima: The impacts on Japanese public opinion of nuclear power." Yale Environment Review (YER), article published 23/03/2015. Available at webpage: https://environment-review.yale.edu/post-fukushima-impacts-japanese-public-opinion-nuclear-power-0 Last Accessed 10/2023.
- Burger, J. Clarke, J. and Gochfeld, M. (2011). "Information needs for siting new, and evaluating current, nuclear facilities: ecology, fate and transport, and human health." *Environmental Monitoring Assessment*, Volume 172, No. 1-4, pp. 121-134.
- Burns, S.G. (2012). "Global nuclear energy law and regulation symposium. The Fukushima Daiichi accident: The international community responds." *Washington University Global Studies Law Review*, Volume 11, No. 4, pp. 739-779.
- Chanchitpricha, C. and Bond, A. (2013). "Conceptualising the effectiveness of impact assessment processes." *Environmental Impact Assessment Review*, Volume 43, pp. 65-72.
- Choudhury, U. (2012). "The impact of the Fukushima Daiichi nuclear crisis on anti-nuclear movements in India." *Social Alternatives*, Volume 31, No. 2, pp. 39-44.
- City of Kyoto, (2018). "Becoming a net-zero emissions city through transformative changes in lifestyle, work-style and urban infrastructure." *(KEAA) Kyoto Environmental Activities Association, ICLEI* - Local

Governments for Sustainability, Japan Office, (RIHN) Research Institute for Humanity and Nature, National Report, 10 December 2017. Available at website: http://copjapan.env.go.jp/talanoa/assets/pdfs/stories/en/20181101-009.pdf Last Accessed 08/2023.

- Cotton, M. (2015). "Structure, agency and post-Fukushima nuclear policy: an alliance-context-actantiality model of political change." *Journal of Risk Research*, Volume 18, No.3, pp. 317-332.
- Davies, L.L. and Jones, A. (2015). "Fukushima's Shadow." Vanderbilt Journal of Transnational Law, Volume 48, No. 4, pp. 1083-1123. Available at webpage: https://scholarship.law.vanderbilt.edu/cgi/viewcontent.cgi?article=1210&context=vjtl Last Accessed 11/2023.
- Downer, J. (2014). "Disowning Fukushima: Managing the credibility of nuclear reliability assessment in the wake of disaster." *Regulation & Governance*, Volume 8, No. 3, pp. 287-309.
- Dudley, N. Buyck, C. Furuta, N. Pedrot, C. Renaud, F. and Sudmeier-Rieux, K. (2015). *Protected Areas Tools for Disaster Risk Reduction. A handbook for practitioners*. Tokyo and Gland, Switzerland: MOEJ and IUCN, 44pp. Available at webpage: https://www.env.go.jp/en/nature/asia-parks/world_6th/EcoDRRhandbook_En.pdf Last Accessed 10/2023.
- Duffield, J.S. (2016). "Japanese energy policy after Fukushima Daiichi: Nuclear ambivalence." *Political Science Quarterly*, Volume 131, No.1, pp. 133-162.
- (The) Economist, Briefing, (2011). *The risks exposed; Japan's nuclear industry*. The Economist; London, Vol. 398, Issue. 8725. March 2011.
- (The) Economist, Asia, (2011). *Living with radiation; Coping with Japan's nuclear disaster.* The Economist Intelligence Unit N.A., Incorporated, Volume 399, Issue 8728, London, UK.
- (The) Economist, Business, (2011). *The troubles of TEPCO; Power in Japan.* The Economist; London, Volume 400, Issue. 8740. July, 2011.
- Edahiro, J. (2009). "A brief history of the environmental movement in Japan (part I)." *JFS, Japan for Sustainability,* Newsletter No. 82, July 21, 2009. Available at website: https://www.japanfs.org/en/news/archives/news_id029180.html Last Accessed 08/2023.
- Environment Canada Report. Environmental Emergencies Program, (1999). "National Environmental Emergencies Contingency Plan." Environmental Emergencies Branch. Canada; Quebec K1A 0H3. Available at website: https://publications.gc.ca/collections/collection_2017/eccc/En40-584-1999-eng.pdf Last Accessed 11/2023.
- Environmental Impact Assessment Division, online (2022). "Environmental impact assessment in Japan." Ministry of the Environment, Government of Japan, National Report. Available at website: https://www.env.go.jp/en/policy/assess/pamph.pdf Last Accessed 08/2023.
- EPA, United States, (2013). "Observations and commentary on remediation of the lands off-site from the Fukushima Daiichi reactors." Report of the United States Embassy Science Fellows Support to the Government of Japan -

Ministry of the Environment. SRNL-RP-2013-00303 EPA/600/R-13/135. Available at website: http://josen.env.go.jp/en/documents/pdf/workshop_july_17-18_2013_04.pdf Last Accessed 09/2023.
- Fam, S.D. Xiong, J. Xiong, G. Yong, D.L. and Ng, D. (2014). "Post-Fukushima Japan: The continuing nuclear controversy." *Energy Policy*, Volume 68, pp. 199-205.
- Fan, M.F. (2010). "Justice, community knowledge, and waste facility siting in Taiwan." *Public Understanding of Science*, Volume 21, No. 4, pp. 418-431.
- Featherstone, S. (2016). "Fukushima five years later." Popular Science, March-April, pp. 72-77. Copyright of Popular Science is property of Bonnier Corporation. POPSCI.COM. Available at webpage: https://www.popsci.com/fukushima-five-years-later/ Last Accessed 11/2023.
- Figueroa, P. (2015). "Governance and risk communication in Fukushima: Notes from Miyakoji." Our World, United Nations University, 14 January 2014. Available at website: https://ourworld.unu.edu/en/governance-and-risk-communication-in-fukushima-notes-from-miyakoji Last Accessed 09/2023.
- Fischer, M. (2015). "Collaboration patterns, external shocks and uncertainty: Swiss nuclear energy politics before and after Fukushima." *Energy Policy*, Volume 86, pp. 520-528.
- Forbes Asia, (2011). *Thoughts on the crisis in Japan*. Forbes, April 11, 2011.
- Fujii, H. (2019). "Development of educational materials for risk communication using the infographics." Ministry of the Environment, Japan, Report, 2019. Available at website: https://www.env.go.jp/content/900406510.pdf Last Accessed 09/2023.
- Fukuda, K. (2015). "Need for a rights-based approach in government support for the victims of Fukushima nuclear accident." *Asia-Pacific Law & Policy Journal*, Volume 16, No. 2, pp. 186-193.
- (The) Fukushima Report, available at website: http://thefukushimareport.com/ As of 11/2023 web-link cannot be retrieved. (or) The Woods Hole Oceanographic Institution, 2013. "Fukushima and the Ocean."Presented on May, 9, 2013. Volume 50. No. 1, Spring 2013. https://www.whoi.edu/know-your-ocean/ocean-topics/ocean-human-lives/pollution/radiation/fukushima-radiation/fukushima-and-the-ocean/.
- G7 Germany, (2022). "G7 climate, energy and environment ministers' communiqué." Japan MOE, Berlin, 27 May 2022, Report. Available at website: https://www.env.go.jp/content/000039438.pdf Last Accessed 08/2023.
- Geels, F.W. (2004). "From sectoral systems of innovation to socio-technical systems: Insights about dynamics and change from sociology and institutional theory." *Research Policy*, Volume 33, No. 6-7, pp. 897-920.
- Glucker, A.N. Driessen, P.P.J. Kolhoff, A. Runhaar, H.A.C. (2013). "Public participation in environmental impact assessment: why, who, and how?" *Environmental Impact Assessment Review*, Volume 43, pp. 104-111.
- GMF, website. (2023) "Welcome to GMF website." Group of European

Municipalities with Nuclear Facilities, declaration summary available at website: https://gmfeurope.org/about-us/ Accessed 08/2023.

- Gonzalez, A.J. (2012). "The recommendations of the ICRP vis-à-vis the Fukushima Dai-ichi NPP accident aftermath." *Journal of Radiological Protection*, Volume 32, No. 1. **DOI** 10.1088/0952-4746/32/1/N1.
- (The) Government of Japan, December (2017). "Japan's third biennial report under the United Nations Framework Convention on Climate Change." Governmental Report, December 2017. Available at website: https://www.env.go.jp/content/900446224.pdf Last Accessed 08/2023.
- (The) Government of Japan, (2019). "The long-term strategy under the Paris Agreement." Cabinet decision, June 11, 2019. Report available at website: https://www.env.go.jp/press/111913.pdf Last Accessed 08/2023.
- Gulati, R. Casto, C. and Krontiris, C. (2014). "How the other Fukushima plant survived." The Globe, Harvard Business Review, Crisis Management, July-August 2014. Available at website: https://hbr.org/2014/07/how-the-other-fukushima-plant-survived Last Accessed 09/2023.
- Hagmann, J. (2012). "Fukushima: probing the analytical and epistemological limits of risk analysis." *Journal of Risk Research*, Volume 15, No. 7, pp. 801-815.
- Hammond, E. (2015). "Nuclear power, risk, and retroactivity." *Vanderbilt Journal of Transnational Law*, Volume 48, No. 4, pp. 1059-1082.
- Hanna, S. Yamada, T. Kondo, H. Watanabe, A. and Ohba, R. (2016). "International workshop at Fukushima, Japan, on dispersion and deposition modeling for nuclear accident releases: Transfer of science from academic to operational models." (Meeting Summaries). *Bulletin of the American Meteorological Society*, Volume 97, February, pp. ES31-ES36.
- Haraguchi, M. (2020). "How can a municipal government continue operations during mega-disasters? An analysis of preparedness using complex adaptive systems." *Disaster Prevention and Management*, Volume 29, No. 5, pp. 779-792.
- Harner, S. (2011). "Japan's energy dependence." Forbes, June 17, 2011. Available at webpage: https://www.forbes.com/sites/stephenharner/2011/06/17/japans-energy-dependence/?sh=4972bde412c6 Last Accessed 10/2023.
- Hasegawa, K. (2016). "On the accident at Fukushima Daiichi nuclear power plant from the inherent safety points of view." *Chemical Engineering Transactions*, Volume 48, pp. 511-516.
- Hayashi, M. and Hughes, L. (2013). "The policy responses to the Fukushima nuclear accident and their effect on Japanese energy security." *Energy Policy*, Volume 59, pp. 86-101.
- Hayes, M. (2016). "Cost of Fukushima nuclear disaster rises to $188 billion." International Construction, 14 December 2016. Website: https://www.international-construction.com/ (or) https://www.khl.com/news/cost-of-fukushima-nuclear-disaster-rises-to-188-bn/1123699.article Last Accessed 09/2023.

- Henry, R. (2013). "Exploring Fukushima to the nth degree." Nuclear Plant Journal, January-February, Volume 31, No. 1, pp. 28-30. Available at website: https://digitaleditions.nuclearplantjournal.com/JF13/files/assets/basic-html/index.html#page28 Last Accessed 11/2023.
- Hibbs, M. (2022). "Why Europe is looking to nuclear power to fuel a green future." *Carnegie Endowment for International Peace*, Commentary, February 18, 2022. Commentary. Available at website: https://carnegieendowment.org/2022/02/18/why-europe-is-looking-to-nuclear-power-to-fuel-green-future-pub-86468 Last Accessed 08/2023.
- Honda A. Wiwattanapantuwong J. and Abe T. (2014). "Japanese university students' attitudes toward the Fukushima nuclear disaster." Journal of Environmental Psychology, Volume 40, pp. 147-156. In: Jacob Bukoski, 2015. Yale Environment Review, article published 23/03/2015. Available at: https://environment-review.yale.edu/post-fukushima-impacts-japanese-public-opinion-nuclear-power-0 (or) https://www.sciencedirect.com/science/article/abs/pii/S0272494414000528?via%3Dihub Last Accessed both 10/2023.
- Huaxia, (2022). "Japan's NRA to resume Tsuruga nuclear safety assessment." Xinhua News, October 27, 2022. Available at webpage: https://english.news.cn/20221027/550f1dec6fce40d58c13844e4b0e0353/c.html Last Accessed 09/2023.
- IAEA, (2013). "The follow-up IAEA international mission on remediation of large contaminated areas off-site the Fukushima Daiichi Nuclear Power Plant." Tokyo and Fukushima Prefecture, Japan 14-21 October 2013. International Atomic Energy Agency, Final Report, NE/NEFW/2013. Available at website: https://www.env.go.jp/content/900483741.pdf Last Accessed 09/2023.
- IAEA, (2017). "The 3rd IAEA-MOE experts meeting on environmental remediation. Tokyo, Minami-Soma City, Date City." Summary Report IAEA, 17-21 April 2017. Available at website: http://josen.env.go.jp/en/news/pdf/news_170417_01.pdf Last Accessed 09/2023.
- IAEA, (2017). "Off-site environmental remediation in Fukushima continuing." IAEA Department of Nuclear Energy, News, March 16, 2017. Available at webpage: https://www.iaea.org/newscenter/news/off-site-environmental-remediation-in-fukushima-continuing Last Accessed 10/2023.
- IAEA International Atomic Energy Agency, (2020). "Information, June 2012, 2020. Fukushima Daiichi Nuclear Power Station until March. Status Updates." Available at webpage: https://www.iaea.org/sites/default/files/20/06/fukushima_update_12june2020.pdf Last Accessed 09/2023.
- IGES, (2018). "Japan's initiative towards expansion of environmental infrastructure ." Clean Asia Initiative Newsletter [CAI], Volume 17, March 2018. Edited by the Institute for Global Environmental Strategies. Available at website:

https://www.env.go.jp/earth/coop/coop/english/cai/pdf/newsletter_e_vol17.pdf Last Accessed 08/2023.
- (Md.) Islam, T. (2013). "People's participation in protected areas of Bangladesh." APC 1st Asia Parks Congress, Japan 2013, Parks Connect., Presentation. Available at webpage: https://www.env.go.jp/en/nature/asia-parks/pdf/wg3/APC_WG4-26_Md.%20Tariqul%20Islam.pdf Last Accessed 10/2023.
- Jade Media, (2011). "Japan struggles to find spot for waste released after March quake, tsunami." Nuclear Waste News, October, page 6. Copyright of Nuclear Waste News is property of Jade Media Partners.
- Japan Government, (1998). "Enforcement regulation of the environmental impact assessment act." Order of the Prime Minister's Office N. 37 of June 12, 1998. Available at website: http://assess.env.go.jp/files/5_global/Enforcement%20Regulation%20of%20the%20EIA%20Act.pdf Last Accessed 08/2023.
- Japan Ministry of the Environment, (2000). "Detailed description of best practices - Japan No. 14." G8 Environmental Futures Forum 2000 on "Domestic Best Practices Addressing Climate Change," Report. Available at website: https://www.env.go.jp/earth/g8_2000/forum/g8bp/detail/japan/japan14.html Last Accessed 08/2023.
- Japan Ministry of the Environment, (2012). "Advancement of environmental management and use of environmental information. Building infrastructures to promote green economy." Government of Japan MOE, report, March 2012. Available at website: https://www.env.go.jp/content/900453304.pdf Last Accessed 08/2023.
- Japan Ministry of the Environment, (2012). "Environmental reporting guidelines." MOE, Government of Japan, Report. Available at website: https://www.env.go.jp/en/policy/economy/erg2012.pdf Last Accessed 08/2023.
- Japan Ministry of the Environment, (2018). "The Basic Environment Plan." MOE, Japan Cabinet Decision on April 17, 2018, Report. Available at website: https://www.env.go.jp/content/000042331.pdf Last Accessed 08/2023.
- Japan Platform, (2020). "Japan: Earthquake & Tsunami. Situation Report 8 April 2011." Report produced by the JP in cooperation with Japan NGO Center for International Cooperation (JANIC). Available at webpage: https://www.japanplatform.org/E/jpf_janic/jpf_janic_20110408.pdf (or) https://www.japanplatform.org/ Last Accessed 09/2023.
- Jawerth, N. (2016). "Five years after Fukushima: Making nuclear power safer." IAEA International Atomic Energy Agency. Available at webpage: https://www.iaea.org/newscenter/news/five-years-after-fukushima-making-nuclear-power-safer Last Accessed 09/2023.
- Jeff, B. (2011). "U.S. Utilities pledge fresh review of nuke plant readiness." *The Energy Daily*, Englewood, Issue 53, March 2011. United States.

- JICA Annual Report, (2018). "Public-private partnerships and partnership with Japanese private sector." Japan International Cooperation Agency, Cooperation with Partners, Available at website: https://www.jica.go.jp/english/publications/reports/annual/2018/c8h0vm0000dxws0g-att/2018_20.pdf Last Accessed 08/2023.
- Jobin, P. (2013). "The Roadmap for Fukushima Daiichi and the sacrifice of Japan's clean-up workers." The Asia-Pacific Journal, Japan Focus. Volume 11, Issue 28, Number 2. Available at webpage: https://apjjf.org/2013/11/28/Paul-Jobin/3967/article.html Last Accessed 09/2023.
- Jobin, P. (2020). "The Fukushima nuclear disaster and civil actions as a social movement." The Asia-Pacific Journal, Japan Focus, Volume 18, Issue 9, Number 1. Available at webpage: https://apjjf.org/2020/9/Jobin.html Last Accessed 09/2023.
- (The) JT Editorial Board, (2020). "Following the crowd, Suga makes a bold climate pledge." *The Japan Times*, published on 29/10/2020. Available at webpage: https://www.japantimes.co.jp/opinion/2020/10/29/editorials/following-crowd-suga-makes-bold-climate-pledge/ Last Accessed 10/2023.
- Kanagawa, H. (2022). "Environmental policy and its enforcement." Environment & Climate Change Laws and Regulations Japan 2022, ICLG report, 23 March, 2022.
- Kastenberg, W.E. (2015). "Ethics, risk, and safety culture: reflections on Fukushima and beyond." *Journal of Risk Research*, Volume 18, No. 3, pp. 304-316.
- Kato, T. Takahara, S. Nishikawa, M. and Homma, T. (2013). "A case study of economic incentives and local citizens' attitudes toward hosting a nuclear power plant in Japan: Impacts of the Fukushima accident." *Energy Policy*, Volume 59, pp. 808-818.
- Khan, M.A. (2013). "Earthquake-Resistant Structures. Design, Build, and Retrofit." ISBN: 978-85617-501-2. "Tsunamis, Earthquakes, and Nuclear Power." Chapter 6. Pp. 141-168. Elsevier Oxford.
- Kikkawa, T. (2014). "The current status of risk communication in Japan." MOE, Japan, Keio University. Presentation available at webpage: https://www.env.go.jp/content/900408606.pdf Last Accessed 10/2023.
- Kim, S.C. and Chung, Y. (2018). "Dynamics of nuclear power policy in the post-Fukushima era: Interest structure and politicisation in Japan, Taiwan and Korea." *Asian Studies Review*, Volume 42, No. 1, pp. 107-124.
- Kim, Y. Kim, M. Kim, W. (2013). "Effect of the Fukushima nuclear disaster on global public acceptance of nuclear energy." *Energy Policy*, Volume 61, pp. 822-828.
- Koike, H. (2014). "Survey on Japanese culture related to safety culture." Nuclear Regulation Authority (NRA) Japan. Workshop on Global Safety Culture - National Factors Relevant to Safety Culture, Presentation Paper, 8-11 April, 2014. Available at webpage:

https://gnssn.iaea.org/NSNI/SC/WS_GSC/Presentations/04%20Koike_Hiroko_Survey%20of%20Japanese%20Culture%20Related%20to%20Safety%20Culture.pdf Last Accessed 09/2023.

- Koyama, K. (2013). "Japan's post-Fukushima energy policy challenges." *Asian Economic Policy Review*, Volume 8, No. 2, pp. 274-293.
- Krupp, F. (2018). "Harnessing the fourth wave of environmentalism." The Fourth Wave of Environmental Innovation, EDF Environmental Defense Fund, 21 March, 2018. Available at website: https://medium.com/the-fourth-wave/harnessing-the-fourth-wave-of-environmentalism-c71afa14eb11 Last Accessed 08/2023
- Kudo, S. Allasiw, D.I. Omi, K. and Hansen, M. (2020). "Translocal learning approach: A new form of collective learning for sustainability." *Resources, Environment and Sustainability*, Volume 2, December 2020, 100009. Abstract quotation. Available at webpage: https://www.sciencedirect.com/science/article/pii/S2666916120300098 Accessed 11/2023.
- Kuroda, A. (2016). "10 Lessons from Fukushima. Reducing risks and protecting communities from nuclear disasters." Fukushima Booklet Committee. pp. 1-72. Available at website: http://fukushimalessons.jp Last Accessed 11/2023.
- Kushida, K.E. (2014). "The Fukushima nuclear disaster and the democratic party of Japan." *The Japanese Political Economy*, Volume 40, No. 1, pp. 29-68.
- Lazo, T. (2013). "Current issues in radiological protection." *Nuclear Plant Journal*, Volume 31, May-June 2013.
- Lin, Y.T.A. (2021). "Best climate practice Japan: Kiko Network." Climate Scorecard, Japan News Brief and Action Alert, 12 May, 2021. Available at website: https://www.climatescorecard.org/2021/05/best-climate-practice-japan-kiko-network/ Last Accessed 08/2023.
- Liu, J. and Faure, M. (2016). "Compensation for nuclear damage : a comparison among the international regime, Japan and China." *International Environmental Agreements: Politics, Law and Economics*, Volume 16, pp. 165-187.
- Lixin, Z. (2013). "Post-Fukushima safety improvement measures for NPPs in China." China Nuclear and Radiation Safety Center, Conference presentation, August 26-29, 2013, Vienna. Available at webpage: https://nucleus.iaea.org/sites/gsan/act/tmonaftermathfukushima/Shared%20Documents/25%20Post-Fukushima%20Safety%20Improvement%20Measures%20for%20NPPs%20in%20China.pdf (or) https://inis.iaea.org/collection/NCLCollectionStore/_Public/52/017/52017999.pdf?r=1 Last Accessed 10/2023.
- Lofquist, L. (2013). "After Fukushima: nuclear power and societal choice." *Journal of Risk Research*, Volume 18, No. 3, pp. 291-303.
- Loss Prevention Bulletin, (2015). *Two die in separate Fukushima incidents*. Loss Prevention Bulletin 241. February 2015.

- Lynas, M. (2011). "If we abandon nuclear power, prepare for catastrophic global warming." *New Statesman*, 21 March 2011. www.newstatesman.com
- McCloy, J. (2019). "6 key environmental issues in Japan you should know." *Green Coast*, 19 September 2019. Available at website: https://greencoast.org/environmental-issues-in-japan/ and https://greencoast.org/author/john-mccloy/page/7/ Last Accessed 08/2023.
- McCurry, J. (2012). "World Report. Japan's Tohoku earthquake: 1 year on." *The Lancet*, World Report, Volume 379, No. 9819, 10th March, pp. 880-881. Available at website: https://www.thelancet.com/journals/lancet/article/PIIS0140-6736(12)60378-X/fulltext Last Accessed 11/2023.
- McLellan, B.C. Zhang, Q. Utama, N. A. Farzaneh, H. and Ishihara, K.N. (2013). "Analysis of Japan's post-Fukushima energy strategy." *Energy Strategy Reviews*, Volume 2, No. 2, pages 190-198.
- Meshkati, N. (2011). "Nuclear Lessons." Notebooks, Technology Review, June 21, Issue: July-August, pp. 8-9. Copyright of Technology Review is the property of Massachusetts Institute of Technology (MIT).
- METI, (2017). "Climate change adaptation good practices by Japanese private sector." Booklet compiled by METI of Japan's "Fiscal Year 2017 Climate Change Adaptation Effect Visualization Project [...]" by Mitsubishi UFJ Morgan Stanley Securities Co., the project consultant. Available at webpage: https://www.sc.mufg.jp/english/company/news/000014701.pdf Last Accessed 10/2023.
- METI, (2017). "Climate change adaptation good practices by Japanese private sector." Ministry of Economy, Trade and Industry, METI, Japan. Report, November 2017. Available at webpage: http://copjapan.env.go.jp/cop23/event_en/nov15/pdf/Climate_Change_Adaptation_Good_Practices_by_Japanese_Private_Sector_en.pdf Last Accessed 10/2023.
- Ming, Z. Yingxin, L. Shaojie, O. Hui, S. and Chunxue, L. (2016). "Nuclear energy in the post-Fukushima era: Research on the developments of the Chinese and worldwide nuclear power industries." *Renewable and Sustainable Energy Reviews*, Volume 58, May 2016, pages 147-156.
- Ministry of the Environment, Japan, (1990). "An act to control toxic substances and hazardous and nuclear wastes, providing penalties for violations thereof, and for other purposes." Philippines Republic Act, No. 6969: "Toxic Substances and Hazardous and Nuclear Waste Control Act 1990." Document available at webpage: https://www.env.go.jp/en/recycle/asian_net/Country_Information/Law_N_Regulation/Philippines/phillipines1.pdf Last Accessed 10/2023.
- Ministry of the Environment, Japan, (1993). "The national action plan for agenda 21." The Council of Ministers for Global Environmental Conservation decided the National Action Plan for Agenda 21 on 24 December 1993. Chapter 35: 'Science and sustainable development.' Available at website: https://www.env.go.jp/en/earth/iec/agenda/agenda35.html Last Accessed

08/2023.
- Ministry of the Environment, Japan, (1994). "Japan's action report on climate change." Environment Agency of Japan, First National Communication Report. Available at webpage: https://www.env.go.jp/content/900446355.pdf Last Accessed 09/2023.
- Ministry of the Environment, Japan, (2000). "Detailed description of best practices. United States of America No. 2." G8 Environmental Futures Forum 2000 on "Domestic Best Practices Addressing Climate Change." Full Report available at webpage: https://www.env.go.jp/earth/g8_2000/forum/g8bp/detail/usa/usa02.html Last Accessed 10/2023.
- Ministry of the Environment, Japan, (2003). "Environmental performance indicators guideline for organizations." MOE, Fiscal Year 2002, April 2003 Report. Available at webpage: https://www.env.go.jp/policy/j-hiroba/PRG/pdfs/e_p_guide.pdf Last Accessed 09/2023.
- Ministry of the Environment, Japan, (2003). "Effective SEA System and case studies." MOE and Mitsubishi Research Institute, Inc., Japan, Report, June 2003. Available at website: http://assess.env.go.jp/files/0_db/seika/0184_02/en_all.pdf Last Accessed 09/2023.
- Ministry of the Environment, Japan, (2003). "Law for enhancing motivation on environmental conservation and promoting of environmental education. " MOEJ, Law No. 130, July 25, 2003. Available at website: https://www.env.go.jp/content/900452874.pdf Last Accessed 08/2023.
- Ministry of the Environment, Japan, (2006). "Study report on comprehensive support strategies for environment and development in the early 21st century. Republic of Kazakhstan." Overseas Environmental Cooperation Center, Japan. Report available at webpage: https://www.env.go.jp/earth/coop/coop/document/c_report/kazakhstan_h17/english/pdf/000.pdf Last Accessed 09/2023.
- Ministry of the Environment, Japan, (2008). "Towards a low carbon society and a sound material-cycle society." MOE Annual Report on the Environment and the Sound Material-Cycle Society in Japan 2008. Available at website: https://www.env.go.jp/content/900457288.pdf Last Accessed 08/2023.
- Ministry of the Environment, Japan, (2009). "International research network for low carbon societies (LCS-RNet)." Clean Asia Initiative, MOE, International Cooperation Office, Short Report. Available at website: https://www.env.go.jp/earth/coop/coop/english/cai/pdf/lcs-rnet_e.pdf Last Accessed 08/2023.
- Ministry of the Environment, Japan, (2011). "Building healthy and satisfied local communities." Reconstruction from the Disaster, Section 1. Chapter 3. Annual Report on the Environment, the Sound Material-Cycle Society and the Biodiversity in Japan 2012. Available at website: https://www.env.go.jp/content/900457371.pdf Last Accessed 08/2023.
- Ministry of the Environment, Japan, (2011). "To achieve a green growth nation

to lead the world." Section 1. Green Economy and Green Innovation, Chapter 4. Annual Report on the Environment, the Sound Material-Cycle Society and the Biodiversity in Japan 2011. Available at website: https://www.env.go.jp/content/900457372.pdf Last Accessed 08/2023.

- Ministry of the Environment, Japan, (2011). "Response to the Great East Japan Earthquake and Nuclear Power Station Accidents." FY 2011 Annual Report of the Environment, Chapter 2. Available at website: https://www.env.go.jp/content/900457370.pdf Last Accessed 09/2023.
- Ministry of the Environment, Japan, (2012). " Recent development of environmental policies in Japan." 1. The Recovery from the Great East Japan Earthquake. MOE Report. Available at website: https://www.env.go.jp/en/focus/docs/files/20120925-20.pdf Last Accessed 08/2023.
- Ministry of the Environment, Japan, (2012). "The National strategy on environment protection to 2020 with visions to 2030." The National Strategy on Environment Protection to 2020, with Visions to 2030 was approved by the Prime Minister in his Decision 1216/QD-TTg on September 05, 2012. Full document available at webpage: https://www.env.go.jp/air/tech/ine/asia/vietnam/files/law/QD1216-English.pdf Last Accessed 10/2023.
- Ministry of the Environment, Japan, (2013). "Observations and commentary on remediation of the lands off-site from the Fukushima Daiichi reactors." Report of the United States Embassy Science Fellows Support to the Government MOE of Japan, EPA/600/R-13/135, Available at website: http://josen.env.go.jp/en/documents/pdf/workshop_july_17-18_2013_04.pdf Last Accessed 08/2023.
- Ministry of the Environment, Japan, (2013). "Comparison between ICRP recommendations and domestic laws and regulations." Booklet 'To Provide Basic Information Regarding Health Effects of Radiation.' Chapter 4.2 'Dose Limits.' Available at website: https://www.env.go.jp/en/chemi/rhm/basic-info/2018/pdf/basic-1st-04-02.pdf Last Accessed 11/2023.
- Ministry of the Environment, Japan, (2013)."BOOKLET to provide basic information regarding health effects of radiation." MOE, 2nd Edition, Chapter 5, 'Assessments by International Organizations' UNSCEAR 2013 Report (9/9) Comparison with Direct Measurements. Available at webpage: https://www.env.go.jp/en/chemi/rhm/basic-info/1st/05-03-09.html Last Accessed 09/2023.
- Ministry of the Environment, Japan, (2013). "Protected areas, natural hazards and disaster recovery." 1st Asia Parks Congress (APC), Japan 2013, Draft Message from WG1 on Natural Disasters and Protected Areas. Available at webpage: https://www.env.go.jp/en/nature/asia-parks/pdf/wg1_message.pdf Last Accessed 10/2023.
- Ministry of the Environment, Japan, (2013). "Japan's sixth national communication under the United Nations Framework Convention on Climate Change." The Government of Japan, December, 2013. Full Report available

at webpage: https://www.env.go.jp/content/900446396.pdf Last Accessed 10/2023.
- Ministry of the Environment, Japan, (2014). "Initiatives for restoration of the environment." Annual Report on the Environment, the Sound Material-Cycle Society, and Biodiversity in Japan. Available at website:https://www.env.go.jp/content/900457394.pdf Last Accessed 08/2023.
- Ministry of the Environment, Japan, (2014). "Expert meeting regarding the status of health management of residents following the accident at the Tokyo Electric Power Company's Fukushima Daiichi Nuclear Power Station." MOE Interim Report, December 2014. Available at website: https://www.env.go.jp/content/900411794.pdf Last Accessed 09/2023.
- Ministry of the Environment, Japan, (2014). "Japan's climate change policies." MOE Report, 18th March, 2014. Presentation available at webpage: https://www.env.go.jp/en/focus/docs/files/20140318-83.pdf Last Accessed 10/2023.
- Ministry of the Environment, Japan, (2015). "Progress on Off-site cleanup efforts in Japan." MOE Policy Report, January 2015. Available at website: http://josen.env.go.jp/en/documents/pdf/progress_on_off_site_cleanup_efforts_in_japan_1501.pdf Last Accessed 09/2023.
- Ministry of the Environment, Japan, (2015). "FY2014 Decontamination Report. A compilation of experiences to date on decontamination for the living environment conducted by the Ministry of the Environment." MOE Report, 2015. Available at website: http://josen.env.go.jp/en/policy_document/pdf/decontamination_report1503_full.pdf Last Accessed 08/2023.
- Ministry of the Environment, Japan, (2015). "Submission by Japan to the UN Framework Convention on Climate Change Communication on Japan's undertakings in adaptation." MOE Japan Report, November 27, 2015. Available at website: https://www.env.go.jp/en/earth/cc/submission151127.pdf Last Accessed 08/2023.
- Ministry of the Environment, Japan, (2015). "Case Studies: From Ridge to Reef." ICRI International Coral Reef Initiative, Secretariat, c/o Biodiversity Policy Division, MOE, Japan. Available at website: https://www.env.go.jp/nature/biodic/coralreefs/pamph/C-community_EN.pdf Last Accessed 08/2023.
- Ministry of the Environment, Japan, (2015). "Overview of decontamination methods." FY2014 Decontamination Report, "A compilation of experiences to date on decontamination for the living environment conducted by the Ministry of the Environment - (MOEJ)." Chapter 2. Available at website: http://josen.env.go.jp/en/cooperation/pdf/decontamination_report1503_02.pdf Last Accessed 11/2023.
- Ministry of the Environment, Japan, (2015). "Basic features of the environmental decontamination in Japan" FY2014 Decontamination Report,

"A compilation of experiences to date on decontamination for the living environment conducted by the Ministry of the Environment - (MOEJ)" Chapter 1. Available at website: http://josen.env.go.jp/en/policy_document/pdf/decontamination_report1503_01.pdf Last Accessed 09/2023.
- Ministry of the Environment, Japan, (2015). "Environment research and technology development fund FY 2015." MOE Policy Report, September 2015. Available at website: https://www.env.go.jp/policy/kenkyu/suishin/english/gaiyou/pdf/2015_pamphlet_eng.pdf Last Accessed 09/2023.
- Ministry of the Environment, Japan, (2015). "Result of selection of model areas for the project to formulate community revitalization plans to achieve 'low-carbon, sound material cycle and natural symbiosis' in fiscal year 2015." MOE, Policy Strategy Division, April 9, 2015. Available at webpage: https://www.env.go.jp/en/policy/plan/crp.html Last Accessed 10/2023.
- Ministry of the Environment, Japan, (2016). "Environment research and technology development fund FY2016." MOE, Environmental Policy Bureau, Office of Environmental Research and Technology, Research Report. Available at webpage: https://www.env.go.jp/policy/kenkyu/suishin/english/gaiyou/pdf/2016_pamphlet_eng.pdf Last Accessed 09/2023.
- Ministry of the Environment, Japan, (2016). "Bilateral cooperation on the dissemination of low carbon technologies towards transformation to decarbonized societies." Joint Statement, the Federal Ministry for the Environment, Nature Conservation, Building and Nuclear Safety of the Federal Republic of Germany, and MOE Japan. 18th May, 2016. Available at website: https://www.env.go.jp/content/900506547.pdf Last Accessed 08/2023.
- Ministry of the Environment, Japan, (2016). "Summary of IAEA-MOE Experts' meeting on environmental remediation of Off-site Areas after the Fukushima Daiichi Nuclear Power Station Accident." MOE, Tokyo, Japan, Meeting Report 4-5- February 2016. Available at website: https://www.env.go.jp/content/900506116.pdf Last Accessed 09/2023.
- Ministry of the Environment, Japan, (2016). "Summary of the 2nd IAEA-MOE experts' meeting on environmental remediation of off-site areas after the Fukushima Daiichi Nuclear Power Station accident." Tokyo and Fukushima, Japan, 14-18 November, 2016. Available at webpage: http://josen.env.go.jp/en/news/pdf/news_161118_01.pdf Last Accessed 10/2023.
- Ministry of the Environment, Japan. (2016). "Ecosystem-based disaster risk reduction in Japan. A handbook for practitioners." Nature Conservation Bureau, MOE, Report, March 2016. Available at website: https://www.env.go.jp/content/900489554.pdf Last Accessed 09/2023.
- Ministry of the Environment, Japan, (2016). "French experience on long term energy & climate planning." Presentation to the Vision Committee, MOEJ,

Tokyo, 29 November 2016. Available at webpage: https://www.env.go.jp/content/900530280.pdf Last Accessed 10/2023.
- Ministry of the Environment, Japan, (2017). "Evolving sustainable energy policy in Nagano Prefecture, Japan: The path towards a 100% renewable energy region." MOE, Nagano, March 2018, Report. Available at website: http://copjapan.env.go.jp/talanoa/assets/pdfs/stories/en/20180601-001.pdf Last Accessed 08/2023.
- Ministry of the Environment, Japan, (2017). "FY2016 JCM feasibility study for low-carbon city in Ayeyarwady Region Study of a low-carbon waste treatment system in Pathein Industrial City." Report, Appendix, Mitsubishi Research Institute, Inc. & Fujita Corporation. Available at webpage: https://www.env.go.jp/earth/coop/lowcarbon-asia/english/project/data/EN_MMR_2016_04-2.pdf Last Accessed 09/2023.
- Ministry of the Environment, Japan, (2018). "Decontamination projects for radioactive contamination discharged by Tokyo Electric Power Company Fukushima Daiichi Nuclear Power Station Accident." Editorial Committee for the Paper on Decontamination Projects, MOE. Available at website: http://josen.env.go.jp/en/policy_document/pdf/decontamination_report1807_01.pdf Last Accessed 08/2023.
- Ministry of the Environment, Japan, (2018). "Decontamination projects for radioactive contamination discharged by Tokyo Electric Power Company Fukushima Daiichi Nuclear Power Station accident." MOE, Policy Document, Chapter 5, 'Effects, Verification, and Risk Communication of Decontamination.' Available at website: http://josen.env.go.jp/en/policy_document/pdf/decontamination_projects_1902_05.pdf Last Accessed 09/2023.
- Ministry of the Environment, Japan, (2018). "Decontamination projects for radioactive contamination discharged by Tokyo Electric Power Company Fukushima Daiichi nuclear power station accident." Chapter 6, "Lessons Learned and Future Challenges." Available at website: http://josen.env.go.jp/en/policy_document/pdf/decontamination_projects_1902_06.pdf Last Accessed 09/2023.
- Ministry of the Environment, Japan, (2018). "Decontamination projects for radioactive contamination discharged by Tokyo Electric Power Company Fukushima Daiichi nuclear power station accident." More information: ICRP International Commission on Radiological Protection. ICRP and Fukushima. Available at website: https://www.icrp.org/page.asp?id=188 Last Accessed 08/2023.
- Ministry of the Environment, Japan, (2018). "Disaster waste management guideline for Asia and the Pacific." MOE report 2018. Available at website: https://www.env.go.jp/content/900512396.pdf Last Accessed 09/2023.
- Ministry of the Environment, Japan, (2018). "Framework and Methods of Decontamination Projects." MOE Report, "Decontamination projects for radioactive contamination discharged by Tokyo Electric Company

Fukushima Daiichi Nuclear Power Station Accident." Chapter 3. Available at webpage: http://josen.env.go.jp/en/policy_document/pdf/decontamination_projects_1902_03.pdf Last Accessed 09/2023.

- Ministry of the Environment, Japan, (2018). "WHO Reports and UNSCEAR 2013 Report (1/3)." MOE, Japan, Chapter 5.1. booklet. Available at webpage: https://www.env.go.jp/en/chemi/rhm/basic-info/1st/pdf/basic-1st-05.pdf Last Accessed 09/2023.
- Ministry of the Environment, Japan, (2018). "Comprehensive radiation monitoring plan and information disclosure." MOE, 2018 report, Chapter 7, 'Spatiotemporal distribution of ambient dose rates.' Available at webpage: https://www.env.go.jp/en/chemi/rhm/basic-info/1st/pdf/basic-1st-07-01-01.pdf Last Accessed 09/2023.
- Ministry of the Environment, Japan, (2018). "Efforts toward recovery from the accident. Activities in areas under evacuation orders." Booklet to Provide Basic Information Regarding Health Effects of Radiation, Chapter 9/9.4. Available at webpage: https://www.env.go.jp/en/chemi/rhm/basic-info/2018/09-04-03.html Last Accessed 10/2023.
- Ministry of the Environment, Japan, (2018). "Environmental remediation in Japan." MOE report, March 2018. Available at webpage: http://josen.env.go.jp/en/pdf/progressseet_progress_on_cleanup_efforts.pdf Last Accessed 10/2023.
- Ministry of the Environment, Japan, (2018). "FY2017 Study of city-to-city collaboration project for low carbon society." MOE, Japan, project report, March 2018. Page 1-57. Mitsubishi Research Institute Inc., Fujita Corporation. Available at webpage: https://www.env.go.jp/earth/coop/lowcarbon-asia/english/project/data/EN_MMR_2017_02.pdf Last Accessed 10/2023.
- Ministry of Environment, Japan, (2019). "Japan's assistance initiatives to address climate change. Responding to needs of the developing countries." MOE, Report, Global Environment Bureau, Japan. Available at website: https://www.env.go.jp/content/900505739.pdf Last Accessed 08/2023.
- Ministry of the Environment, Japan, (2019). "Toward sustainable transformation in the post-COVID-19 Era - Circulating and Ecological Sphere (CES) and Societal Innovation." Exhibition, Virtual Japan Pavilion - Innovation for 2050 net-zero - Available at website: http://copjapan.env.go.jp/cop/virtualjapanpavilion2021/en/exhibition/lifestyle.html Last Accessed 08/2023.
- Ministry of the Environment, Japan, (2019). "International symposium on remediation of radioactive contamination in the environment." MOE Environmental Remediation, News & Topics, July 11, 2019. Information available at webpage: http://josen.env.go.jp/en/news/ Last Accessed 10/2023.
- Ministry of the Environment, (2020). "Environmental Remediation. Results and Effects of Decontamination." Government of Japan MOE Report. Available

at website: http://josen.env.go.jp/en/decontamination/ Last Accessed 08/2023.
- Ministry of the Environment, Government of Japan, (2020). "Joint declaration between United Nations Industrial Development Organization and the Ministry of the Environment of Japan." Press & Public Relations Release. Available at webpage: http://www.env.go.jp/en/headline/2481.html Last Accessed 09/2023.
- Ministry of the Environment, Japan, (2020). "Setting of standard limits for radioactive materials in foods and distribution/consumption restrictions." Booklet to Provide Basic Information Regarding Health Effects of Radiation, 2nd edition, Chapter 8: Radioactive Materials in Foods. Report available at webpage: https://www.env.go.jp/en/chemi/rhm/basic-info/1st/08-01-01.html Last Accessed 09/2023.
- Ministry of the Environment, (2020). "About the conclusion of 'Cooperative Cooperation Agreement on future-oriented environmental measures for reconstruction of Fukushima...that challenges from the environment, and hope for the future." Japanese Government information, published 27/08/2020. Available at website: https://www.gov-base.info/en/2020/08/27/125124 (or) https://www.gov-base.info/ Last Accessed 09/2023.
- Ministry of the Environment, (2020). Quote: "The Ministry of the Environment has been working on the environmental restoration of Fukushima since 2012, such as decontamination and treatment of special waste." Japanese Government information, published 27/08/2020. Available at webpage: https://www.gov-base.info/en/2020/08/27/125124 (This original web-link dated 2020.08.27 is not available as of 10/2023). MOE Gov Base Archive currently available at this webpage: https://www.gov-base.info/page/15?s=Fukushima Last Accessed 10/2023.
- Ministry of the Environment, Japan, (2020). "Review results on SAICM national implementation plan of Japan." MOE Report, March 2020. Available at webpage: https://www.env.go.jp/content/900414530.pdf Last Accessed 10/2023.
- Ministry of the Environment, Japan, (2020). "Special Decontamination Areas and Intensive Contamination Survey Areas." Chapter 9: 'Efforts towards Recovery from the Accident,' 9.1 'Decontamination.' MOE, Booklet to Provide Basic Information Regarding Health Effects of Radiation (3rd edition). Available at webpage: https://www.env.go.jp/en/chemi/rhm/basic-info/1st/09-01-04.html Last Accessed 10/2023.
- Ministry of the Environment, Japan, (2021). "Effects of Radioactive Fallout due to Atmospheric Nuclear Testing." Volume 1, Chapter 2.1, 'Exposure Routes' study. Available at webpage: https://www.env.go.jp/en/chemi/rhm/basic-info/1st/pdf/basic-1st-02.pdf Last Accessed 09/2023.
- Ministry of the Environment, Japan, (2021). "Annex I. Recommendations for ocean energy and offshore renewables accelerated development and deployment." ANNEXES Joint G20 Energy-Climate Ministerial

Communiqué, July 23, 2021. "Energy Transition and Climate Sustainability Working Groups." Annexes available at webpage: https://www.env.go.jp/press/files/jp/116565.pdf (or) https://www.meti.go.jp/press/2021/07/20210726010/20210726010-1.pdf Last Accessed 10/2023.

- Ministry of the Environment, Japan, (2021). "Practical guide for Scenario Analysis in line with the TCFD recommendations 3rd edition." MOE, Climate Change Policy Division. Report available at: https://www.env.go.jp/content/900498777.pdf Last Accessed 10/2023.
- Ministry of the Environment, Japan, (2021). "Practical guide for scenario analysis in line with the TCFD recommendations 3rd edition." MOE Climate Change Policy Division, March 2021. Report Page 3-70. Available at webpage: https://www.env.go.jp/policy/policy/tcfd/TCFDguide_3rd_EN.pdf Last Accessed 10/2023.
- Ministry of the Environment, Japan, (2022). "Booklet to provide basic information regarding health effects of radiation." 2nd Edition, Chapter 6 'Situation concerning the Accident,' Section 6.3: 'Efforts and Progress for Decommissioning.' Available at website: https://www.env.go.jp/en/chemi/rhm/basic-info/1st/index.html (or) https://www.env.go.jp/en/chemi/rhm/basic-info/1st/pdf/basic-1st-06.pdf (or) https://www.env.go.jp/en/chemi/rhm/basic-info/1st/06-03-09.html Last Accessed 08/2023.
- Ministry of the Environment, Japan, (2022). "Partnerships & information-sharing with international institutions." Archive of Technical References related to Disaster Waste Management Guideline for Asia and the Pacific, March 11, 2022. Available at webpage: http://kouikishori.env.go.jp/en/international_organizations_cooperation/ Last Accessed 09/2023.
- Ministry of the Environment, Japan, (2022). "Disaster waste management information site." Webpage on State of Disaster Waste Treatment & Archives, Cabinet Office Disaster Management Information. Available at website: http://kouikishori.env.go.jp/en/ Last Accessed 09/2023.
- Mochizuki, Y. (2014). "Message from Minister of the Environment, Japan." *Japan Environment Quarterly (JEQ)*, Vol. 8, December 2014. Available at website: https://www.env.go.jp/en/focus/jeq/issue/vol08/feature.html Last Accessed 09/2023.
- Murakami, M. Sato, A. Matsui, S. Goto, A. Kumagai, A. and Tsubokura, M. *et al.,* 2017. "Communicating with residents about risks following the Fukushima nuclear accident." *Asia Pacific Journal of Public Health*, Volume 29, No. 2_suppl., pp. 74S-89S. https://doi.org/10.1177/1010539516681841
- Nakamura, A. Kikuchi, M. (2011). "What we know, and what we have not yet learned: Triple disasters and the Fukushima nuclear fiasco in Japan." *Public Administration Review*, Volume 71, No. 6, (November-December 2011), pp. 893-899.

- (The) National Diet of Japan, (2012). National Report "The Fukushima Nuclear Accident Independent Investigation Commission." The National Diet of Japan, publication available at website: https://warp.da.ndl.go.jp/info:ndljp/pid/3856371/naiic.go.jp/en/. Last Accessed 09/2023.
- NEA/OECD, (2010). "Protocol on strategic environmental assessment to the Espoo Convention (Kiev Protocol)." Nuclear Energy Agency, Topics section, Division of Nuclear Law, 2022. Available at website: https://www.oecd-nea.org/jcms/pl_29149/protocol-on-strategic-environmental-assessment-to-the-espoo-convention-kiev-protocol Last Accessed 08/2023.
- NECG, (2019). "#26 - Japan - Nuclear power and electricity reform." Nuclear Economics Consulting Group, 26 February, 2019. Report available at webpage: https://nuclear-economics.com/wp-content/uploads/2019/02/26-Japan-nuclear-power-and-electricity-reform-update.pdf Last Accessed 10/2023.
- News Reports, Jade Media, 2013. "Nuclear waste news." Nuclear Waste News, October 24th, 2013, Jade Media Partners LLC. Available at website: https://www.thefreelibrary.com/Japan.-a0350573515 Last Accessed 10/2023.
- Nikkei Asia, (2021). "Japan watchdog halts Tsuruga nuclear safety assessments." Nikkei Asia, August 18, 2021. Available at webpage: https://asia.nikkei.com/Business/Energy/Japan-watchdog-halts-Tsuruga-nuclear-safety-assessment (or) https://www.japantimes.co.jp/news/2023/04/05/national/tsuruga-reactor-safety-assessment-halt/ Last Accessed 09/2023.
- NRA, Japan, (2020). "National report of Japan. For the Seventh Review Meeting. Joint convention on the safety of spent fuel management and on the safety of radioactive waste management." Nuclear Regulation Authority, Report, October 2020. Available at webpage: https://www.nra.go.jp/data/000366720.pdf Last Accessed 10/2023.
- NRA, Japan, (2020). "FY 2020 Annual Report." Nuclear Regulation Authority, Japan, Report, Available at webpage: https://www.nra.go.jp/data/000384155.pdf Last Accessed 10/2023.
- NRA, Japan, (2020). "National Report of Japan. For the seventh review meeting; joint convention on the safety of spent fuel management and on the safety of radioactive waste management." Nuclear Regulation Authority Report, October 2020. Available at webpage: https://www.nra.go.jp/data/000366720.pdf Last Accessed 10/2023.
- NRC, Japan, (2020). "Plant-specific Japan lessons-learned activities." U.S. Nuclear Regulatory Commission, Japan Lessons Learned information page. Webpage has been reviewed under a new title in 2021: "Plant-Specific Safety Enhancements after Fukushima." Available at webpage: https://www.nrc.gov/reactors/operating/ops-experience/japan-dashboard/japan-plants.html Last Accessed 10/2023.
- Nuclear Emergency Response Headquarters Government - TEPCO Integrated

Response Office, Report Appendix 1-3, "Current Status of 'Roadmap towards Restoration from the Accident at Fukushima Daiichi Nuclear Power Station, TEPCO' (Step 2 completion)." December 16, (2011). Available at website: https://www.tepco.co.jp/en/press/corp-com/release/betu11_e/images/111216e11.pdf Last Accessed 09/2023.

- Nuclear News, (2011). "Organizing petition NRC to halt permit process in wake of Japan events. " *Nuclear Waste News*, Volume 31, No. 8, pp. 2-3.
- NWMO, Nuclear Waste Management Organization, (2021). "The NWMO 2020 annual report celebrates progress and resilience." NWMO News and Activities, March 23, 2021 Toronto, Ont. Available at website: https://www.nwmo.ca/en/More-information/News-and-Activities/2021/03/23/17/02/The-NWMO-2020-annual-report-celebrates-progress-and-resilience Last Accessed 08/2023.
- Omori, N. (2021). "Post-Fukushima educational practices." Citizen's Nuclear Information Center, Information Report, February 11, 2021. Available at webpage: https://cnic.jp/english/?p=5314 Last Accessed 09/2023.
- O'Rourke, M. (2011). "In the wake of the quake: Rethinking nuclear safety." *Risk Management Magazine*, Volume 58, No. 4, May, pp. 24-26.
- Owen, D.H. and Wahl, Z. (2010). "Defining four pillars for successful applied knowledge transfer." In book edition: R.J. Howlett (ed.): *Innovation through Knowledge Transfer*, 2010, SIST 9, pp. 83-93, Springer-Verlag, Berlin, Heidelberg 2011.
- Peterson, S. (2012). "The right response." *Electric Perspectives*, May-June, pp. 76-89. Copyright of Electric Perspectives is the property of Edison Electric Institute Inc. Available at website: https://lsc-pagepro.mydigitalpublication.com/publication/?m=6643&i=113534&p=78&ver=html5 Last Accessed 11/2023.
- Pineda-Solano, A.L. Carreto-Vazquez, V.H. and Mannan, M.S. (2013). "The Fukushima Daiichi accident and its impact on risk perception and risk communication." *Chemical Engineering Transactions*, Volume 31, pp. 517-522.
- Pistner, C. Englert, M. (2017). "Nuclear power and nuclear safety post Fukushima." Institute for Applied Ecology, Oko-Institut e.V. DPG-AKE-AGA: Nuclear Energy and Security, Munster, 29/03/2017. Available at webpage: https://www.oeko.de/fileadmin/oekodoc/DPG_Nuclear_Safety.pdf
- Polonen, I. Hokkanen, P. and Jalava, K. (2011). "The effectiveness of the Finnish EIA system – What works, what doesn't, and what could be improved?" *Environmental Impact Assessment Review*, Volume 31, No. 2, pp. 120-128.
- Pope, J. Bond, A. Morrison-Saunders, A. and Retief, F. (2013). "Advancing the theory and practice of impact assessment: Setting the research agenda." *Environmental Impact Assessment Review*, Volume 41, July, pp. 1-9.
- Professional Engineering News, (2011). "Fight for future of nuclear in wake of Japan accident. Nuclear confidence shaken" Professional Engineering.

Copyright of Professional Engineering is property of Professional Engineering Publishing.
- Radiation Health Management Division, Ministry of the Environment, Japan, (2022). "Accident at TEPCO's Fukushima Daiichi NPS and Thereafter (Initiatives by Ministries and Agencies)." Booklet to Provide Information Regarding Health Effects of Radiation. Volume 2. National Institutes for Quantum Science and Technology. Available at website: https://www.env.go.jp/en/chemi/rhm/basic-info/1st/pdf/basic-1st-vol2.pdf Last Accessed 09/2023.
- Rangarajan, S. (2011). "Why is 'Radioactivity' such a scary word?" *Chemical Business*, April 2011. Colour Publications Pvt. Ltd. https://colourpublications.in/pages/books/ Accessed 11/2023. As of 11/2023 direct article cannot be retrieved. The web-link refers to the publishing outlet.
- Rich, M. and Ueno, H. (2019). "Fukushima, Beaten Down by Nuclear Disaster, Takes Big Typhoon Hit." *The New York Times* newspaper, Asia Pacific, October 15, 2019. Available at website: https://www.nytimes.com/2019/10/15/world/asia/typhoon-hagibis-fukushima-japan.html Last Accessed 11/2023.
- RoSPA (2011). "News: Government outlines next moves in nuclear review." The RoSPA Occupational Safety & Health Journal, August, pp. 1-2. Copyright of RoSPA Occupational Safety & Health Journal is property of Royal Society for the Prevention of Accidents.
- Roux-Dufort, C. and Metais, E. (1999). "Building core competencies in crisis management through organizational learning: The case of the French Nuclear Power Producer." *Technological Forecasting and Social Change*, Volume 60, No. 2, pp. 113-127.
- Rozema, J.G. Bond, A.J. Cashmore, M. and Chilvers, J. (2012). "An investigation of environmental and sustainability discourses associated with the substantive purposes of environmental assessment." *Environmental Impact Assessment Review*, Volume 33, No. 1, pp. 80-90.
- Runhaar, H. (van) Laerhoven, F. Driessen, P. and Arts, J. (2013). "Environmental assessment in The Netherlands: Effectively governing environmental protection? A discourse analysis." *Environmental Impact Assessment Review*, Volume 39, pp. 13-25.
- Runhaar, H. Runhaar, P.R. Oegema, T. (2010). "Food for thought: Conditions for discourse reflection in the light of environmental assessment." *Environmental Impact Assessment Review*, Volume 30, No. 6, pp. 339-346.
- Saito, W.H. (2017). "What Fukushima disaster taught me about risk management in cybersecurity." *Forbes*, published 20/04/2017. Available at webpage: https://www.forbes.com/sites/williamsaito/2017/04/20/what-fukushima-disaster-taught-me-about-risk-management-in-cybersecurity/?sh=5e7cc3fd681e Last Accessed 09/2023.
- Samet, J.M. and Chanson, D. (2015). "Fukushima Daiichi Power Plant Disaster: How many people were affected? 2015 Report." Green Cross, Reliefweb,

published 11/03/2015. Available at webpage: https://reliefweb.int/sites/reliefweb.int/files/resources/2015_fukushima_report.pdf Last Accessed 09/2023.
- Saunders, F. (2017). "First person: M.V. Ramana." *American Scientist*, Research Triangle Park, Volume 105, January-February 2017, pp. 8-9.
- Schmitt, K. (2012). "Automations influence on nuclear power plants: A look at three accidents and how automation played a role." *Work*, Volume 41, pp. 4545-4551. IOS Press.
- Schwarz, P.M. and Cochran, J.A. (2012). "Renaissance or requiem: Is nuclear energy cost effective in a post-Fukushima world?" *Contemporary Economic Policy*, Volume 31, No. 4, pp. 691-707.
- Shimura, T. Kunugita, N. *et al.*, 2015. "Radiation occupational health interventions offered to radiation workers in response to the complex catastrophic disaster at the Fukushima Daiichi Nuclear Power Plant." *Journal of Radiation Research*, Volume 56, No. 3, pp. 413-421.
- Shinkawa, T. (2013). "Revised mid-and-long-term Roadmap towards the Decommissioning of TEPCO's Fukushima Daiichi NPP Units 1-4." Agency for Natural Resources and Energy, METI, July 2013, METI report. Available at webpage: https://www.env.go.jp/press/files/jp/22699.pdf Last Accessed 09/2023.
- Shirouzu, N. Dawson, C. (2011). "In depth: Design flaw fueled nuclear disaster." The Wall Street Journal Asia; Hong Kong, July 4th, 2011. Dow Jones & Company Inc.
- Siegrist, M. Sūtterlin, B. Keller, C. (2014). "Why have some people changed their attitudes toward nuclear power after the accident in Fukushima?" *Energy Policy*, Volume 69, pp. 356-363.
- Silverberg, E. and Smith, E. (2019). "Does Japan have a global environmental strategy?" *The Diplomat*, 06 November, 2019. Available at website: https://thediplomat.com/2019/11/does-japan-have-a-global-environmental-strategy/ Last Accessed 08/2023.
- Sinclair, A.J. Diduck, A. and Fitzpatrick, P. (2008). "Conceptualizing learning for sustainability through environmental assessment: critical reflections on 15 years of research." *Environmental Impact Assessment Review*, Volume 28, Issue 7, October, pp. 415-428. https://doi.org/10.1016/j.eiar.2007.11.001
- Siripala, T. (2020). "Japan's 3/11 recovery stalled by Fukushima decommissioning delays." The Diplomat, Tokyo Report, Environment, East Asia. Published 13/03/2020. Available at website: https://thediplomat.com/2020/03/japans-3-11-recovery-stalled-by-fukushima-decommissioning-delays/ Last Accessed 09/2023.
- Skeen, D. (2013). "Fukushima, a game changer." Nuclear Plant Journal, Volume 31, No. 3, May-June 2013, pp. 22-24. Available at webpage: https://nuclearplantjournal.com/uploads/digital/MJ13.pdf Last Accessed 11/2023.
- Srinivasan, T.N. and Gopi Rethinaraj, T.S. (2013). "Fukushima and thereafter: Reassessment of risks of nuclear power." *Energy Policy*, Volume 52, pp. 726-

736.

- Stapczynski, S. and Suzuki, I. (2016). "Japan Fukushima cost seen almost doubling to $188 Billion." *Bloomberg-Quint* news article, published 09/12/2016. Available at webpage: https://www.bloombergquint.com/business/japan-fukushima-cost-seen-nearly-doubling-to-21-5-trillion-yen Last Accessed 09/2023.
- Strickland, E. (2012). "Can Japan phase out nuclear power? The country wants to go nuclear-free, but many obstacles remain" *NA-IEEE SPECTRUM* November, pp.13-14. www.SPECTRUM.IEEE.ORG (or) https://spectrum.ieee.org/can-japan-phase-out-nuclear-power Last Accessed 10/2023.
- Suami, T. (2015). "Legal support to Fukushima municipalities: Law school, lawyers, and nuclear disaster victims." Asian-Pacific Law & Policy Journal, Volume 16, No. 2, pp. 158-185. Available at webpage: http://manoa.hawaii.edu/aplpj/wp-content/uploads/sites/120/2016/01/APLPJ_16.2_Suami.pdf Last Accessed 11/2023.
- Suzuki, A. (2014). "Managing the Fukushima Challenge." *Risk Analysis*, Volume 34, No. 7, pp. 1240-1256.
- Suzuki, K. (2019). "Environmental impact assessment of renewable energy in Japan." Environmental Impact Assessment Division, Ministry of the Environment, Japan. Webpage available at: https://www.nedo.go.jp/content/100899753.pdf Last Accessed 08/2023.
- Tabuchi, H. (2012). "Nuclear operator in Japan exonerates itself in report." *New York Times edition*, Today's Paper, June 21, 2012. Available at webpage: https://www.nytimes.com/2012/06/21/world/asia/tepco-operator-of-fukushima-exonerates-itself-in-report.html Last Accessed 09/2023.
- Takahashi, Y. (2016). "Results of the 18th tripartite environment ministers meeting among Korea, China and Japan (TEMM18)." Japan Environment Quarterly (JEQ), Volume 14, August 2016. Available at webpage: https://www.env.go.jp/en/focus/jeq/issue/vol14/topics2.html#c1 Last Accessed 10/2023.
- Tanigawa, K. Hosoi, Y. Hirohashi, N. Iwasaki, Y. and Kamiya, K. (2012). "Loss of life after evacuation: lessons learned from the Fukushima accident." *The Lancet*, Volume 379, No. 9819, March 10th, 2012. Pp. 889-891. www.thelancet.com.
- Tanimoto,T. Uchida, N. Kodama, Y. Teshima, T. and Taniguchi, S. (2011). "Safety of workers at the Fukushima Daiichi nuclear power plant." *The Lancet*, Volume 377, No. 9776, pp. 1489-1490, April 15, 2011. www.thelancet.com.
- Tateiwa, K. (2015). "Fukushima Daiichi Update." *Nuclear Plant Journal*, Volume 33, No. 3, May-June, pp. 32-35. https://digitaleditions.nuclearplantjournal.com/MJ15/files/assets/basic-html/index.html#32 Last Accessed 11/2023.
- TEPCO, (2022). "Safety measures of nuclear power station." Tokyo Electric

Power Company, Power Supply Facilities, 'Creating disaster-resistant nuclear power station.' Full news report available at website: https://www.tepco.co.jp/en/challenge/csr/nuclear/stations-e.html Last Accessed 10/2023.

- Thatcher, A. Vasconcelos, A.C. and Ellis, D. (2015). "An investigation into the impact of information behavior on information failure: The Fukushima Daiichi nuclear power disaster." *International Journal of Information Management*, Volume 35, No. 1, pp. 57-63.
- Thibierge, S. (2012). "Fukushima, la vie après." Art-Press, Volume 423, pp. 72-75. Copyright of Art-Press is the property of Art-Press (International).
- Thomson, E. (2011). "China's nuclear energy in light of the disaster in Japan." *Eurasian Geography and Economics*, Volume 52, No. 4, pp. 464-482.
- Tsujikawa, N. Tsuchida, S. and Shiotani, T. (2015). "Changes in the factors influencing public acceptance of nuclear power generation in Japan since the 2011 Fukushima Daiichi nuclear disaster." *Risk Analysis,* Volume 36, No. 1, pp. 98-113.
- UCS, (2011). "Emergency planning and preparedness for nuclear disasters." The Union of Concerned Scientists (UCS), Offsite Emergency Planning Report, December 2011. Available at website: https://www.ucsusa.org/sites/default/files/2019-09/fact-sheet-emergency-planning.pdf Last Accessed 09/2023.
- UK Environment Agency, (2021). "Regulating for people, the environment and growth, 2020." Applies to England. Research and Analysis Report, 29 December 2021. Available at website: https://www.gov.uk/government/publications/regulating-for-people-the-environment-and-growth-2020/regulating-for-people-the-environment-and-growth-2020 Last Accessed 08/2023.
- United Nations, FCCC/IDR.7/JPN, (2019). "Report on the technical review of the seventh national communication of Japan." U.N. Framework Convention on Climate Change, 24 January 2019. FCCC/IDR.7/JPN. Available at website: https://www.env.go.jp/content/900446251.pdf Last Accessed 09/2023.
- University of Maryland, (2020). "Assessing natural hazard risks to nuclear facilities." Division of Research, University of Maryland, Headlines article. Available at webpage: https://spac.umd.edu/news/story/assessing-natural-hazard-risks-to-nuclear-facilities Last Accessed 09/2023.
- U.S. Department of Energy report, (2000). "Waste Isolation Pilot Plant Biennial Environmental Compliance Report . " DOE/WIPP 99-2171 ; U.S. DOE Carlsbad Area Office, New Mexico, United States.
- U.S. Department of Energy Report, (2006) "Waste Isolation Pilot Plant Biennial Compliance Report." Washington Regulatory and Environmental Services. DOE/WIPP 06-2171; U.S. DOE - Office of Environmental Management (EM).Carlsbad Field Office, New Mexico, United States.
- United States Nuclear Regulatory Commission, (2011)."Commissioner Magwood's Comments on SECY-11-0137, 'Prioritization of Recommended

Actions to be Taken in Response to Fukushima Lessons Learned.'" Decision ITEM: SECY-11-0137. Report available at website: https://www.nrc.gov/reading-rm/doc-collections/commission/cvr/2011/2011-0137vtr.pdf Last Accessed 09/2023.

- Verger, R. (2014). "Three years after." *Big Shots*, March, pp. 1-2. Copyright of Newsweek Global property of Newsweek L.L.C.
- Visschers,V.H.M. and Siegrist, M. (2013). "How a nuclear power plant accident influences acceptance of nuclear power: Results of a longitudinal study before and after the Fukushima disaster." *Risk Analysis*, Volume 33, No. 2, pp. 333-347.
- Vivoda, V. (2012). "Japan's energy security predicament post-Fukushima." *Energy Policy*, Volume 46, pp. 135-143.
- Wako, T. (2012). "Industrial wastewater management in Japan." Environment Management Bureau, Ministry of the Environment, Japan. Technical Report available at webpage: https://www.env.go.jp/en/focus/docs/files/20120801-51.pdf Last Accessed 10/2023.
- Walker, M.J. and Henry, E.M. (2012). "Response to the changing perspectives of U.S. and Japanese nuclear energy policies in the aftermath of the Fukushima Daiichi disaster (by Daniel A. Dorfman)." *Pace Environmental Law Review*, Volume 30, No. 1, Fall, pp. 291-298.
- Walter, L. (2012). "Report: United States not prepared for Fukushima-like emergency." *EHS Today*, March, 2012. Website:www.ehstoday.com. (or) https://www.ehstoday.com/emergency-management/article/21915198/report-united-states-not-prepared-for-fukushimalike-emergency Last Accessed 09/2023.
- Wecker, K. (2019). "Germany's atomic phaseout: How to dismantle a nuclear power plant." *Deutsche Welle (DW)*, Environment Article, published 11/03/2019. Available at website: https://www.dw.com/en/germanys-atomic-phaseout-how-to-dismantle-a-nuclear-power-plant/a-47823766 Last Accessed 10/2023.
- Wheeler, B. and Dotson, S. (2011). "Japan's nuclear crisis: Timeline of events." *Power Engineering*, June 2011. www.power-eng.com. (or) https://www.power-eng.com/nuclear/japans-nuclear-crisis-timeline-of-events/ Last Accessed 09/2023.
- Wheeler, B. (2012). "Understanding the future of nuclear after Fukushima." Power Engineering, September 1, 2012. Available at website: www.power-eng.com or https://www.power-eng.com/nuclear/understanding-the-future-of-nuclear-after-fukushima/ Last Accessed 11/2023.
- Wohns, A. (2014). "Fukushima's lessons for Boston: Debating the future of nuclear energy." *Harvard International Reviews*, Volume 35, Winter, pp. 4-5.
- (The) World Bank, (2017). "Resilient infrastructure public-private partnerships (PPPs): Contracts and procurement. The case of Japan." *World Bank DRM*

Hub, Tokyo, International Bank for Reconstruction and Development, Report, Available at website: https://thedocs.worldbank.org/en/doc/221901515466795175-0090022018/original/ResilientInfrastructurePPPsContractsandProcurementJapanCase.pdf Last Accessed 08/2023.
- (The) World Bank, (2017). "Sharing Japanese expertise in emergency preparedness and response (EP&R) systems at national and local levels." *WB, IBRD, IDA*, Featured Story, October 13, 2017. Available at webpage: https://www.worldbank.org/en/news/feature/2017/10/12/sharing-japanese-expertise-in-emergency-preparedness-and-response-systems-at-national-and-local-levels Last Accessed 10/2023.
- World Nuclear Association, (2020). "Nuclear Power in Japan." World Nuclear Association, Country Profiles report, updated September 2020. Available at webpage: https://world-nuclear.org/information-library/country-profiles/countries-g-n/japan-nuclear-power.aspx Last Accessed 10/2023.
- Yamaguchi, M. (The Associated Press), (2017). "Court Holds TEPCO, govt liable for Fukushima safety failures." *The Seattle Times* - Business - Nation & World - March, 17, 2017.
- Yamamura, E. (2015). "Transparency and views regarding nuclear energy before and after the Fukushima accident: Evidence on micro-data." *Pacific Economic Review*, Volume 20, No. 5, pp. 761-777.
- Yamasaki, J. Ikaga, T. Itsubo, N. (2019). "Eco-efficiency assessment of Japanese Municipalities based on environmental impacts and gross regional product." *Sustainability*, Volume 11, No. 15, pp. 4045; https://doi.org/10.3390/su11154045 Last Accessed 08/2023.
- Yamasaki, J. Ikaga, T. and Itsubo, N. (2020). "Eco-efficiency assessment by industry for Japanese municipalities nationwide based on gross regional product and environmental damage." *Journal of Environmental Engineering (Japan)*, Volume 85, No. 776, pp. 745-755.
- Yeo, S.K. Cacciatore, M.A. Brossard, D. Scheufele, D.A. Runge, K. Su, L.Y. Kim, J. Xenos, M. and Corley, E.A. (2013). "Partisan amplification of risk: American perceptions of nuclear energy risk in the wake of the Fukushima Daiichi disaster." *Energy Policy*, Volume 67, pp. 727-736. https://doi.org/10.1016/j.enpol.2013.11.061
- Yoshida, A. Noda, T. and Honda, M. (2020). "Regional binding in information networks of open data promotion in local governments of Japan." In: Baghdadi, Y., Harfouche, A., Musso, M., (eds) *ICT for an Inclusive World*. Lecture Notes in Information Systems and Organisation, book series, (LNISO, Volume 35). Pp. 105-111- Springer, Cham. https://doi.org/10.1007/978-3-030-34269-2_8

Suggested Literature

- Adamantiades, A. Kessides, I. (2009). "Nuclear power for sustainable development: Current status and future prospects." *Energy Policy*, Volume 37, No. 12, pp. 5149-5166.
- Agency for Natural Resources and Energy, Ministry of Economy, Trade and industry, (2019). "Important Stories on Decommissioning 2019." Report on Fukushima Daiichi Nuclear Power Station, now and in the future. Available at webpage: https://www.meti.go.jp/earthquake/nuclear/hairo_osensui/images/reactorpamph2019en.pdf Last Accessed 09/2023.
- American Nuclear Society (ANS), Special Committee on Fukushima, "Full Report: Fukushima Daiichi," March (2012), Revised on June 2012. Available at webpage: http://fukushima.ans.org/report/Fukushima_report.pdf Last Accessed 10/2023.
- (The) Asahi Shimbun, August 30, (2022). "Partial lifting of evacuation order fails to bring life back to Futaba." August 30, 2022. Available at webpage: https://www.asahi.com/ajw/articles/14706619 Last Accessed 09/2023.
- Berglund, J. (2020). "After Fukushima: Safety culture and fostering critical thinking." *Safety Science*, Volume 124, April 2020, 104613.
- Butler D. (2011) "Radioactivity spreads in Japan." *Nature*; Volume 471, pp. 555-556. 29 March 2011.
- CBS News (2016). "Fukushima meltdown apology: 'It was a cover-up.'" Available at website: https://www.cbsnews.com/news/fukushima-tepco-power-japan-nuclear-meltdown-apologizes-cover-up/ Last Accessed 08/2023.
- Center for Health Care Strategies, "Leveraging community knowledge through community-based participatory research." Audrey Nuamah, Anna Spencer, Center for Health Care Strategies, October 17, 2019.
- Chen, Y.F. and Yang, Y. (2012). "Taming the nuclear dragon? The prospect and potential of cross-Strait cooperation on nuclear security." *Journal of Asian Public Policy*, Volume 5, No. 2, pp. 155-167.
- Colthorpe, A. October 25, (2021). "Japan's policymakers approve higher 2030 renewable energy target." PVTECH News, Markets & Finance, Policy. Webpage available at: https://www.pv-tech.org/japans-policymakers-approve-higher-2030-renewable-energy-target/ Last Accessed 08/2023.
- Dietz, S. and Morton, A. (2011). "Strategic appraisal of environmental risks: A contrast between the United Kingdom's Stern Review on the economics of climate change and its committee on radioactive waste management." *Risk Analysis*, Volume 31, No.1, pp. 129-142.

- Dorfman, D.A. (2012). "The changing perspectives of U.S. and Japanese nuclear energy policies in the aftermath of the Fukushima Daiichi disaster." *Pace Environmental Law Review,* Volume 30, No. 1, Fall, pp. 255-290.
- EPA-U.S., (2022). "Cleaner power plants." Environmental Protection Agency report, web-page updated on July 26, 2022. Available at website: https://www.epa.gov/mats/cleaner-power-plants Last Accessed 09/2023.
- Eurasia Review, News & Analysis, (2020). " Fortum begins environmental impact assessment procedure for Loviisa Nuclear Power Plant." ER 13-08-2020. Website:https://www.eurasiareview.com/13082020-fortum-begins-environmental-impact-assessment-procedure-for-loviisa-nuclear-power-plant/ Last Accessed 09/2020.
- Ferguson, C.D. and Jansson, M. (2013). "Regulating Japanese nuclear power in the wake of the Fukushima Daiichi Accident." Federation of American Scientists (FAS), FAS Issue Brief, May 2013. Webpage available at: https://uploads.fas.org/2013/05/Regulating_Japanese_Nuclear_13May131.pdf Last Accessed 08/2023.
- Fuji Johnson, G. (2007). "The discourse of democracy in Canadian nuclear waste management policy." *Policy Sciences*, Volume 40, pp. 79-99.
- Fukushima Prefectural Government, (2012). "Plan for revitalization in Fukushima Prefecture. (Second Version) [Outline]." Published by: Revitalization & Comprehensive Planning Division, Planning & Coordination Department, Fukushima Prefectural Government, December 2012. Available at webpage: https://www.pref.fukushima.lg.jp/download/1/plan_for_revitalization2_outline.pdf Last Accessed 10/2023.
- Hultquist, C. and Cervone, G. (2018). "Citizen monitoring during hazards: validation of Fukushima radiation measurements." *GeoJournal*, Volume 83, No. 2, pp. 189-206. DOI: 10.1007/s10708-017-9767-x
- International Atomic Energy Agency, 2020. "Country Nuclear Power Profiles. Japan." (IAEA) Country Energy Overview. Webpage available at: https://cnpp.iaea.org/countryprofiles/Japan/Japan.htm Last Accessed 08/2023.
- Japan's Agency for Natural Resources and Energy, Government of Japan (GOJ) report, (2018). "Strategic Energy Plan." July 2018. Webpage available at: https://www.enecho.meti.go.jp/en/category/others/basic_plan/5th/pdf/strategic_energy_plan.pdf Last Accessed 08/2023.
- Japan, Ministry of the Environment, (2013). "Environmental impact assessment in Japan." Environmental Impact Assessment Network Report: Revision of the Environmental Impact Assessment Act. Available at webpage: http://assess.env.go.jp/5_global/OutlineofEnvironmentalImpact_inJapan/index.html and
http://assess.env.go.jp/files/1_seido/pamph_e.pdf and
http://assess.env.go.jp/files/5_global/OutlineofEnvironmentalImpact_pdf/e_02.pdf Last Accessed 08/2023.
- Jobin, P. (2020). "The Fukushima nuclear disaster and civil actions as a social movement." *The Asia-Pacific Journal*, Vol. 18, Issue 9, Number 1, Article ID 5392.

- Juraku, K. (2016). "Deficits of Japanese nuclear risk governance remaining after the Fukushima accident: Case of contaminated water management." In Kamae, K. (eds) Earthquakes, Tsunamis and Nuclear Risks, pp.157-169. Springer, Tokyo.
- Kanagawa, H. Nakayama, Y. (2020). ICLG Study "Japan: Environment & Climate Laws and Regulations 2020." Available at webpage: https://iclg.com/practice-areas/environment-and-climate-change-laws-and-regulations/japan Last Accessed 09/2023.
- Kinsella, W.J. Kelly, A.R. and Autry, M.K. (2013). "Risk, Regulation, and Rhetorical Boundaries: Claims and challenges surrounding a purported nuclear renaissance." *Communication Monographs*, Volume 80, No. 3, pp. 278-301.
- Krutli, P. Stauffacher, M. Flueler, T. and Scholz, R.W. (2010). "Functional-dynamic public participation in technological decision-making: site selection processes of nuclear waste repositories." *Journal of Risk Research*, Volume 13, No. 7, pp. 861-875.
- Kuroda, Y. Koyama, Y. Sato, N. Ando, R. (2019). "Re-building trust with local communities after the Nuclear accident: Making of 'Information booklet for Returnees' from native's point of view." The Consultancy Meeting on STS Education Support on Return in the Context of Low-dose Radiation, 2019. Available at website: https://www.env.go.jp/content/900406510.pdf Last Accessed 11/2023.
- Kuroda, Y. (2018). "Rehabilitation of living conditions after NPP accident: the practical experience and lessons learned from working with Iitate people." RICOMET Conference, 2018.06.13 Antwerp. https://kaken.nii.ac.jp/en/grant/KAKENHI-PROJECT-18K11779/ Last Accessed 11/2023.
- Ministry of the Environment, Japan, (2012). "Environmental Impact Assessment in Japan." MOE, Environmental Impact Assessment Division, Report, May 2012. Available at webpage: https://www.env.go.jp/en/focus/docs/files/20120501-04.pdf Last Accessed 10/2023.
- Ministry of the Environment, Japan, (2013). "Asia Protected Areas Charter." MOE doc. of 17 November, 2017. Available at webpage: https://www.env.go.jp/en/nature/asia-parks/pdf/3-1_asia_protected_areas_charter.pdf Last Accessed 10/2023.
- MOE, Japan, (2020). "The inspection results of large container bags for removed soil in Temporary Storage Sites (TSS) after heavy rain by typhoon Hagibis." Waste & Recycling news, March 17, 2020. Available at webpage: https://www.env.go.jp/en/headline/2440.html Last Accessed 09/2023.
- Morton, A. Airoldi, M. and Phillips, L.D. (2009). "Nuclear risk management on stage: A decision analysis perspective on the UK's committee on radioactive waste management." *Risk Analysis*, Volume 29, No. 5, pp. 764-779.
- Nagasaki, A. (2021). "Environmental Law 2021. Japan." Chambers and Partners, November 30, 2021. Website available at:

https://practiceguides.chambers.com/practice-guides/comparison/711/9875/15767-15769-15771-15774-15776-15779-15782-15785-15788-15793-15796-15798-15801-15803-15807-15811-15814 Last Accessed 08/2023.

- NRC Japan's Lessons Examples from direct available websites:
https://www.nrc.gov/reactors/operating/ops-experience/japan-dashboard.html - Last Accessed 10/2023.

b. https://public-blog.nrc-gateway.gov/tag/fukushima/ - Last Accessed 10/2023.

- NRA, Japan, (2022). "The flow of review and inspection for checking conformity to New Regulatory Requirements." Presentation available at: https://www.nra.go.jp/data/000118257.pdf Last Accessed 10/2023/ NRA's direct available webpage.

- NRA Commission document decided on 22 July (2022). "Review results document on the application for approval to amend the implementation plan pertaining to Specified Nuclear Facility (Installation of ALPS Treated Water Discharge Facility) of Tokyo Electric Power Company Holdings Fukushima Daiichi Nuclear Power Station. page 3. NRA Japan. Doc. Available at webpage: https://www.nra.go.jp/data/000399110.pdf Last Accessed 10/2023.

- Nuclear Regulatory Authority, Japan, (2019). "Annual Report." Chapter 1 "Ensuring Trust in Nuclear Regulatory Administration." Available at webpage: https://www.nra.go.jp/data/000347153.pdf Last Accessed 11/2023.

- OECD study project "Assessing the impacts of the policy mix for knowledge transfer between industry and science."/ "2017-18 project implemented by the Working Party on Innovation and Technology Policy (TIP) under the auspices of the OECD Committee for Science and Technological Policy (CSTP)." OECD reference websites available at: (1) https://www.oecd.org/sti/inno/working-group-on-innovation-and-technology-policy.htm#:~:text=The%20core%20objective%20of%20the%20TIP%20is%20to,foster%20the%20creation%20of%20science%20and%20technology-based%20firms. (2) https://stip.oecd.org/knowledge-transfer/case-studies - Last Accessed 07/2023.

- Ortiz-Moya, F. Kataoka, Y. and Saito, O., *et al., (*2021). "Sustainable transitions towards a resilient and decentralised future: Japan's Circulating and Ecological Sphere (CES)." *Sustainability Science*, Volume 16, pp. 1717-1729.

- Ozawa, H. Umeda, S. and Nishimura & Asashi, (2015). "Environmental law and practice in Japan: overview." Thomson Reuters, Practical Law, Available at website: https://uk.practicallaw.thomsonreuters.com/6-502-8920?contextData=(sc.Default)&transitionType=Default&firstPage=true Last Accessed 01/2021.

- Radiological Impact Assessment Report Regarding the Discharge of ALPS Treated Water into the Sea (design stage)." TEPCO report, November 2021.

Webpage available: https://www.tepco.co.jp/en/hd/newsroom/press/archives/2021/pdf/211117e0102.pdf Last Accessed 08/2023.

- Ramana, M.V. (2013). "Shifting strategies and precarious progress: Nuclear waste management in Canada." *Energy Policy*,Volume 61, pp. 196-206.
- Report of (JST) Japan Science and Technology Agency, April (2021). "Mobilizing Science, Technology and Innovation for SDGs. Japanese Actions in STI for SDGs." Page 22. Webpage available at: https://www.jst.go.jp/sdgs/en/pdf/sti_for_sdgs_report_en_apr_2021.pdf Last Accessed 08/2023.
- Reuters Agency Staff: Yuka Obayashi, Kentaro Hamada, (2016). "Japan doubles Fukushima disaster-related cost to $188bln." Reuters-Utilities-Electric, published 9/12/2016. Available at webpage: https://www.reuters.com/article/tepco-fukushima-costs-idUST9N1DC00J Last Accessed 09/2023.
- Sun, Y. and Yan,T. (2019). "The use of public health indicators to assess individual happiness in post-disaster recovery." *International Journal of Environmental Research and Public Health,* Volume 16, No. 21: 4101. Available at webpage: https://www.ncbi.nlm.nih.gov/pmc/articles/PMC6862458/ Last Accessed 10/2023.
- U.S. Nuclear Waste Technical Review Board, (2017). Official website, available at webpage: https://www.nwtrb.gov/about-us/mission#:~:text=The%20mission%20of%20the%20U.S.%20Nuclear%20Waste%20Technical,Department%20of%20Energy%E2%80%99s%20%28DOE%29%20nuclear%20waste%20management%20activities. Last Accessed 10/2023.
- U.S. Senate Hearing 112-959. (2012) "Lessons from Fukushima one year later: NRC's implementation of recommendations for enhancing nuclear reactor safety in the 21st century." U.S. Subcommittee on clean air and nuclear safety and the Committee on environment and public works U.S. Senate. March 15, 2012. Available at webpage: https://www.govinfo.gov/content/pkg/CHRG-112shrg25036/html/CHRG-112shrg25036.htm Last Accessed 10/2023.
- Walker, W. (2000). "Entrapment in large technology systems: institutional commitment and power relations." *Research Policy*, Volume 29, No. 7-8, pp. 833-846.
- Westerhoff, L. Keskitalo, E.C.H. McKay, H. Wolf, J. Ellison, D. Botetzagias, I. and Reysset, B. (2010). "Planned Adaptation Measures in Industrialised Countries: A comparison of select countries within and outside the EU." Chapter 7, pp. 271-338. In book edition: E.C.H. Keskitalo (eds) *Developing Adaptation Policy and Practice in Europe: Multi-level Governance of Climate Change*, Springer Science+Business Media B.V. 2010.
- WNA, (2023) Updated Contents. "Fukushima Daiichi Accident." reported on: World Nuclear Association website, available online at: https://www.world-

nuclear.org/information-library/safety-and-security/safety-of-plants/fukushima-daiichi-accident.aspx - Last Accessed 07/2023.

- World Nuclear Association, (2018). WNA Report updated available at website: https://www.world-nuclear.org/focus/fukushima/the-situation-at-fukushima.aspx Last Accessed 09/2023.
- Yamamoto, T. (2022). "12.1 trillion yen spent so far on Fukushima nuclear disaster." The Asahi Shimbun, 7 November, 2022.
- Yamashita, S. and Takamura, N. (2015). "Post-crisis efforts towards recovery and resilience after the Fukushima Daiichi Nuclear Power Plant accident." *Japanese Journal of Clinical Oncology*, Volume 45, No. 8, August 2015, pages 700-707.

END.

Index

A

Adaptive Management,12, 168

C

Collective Knowledge, 43
Commission, 6, 9, 16, 45, 47, 48, 87, 88, 98, 99, 158, 168, 171, 174, 177, 179, 180, 187, 188, 189, 228, 230, 231, 232, 233, 235, 238, 255
Community, 11, 16, 18, 19, 20, 28, 31, 37, 38, 39, 45, 47, 56, 66, 68, 71, 76, 80, 83, 84, 86, 90, 93, 94, 95, 152, 154, 156, 158, 162, 168, 169, 170, 172, 176, 180, 184, 185, 186, 192, 195, 198, 204, 206, 207, 208, 241, 243, 253, 256,
Comparative Review, 132, 138, 201, 244

D

Disaster Management, 7, 10, 14, 18, 20, 26, 31, 37, 47, 86, 98, 140, 141, 180, 196, 208, 211, 221, 257, 259, 260, 261, 263
Disaster Risk, 3, 5, 10, 12, 13, 14, 18, 24, 27, 47, 53, 67, 75, 76, 88, 90, 93, 94, 95, 97, 149, 152, 173, 181, 186, 194, 199, 205, 206, 207, 213, 216, 230, 237, 244, 260
DRR Participatory Approaches, 95

E

Energy Compliance, 155, 157, 158, 160
Energy Designs, 237, 256
Energy Innovation, 1, 12, 31, 43, 96, 131, 134, 162
Environmental Adaptation, 51, 81, 149, 166, 201
Environmental Impact Assessment, 36, 40, 51, 131, 134, 142, 157, 201
Environmental Review, 19

F

Facilities, 11, 14, 34, 40, 44, 48, 49, 52, 53, 66, 67, 68, 69, 73, 88, 93, 97, 142, 149, 151, 156, 157, 158, 161, 165, 166, 171, 175, 182, 191, 193, 194, 196, 209, 214, 221, 225, 227, 235, 236, 238, 242, 257, 260

G

Governance Learning, 40

H

Hazards, 5, 7, 10, 58, 60, 89, 95, 158, 162, 166, 171, 176, 194, 195, 211, 213, 215

I

Institutional Shifts, 88
IT Exchanges, 158, 233

J

Japan Disaster Crisis, 246

K

Knowledge Transfers, 12, 39, 44, 56, 83, 86, 134, 138, 141, 152, 154, 159, 160, 217, 257

L

Local Learning, 96, 141, 148, 237

M

Multilateral Coordination, 158, 194

N

Nuclear Power Plants, 4, 9, 20, 22, 25, 29, 33, 34, 56, 65, 155, 162, 166, 185, 190, 231, 232, 261
Nuclear Debate, 4
Nuclear Governance, 134

P

Participation Initiatives, 143
Planning, 2, 6, 7, 12, 16, 18, 19, 20, 21, 23, 31, 37, 39, 40, 44, 45, 51, 52, 56, 59, 69, 70, 71, 75, 77, 82, 84, 89, 96, 98, 131, 133, 134, 136, 137, 139, 141, 143, 145, 146, 150, 151, 153, 155, 157, 158, 159, 162, 164, 169, 170, 173, 181, 186, 200, 202, 208, 210, 215, 221, 226, 227, 231, 245, 257
Post-Disaster, 67, 131, 153, 180, 214
Post-Recovery, 93, 158, 169, 174, 180, 184, 233, 234
Protocols, 16, 51, 74, 89, 92, 131, 135, 157, 158, 163, 165, 171, 176, 185, 189, 236
Public-Private Partnerships, 71, 225, 244,
Public Safety, 16, 33, 36, 39, 75, 150, 226, 230, 232, 241, 242

R

Regional Knowledge, 12, 53, 87, 167
Regional Innovation, 3, 49, 65, 159
Regional Research, 76, 202
Risk Management, 3, 13, 61, 90, 93, 95, 140, 143, 146, 164, 181, 184, 187, 188, 193, 195, 197, 198, 204, 216

S

Safety, 3, 4, 5, 7, 8, 14, 16, 19, 24, 26, 27, 28, 32, 33, 36, 37, 39, 46, 47, 48, 56, 59, 64, 65, 67, 68, 69, 73, 74, 75, 76, 82, 87, 88, 89, 90, 92, 93, 94, 95, 97, 98, 99, 101, 131, 150, 152, 154, 161, 162, 165, 166, 170, 172, 173, 174, 175, 176, 177, 179, 182, 183, 184, 185, 187, 189, 190, 191, 193, 194, 195, 197, 201, 202, 203, 204, 205, 206, 209, 210, 211, 214, 215, 216, 217, 219, 221, 222, 226, 228, 229, 230, 231, 232, 233, 234, 235, 237, 238, 239, 241, 242, 245, 253, 254, 255, 256, 257
Science Technology and Society, 1, 12, 40, 43

T

Taiwan Disaster Prevention, 19
Technology Innovation, 1, 3, 23, 48, 61, 65, 96, 153, 168, 237

Printed in the USA
CPSIA information can be obtained
at www.ICGtesting.com
LVHW021105080924
790463LV00018B/193/J

9 781680 535501